Differential equations

Book 1

Mathematical methods

MST224

Cover image: This shows a simulation of the patterns formed by smoke particles moving in air, which is itself in turbulent motion. The positions of the particles are described by relatively simple differential equations, yet the patterns that they form are complex and intriguing. Similar patterns are also relevant to understanding how clouds produce rain, and are a subject of ongoing research at The Open University.

This publication forms part of an Open University module. Details of this and other Open University modules can be obtained from the Student Registration and Enquiry Service, The Open University, PO Box 197, Milton Keynes MK7 6BJ, United Kingdom (tel. +44 (0)845 300 6090; email general-enquiries@open.ac.uk).

Alternatively, you may visit the Open University website at www.open.ac.uk where you can learn more about the wide range of modules and packs offered at all levels by The Open University.

To purchase a selection of Open University materials visit www.ouw.co.uk, or contact Open University Worldwide, Walton Hall, Milton Keynes MK7 6AA, United Kingdom for a brochure (tel. +44 (0)1908 858779; fax +44 (0)1908 858787; email ouw-customer-services@open.ac.uk).

The Open University has had Woodland Carbon Code Pending Issuance Units assigned from Doddington North forest creation project (IHS ID103/26819) that will, as the trees grow, compensate for the greenhouse gas emissions from the manufacture of the paper in MST224 *Block 1*. More information can be found at https://www.woodlandcarboncode.org.uk/

The Open University, Walton Hall, Milton Keynes, MK7 6AA.

First published 2013.

Edited, designed and typeset by The Open University, using the Open University TeX System.

Printed in the United Kingdom by Halstan & Co. Ltd, Amersham, Bucks.

ISBN 978 1 7800 7479 5

1.1

Contents

Contents

Getting started

Introduction

Welcome to MST224 *Mathematical methods*. This module is designed to teach you the mathematics needed to study the physical sciences and other subjects (such as economics) where mathematics is used to model phenomena in the real world.

Everything that you will learn in this module has applications in a wide range of topics. Because the same mathematical techniques appear in different contexts, the mathematical knowledge required by a really good scientist need not be that extensive. This module will teach you most of the essential tools. If you go on to further study, you will find that while some additional mathematical ideas may be needed, most of the time you will be discovering the power of what you have learned in this module.

Because it is easier to learn just one new thing at a time, this module will concentrate on teaching the mathematics. It will not attempt to teach new topics in physical sciences, but in some cases the best way to illustrate a topic is in the context of a real-world example. In cases where a little science is required, it will always be explained. *The assessment materials will test only your knowledge and understanding of the mathematics.*

To illustrate the relevance of the mathematics to the real world, some additional material will be included in brown boxes such as the one below. We recommend that you read the material in these boxes, but do not get stuck or discouraged if you do not understand everything. All of the material in this style of boxed text is non-examinable, but it is hoped that you will enjoy reading about the applications and will want to learn more.

Note that green boxes contain essential information that *must* be read and understood.

The 'unreasonable effectiveness of mathematics'

As an illustration of why studying the mathematics underlying physical sciences can be so rewarding, consider Figure 1. The Cartwheel galaxy collided with another galaxy – presumably the small blue object to the left of the image – roughly 200 million years before the image that we now see.

Unleashing awesome energy, the collision sent a shock wave into the sparse gas around it. Expanding at nearly 100 kilometres per second, this 'cosmic tsunami' ploughed up a concentration of hydrogen gas and dust, creating conditions favourable for the birth of new stars around the galaxy's rim. The new stars in the rim are massive and extremely bright. Many have lived fast, died young and exploded,

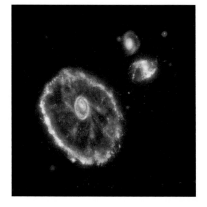

Figure 1 The Cartwheel galaxy (a composite image in false colour)

leaving behind burnt-out cores that are 5×10^{13} times denser than iron. Others have formed black holes that swallow up surrounding matter; as matter falls into a black hole, never to be seen again, it can produce intense bursts of X-rays. All these processes of galaxy collision, shock wave creation, star birth and death, and the creation of X-rays are explained in terms of mathematical models covering situations that are far from familiar everyday experience, but nevertheless trusted by physicists and astronomers. It is a remarkable testament to the power of mathematics, and our understanding of physical laws, that this is possible.

The ring in the image of the Cartwheel galaxy is about 1.4×10^{21} metres in diameter. The image in Figure 2 reveals the equally strange world of the very tiny. It shows something called a *quantum corral* imaged by an immensely powerful microscope (a so-called *scanning tunnelling microscope*). The lumps around the edge of the corral are individual iron atoms standing proud of a flat copper surface, and the diameter of the corral is about 10^{-8} metres. Of most interest to scientists are the ripples inside the corral. These show concentrations of electrons that form patterns similar to water waves inside a bucket or the vibration patterns on the surface a drum. These analogies are close, though not exact. The interesting thing, from our point of view, is that water waves, drum vibrations and the concentrations of electrons in a quantum corral can all be understood using similar mathematical techniques applied to slightly different equations. In the case of the electrons, we are completely beyond the comfortable familiarity of everyday life, but the tools of mathematics again provide the keys to understanding. The calculations are demanding and use sophisticated physical principles, but most of the mathematics is built on what you will study in this module.

It cannot always have been obvious that all this would be possible. The Nobel laureate Eugene Wigner has spoken about what he called 'the unreasonable effectiveness of mathematics in the Natural Sciences'. For example, he points out that Newton was able to verify his law of gravitation to within 4%, but the law turned out to be accurate to better than one part in a million: outrageous fortune or unerring instinct? He concludes that:

> The miracle of the appropriateness of the language of mathematics for the formulation of the laws of physics is a wonderful gift which we neither understand nor deserve.

(Eugene Wigner, 1960)

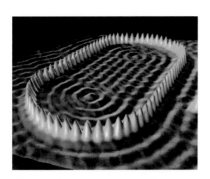

Figure 2　Iron atoms forming a 'quantum corral' (an image in false colour produced by a scanning tunnelling microscope)

Study guide

The module is divided into thirteen units, which you will study at a rate of roughly one per fortnight. Each unit will emphasise one major topic or technique. The units are grouped into four books, dealing with connected sets of topics.

The first book is primarily about differential equations, but this first unit is an exception. It reviews material that you will need in order to make a good start on MST224. The material is broad-ranging, so this unit contains more pages than others, but it may take no longer to study. This is because most of its topics have been covered in previous modules. If you find some things familiar, you may not need to study everything in great detail.

To help you to judge where to put your effort, most subsections begin with a diagnostic test. If you can answer the test questions correctly, it is probably safe to skim through some subsections, just checking that you remember the key ideas. If you choose not to study a subsection in detail, do check any new terms that are introduced, and make sure that you understand them. (New terms are set in bold type.)

If you do not have time to study the whole unit, make sure that you are familiar with the basic properties of the exponential and trigonometric functions (Sections 2 and 3), and with techniques for differentiation and integration (Sections 5 and 6). These topics are required in almost every part of the module, and without a reasonable knowledge of them you will get stuck later on.

The unit contains a number of 'standard formulas': for example, for the solution of a quadratic equation, for expanding $\sin(a + b)$ and $\cos(a + b)$, and for the derivatives and integrals of standard functions. It will be helpful if you are able to remember such formulas, but not essential; they are all given in the module Handbook. You *do* need to be aware that these formulas exist, know when they are needed and how they are used, and be able to find them quickly in the Handbook.

1 Some elementary functions

Functions play a central role in mathematics. After a brief look at some general ideas about functions (in Subsection 1.1), this section reviews some very simple but nevertheless important types of function: linear functions, quadratic functions and powers. It also looks briefly at how functions may be combined by *composition*.

1.1 Functions, variables and parameters

Consider the following example of defining a function. At midday on 1 June, a reservoir contains 2×10^6 cubic metres of water. For the next 50 days, the reservoir loses 15 cubic metres per minute. Suppose that at a time t minutes after midday on 1 June, the reservoir contains V cubic metres of water. Then we might use the equation

$$V = 2 \times 10^6 - 15t \quad (0 \le t \le 72\,000) \tag{1}$$

to model the volume of water in the reservoir for the 50 days ($= 72\,000$ minutes) after midday on 1 June. The letters V and t represent measurable quantities. V and t are called **variables**. Here, V depends on t, so V is called the **dependent variable** and t the **independent variable**. The comment in parentheses simply says that t lies between 0 and $72\,000$.

A **function** is a *process* or *rule* that can be applied to each of a specified set of input values to produce a definite output value. One example is: 'given t between 0 and $72\,000$, calculate $2 \times 10^6 - 15t$'. If we denote this function by f, then we can write equation (1) as $V = f(t)$, where $f(t)$ is the result of applying the rule f to the input value t.

We sometimes say that the function 'maps' each input value to its corresponding output value.

The **domain** of a function is the set of permitted input values. The function f associated with equation (1) has as domain the set of real numbers t with $0 \le t \le 72\,000$ – that is, the interval $[0, 72\,000]$. The **image set** of a function is the set of output values. The function f associated with equation (1) has as image set the set of values of $2 \times 10^6 - 15t$ with $0 \le t \le 72\,000$ – that is, the interval $[920\,000, 2\,000\,000]$. This is the range of volumes of water (measured in cubic metres) in the reservoir over the 50 days following midday on 1 June.

To define a function fully, we must give both the function rule and the domain. So the function corresponding to equation (1) is

$$f(t) = 2 \times 10^6 - 15t \quad (0 \le t \le 72\,000), \tag{2}$$

where the expression $2 \times 10^6 - 15t$ on the right-hand side gives the *rule* or *formula* that specifies the function, and the conditions in parentheses indicate the domain (the range of input values for which the function is valid).

To define a function, a process must produce a unique output value for each allowed input. So, for example,

$$f(x) = \pm\sqrt{x} \quad (x \geq 0)$$

does *not* define a function f because $\pm\sqrt{x}$ does *not* specify a *unique* value for a given x.

We write $\pm\sqrt{x}$ to denote the positive and negative square roots of x because, by convention, $\sqrt{x}$ denotes only the positive square root.

You may have noticed a subtle difference between equations (1) and (2). The former gives a relationship between the variables V and t, but the latter defines a function – the abstract rule underlying this relationship. In this module, however, functions will often be labelled in a way that blurs this distinction. For example, we may write $V = V(t)$ rather than introducing a separate symbol, such as f, for the function relating V to t. In this notation, $V(30)$ is the value of V when $t = 30$. This is the volume of water in the reservoir 30 minutes after midday on 1 June. But $V(t)$ is generally taken to represent the function itself. If there is any doubt, the context will make it clear whether we are referring to a function or just one of its values.

We can also consider a generalisation of the reservoir model. Suppose that the reservoir initially contains V_0 cubic metres of water and that the rate of loss is L cubic metres per minute. We will assume that this situation persists for $72\,000$ minutes after a starting time $t = 0$. Then we have

$$V = V(t) = V_0 - Lt \tag{3}$$

for $0 \leq t \leq 72\,000$. We now have an equation involving several symbols, with differing roles. Assuming that we want to use equation (3) to describe how V changes with time t, we continue to call t the independent variable and V the dependent variable. The function $V(t)$ tells us how to relate a time t to V. The quantities V_0 and L do *not* depend on t. They may, however, take different values in different uses of equation (3) – in an application to a different reservoir, for example. V_0 and L are called **parameters**. Whatever the values of the parameters V_0 and L, equation (3) gives a similar form of relationship between V and t: for example, the independent variable t appears in a similar way in any of the expressions $12\,000 - 5t$, $300 - 6.6t$ and $14 - 2t$.

Often, having defined a function that maps x to y (say), it is useful to define another function that reverses this operation, so that if $y = f(x)$, we might wish to define another function g such that $x = g(y)$. In this case g is called the **inverse function** of f. As an example, if $f(x) = x^2$ with domain $x \geq 0$, then solving $y = f(x)$ for x gives the inverse function $x = g(y) = \sqrt{y}$. By definition, the domain of the inverse function $g(y)$ is the image set of $f(x)$, and the image set $g(y)$ is the domain of $f(x)$.

We ignore the negative solution $-\sqrt{y}$ because we know $x \geq 0$.

Exercise 1

Consider the function

$$f(x) = 2x^2 + 6 \quad (x \geq 0).$$

(a) State the domain and image set of f.

(b) Find the inverse function, and state its domain and image set.

A note on units and dimensions

If you have taken a science course previously, you will be aware that most physical quantities have units or dimensions associated with them. This module will often use SI units: the SI units of distance and time are metres and seconds (denoted by m and s, respectively), and the SI units of volume are cubic metres (denoted by m^3). In equations where symbols represent physical quantities, there are two acceptable ways of combining units and symbols; both are correct, but they must not be mixed together.

Method A   The units are incorporated into the symbols

For example, the volume of the reservoir is written as $V = 10^6 \, m^3$, where m denotes metres. In this convention, the symbol V has units of m^3.

Then, if we use an equation like (3), with initial volume $V_0 = 10^6 \, m^3$, rate of water loss $L = 10 \, m^3 \, s^{-1}$ and time $t = 1000 \, s$, we write

$$V = 10^6 \, m^3 - (10 \, m^3 \, s^{-1} \times 1000 \, s)$$
$$= 10^6 \, m^3 - 10\,000 \, m^3$$
$$= 990\,000 \, m^3.$$

The notation $m^3 \, s^{-1}$ is shorthand for 'metres cubed per second'.

Method B   The symbols are pure numbers

For example, the volume of the reservoir is written as V cubic metres, where $V = 10^6$ is a number with no units. In this convention, the units are stated in the text, but the equations involve pure numbers.

In this approach, if we use an equation like (3) with initial volume $V_0 = 10^6$ (in cubic metres), rate of water loss $L = 10$ (in cubic metres per second) and time $t = 1000$ (in seconds), then we write

$$V = 10^6 - (10 \times 1000) = 990\,000.$$

It is then helpful to round off the calculation with a sentence that includes appropriate units, for example stating that the volume in the reservoir at time 1000 seconds is 990 000 cubic metres.

This module generally adopts the latter approach, so units will not appear in equations. If units are required in the final answer, the wording of the question will guide you as to what they should be.

1.2   Linear functions

A **linear function** relating y to x is one of the general form

$$y = y(x) = mx + c,$$

where m and c are constants. The graph of such a function is a straight line (hence the term 'linear'), as in Figure 3. The constant c represents the value of y at the point where the line crosses the y-axis. The **gradient** (or **slope**) of the graph is the same everywhere, and is equal to m. That is, for any two points (x_1, y_1) and (x_2, y_2) on the graph, we have

$$m = \frac{y_2 - y_1}{x_2 - x_1}.$$

In this module, if no domain is specified for a function, and there are no obvious points where it is not defined, you can assume that the domain is $\mathbb{R}$, i.e. the set of all real numbers.

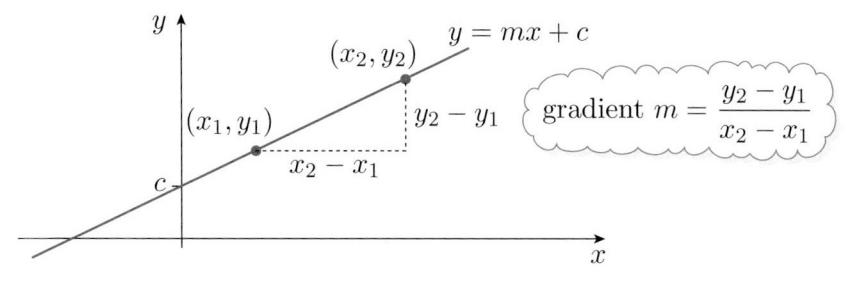

Figure 3   The graph of the linear function $y(x) = mx + c$

One situation where linear functions arise is when an object moves in a straight line with constant speed. Let us look at an example.

At 11.00 pm, a smuggler's boat passes a detector buoy that is 2 kilometres from a port. The boat then moves at a steady 5 metres per second on a straight course directly away from the port (along the line AZ in Figure 4). A coastguard vessel leaves the port in pursuit at midnight, travelling at 7 metres per second. When will it catch the smuggler's boat?

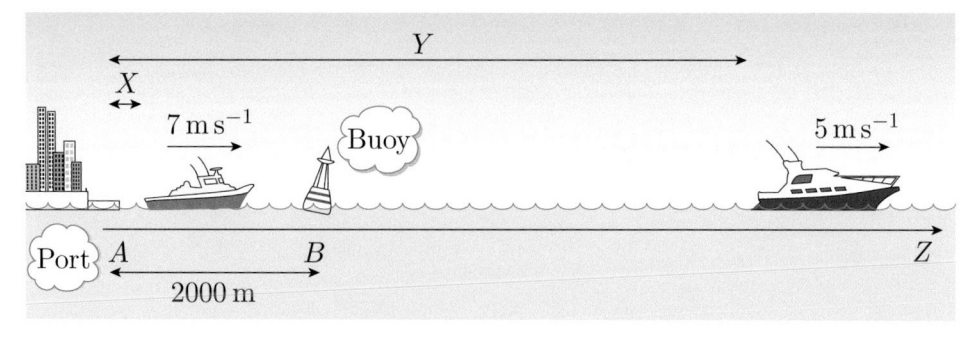

Figure 4   A boat chase modelled with linear functions

Suppose that we choose to measure time in seconds, starting from midnight, and distance in metres, measured from the port A. Let X metres be the distance of the coastguard vessel from A at time t seconds after midnight, and let Y metres be the distance of the smuggler's boat from A at the same time. We can readily obtain an expression for X in terms of t, since $X = 0$ when $t = 0$, and the coastguard vessel travels at a constant speed of 7 metres per second: we have

$$X = 7t.$$

We also want an expression giving Y in terms of t. The boat is moving at a constant speed of 5 metres per second, so Y will be related to t by a linear equation of the form

$$Y = 5t + c,$$

where c is a constant. We also know that (at point B) $Y = 2000$ at 11.00 pm, which is 1 hour, or 3600 seconds, before midnight and so corresponds to $t = -3600$.

Exercise 2

(a) Find the value of c such that $Y = 5t + c$ satisfies the condition $Y = 2000$ at $t = -3600$.

(b) (i)   When will the coastguard vessel catch the smuggler's boat?

   (ii)   The limit of territorial waters is 100 kilometres from A. Will the vessel catch the boat within territorial waters?

Simultaneous linear equations

Surveying equipment often uses laser beams, which travel in straight lines and can therefore be described by linear equations. We might wish to locate a point in space by finding the position where two laser beams cross. This is one of a wide variety of situations where we need to find the intersection of two straight-line graphs, which is equivalent to the algebraic problem of solving two **simultaneous linear equations**. Consider, for example, the following linear equations (graphed in Figure 5):

These equations are linear, since they can be rewritten in the form $y = mx + c$.

$$4x + 3y = -1, \tag{4}$$
$$3x + y = 3. \tag{5}$$

There are many ways of solving these equations: one powerful method is **Gaussian elimination**. Let us see how this works for equations (4) and (5).

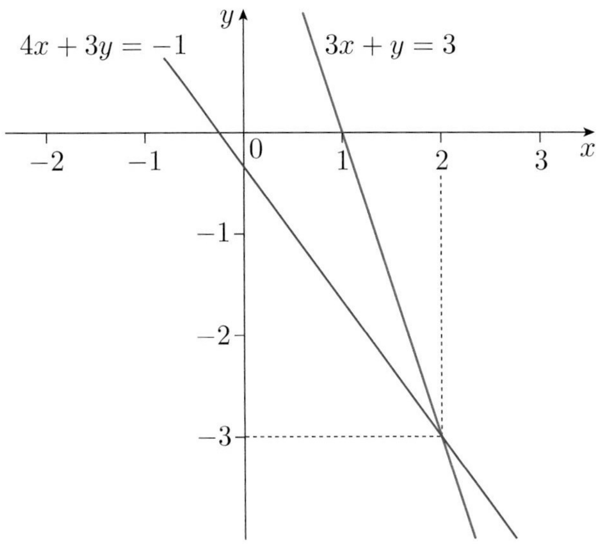

Figure 5 Graphical representation of the equations $4x + 3y = -1$ and $3x + y = 3$, and their solution

The aim of the method is to subtract a multiple of the first equation from the second in order to eliminate the x terms. First, we multiply equation (4) by $\frac{3}{4}$, to obtain an equation with the same coefficient of x as in equation (5):

$$\tfrac{3}{4} \times 4x + \tfrac{3}{4} \times 3y = \tfrac{3}{4} \times (-1),$$

which simplifies to

$$3x + \tfrac{9}{4}y = -\tfrac{3}{4}. \tag{6}$$

Now we subtract equation (6) from equation (5). This eliminates x, and gives

$$y - \tfrac{9}{4}y = 3 - \left(-\tfrac{3}{4}\right) = 3 + \tfrac{3}{4} = \tfrac{15}{4},$$

that is, $-\tfrac{5}{4}y = \tfrac{15}{4}$, so $y = -3$.

To find x, we substitute this value of y into equation (4), to obtain

$$4x + 3(-3) = -1,$$

which gives $4x = -1 + 9 = 8$, and hence $x = 2$.

So the solution of equations (4) and (5) is $x = 2$, $y = -3$.

You may like to check these values by substituting them into equations (4) and (5).

Exercise 3

Use Gaussian elimination to solve the following equations for u and v:

$$2u - 5v = 19,$$
$$3u + 4v = -29.$$

1.3 Quadratic functions

A **quadratic function** relating y to x is a function of the general form

$$y = y(x) = ax^2 + bx + c, \tag{7}$$

where a, b and c are constants, and $a \neq 0$. The graph of such a quadratic function is a **parabola**, and may open 'up' or 'down', depending on the sign of a, as illustrated in Figure 6.

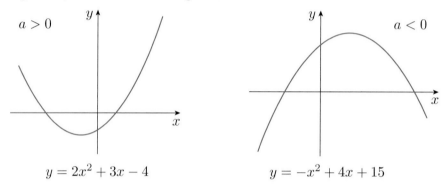

$a > 0$

$y = 2x^2 + 3x - 4$

$a < 0$

$y = -x^2 + 4x + 15$

Figure 6   Graphical representation of two quadratic functions

If $a > 0$, then the graph opens 'up' and positive values of y may become arbitrarily large, but there is a smallest (minimum) value that y can take. If $a < 0$, then the graph opens 'down', and negative values of y may become arbitrarily large in magnitude, but there is a largest (maximum) value that y can take.

For example, suppose that a ball is thrown directly upwards at time $t = 0$ seconds, with initial velocity $10\,\mathrm{m\,s}^{-1}$, from a height of 2.0 metres (see Figure 7).

The ball moves under the influence of gravity. Its position, y metres above the ground after t seconds, is given by

$$y = -4.9t^2 + 10t + 2.$$

Suppose that we want to find when the ball will hit the ground – that is, the value of t when $y = 0$. Then we need to solve the **quadratic equation**

$$-4.9t^2 + 10t + 2 = 0. \tag{8}$$

You will have met the formula for the solution of a general quadratic equation before. It is given below.

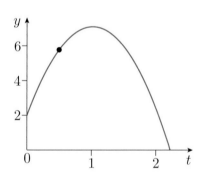

Figure 7   A ball is thrown vertically upwards

This equation may be taken on trust.

Procedure 1   Solution of a quadratic equation

The quadratic equation

$$ax^2 + bx + c = 0,$$

where a, b and c are constants, and $a \neq 0$, can be solved for x using the formula

$$x = \frac{-b \pm \sqrt{b^2 - 4ac}}{2a}. \qquad (9)$$

The solutions of a quadratic equation are often referred to as its **roots**.

Notice that the **sum of the roots** is $-b/a$, which is a useful check.

The term 'root' is also used for a solution of other sorts of equation, as you will see in Section 4.

Using this formula to solve equation (8) for t gives

$$t = \frac{-10 \pm \sqrt{100 + 39.2}}{-9.8} = 2.2 \text{ or } -0.18$$

(to two significant figures). Here the solution $t = -0.18$ refers to a time before the ball is thrown, so it can be discarded. The ball hits the ground about 2.2 seconds after it is thrown.

In this example, the quadratic equation has two solutions, but this is not always true. Look at the graphs in Figure 6, and imagine moving them up and down (which corresponds to varying the value of c). It is clear that the x-axis may meet a quadratic graph in two places, or it may touch at just one place (where the graph has a maximum or minimum value), or it may not meet the graph at all. Examples of these three cases are shown in Figure 8.

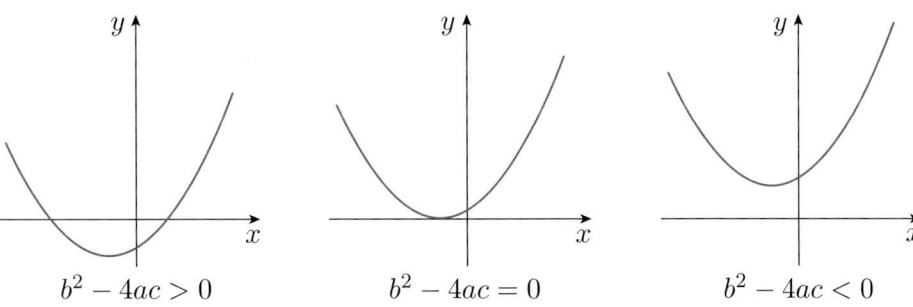

Figure 8   Graphs of the quadratic equation $y = ax^2 + bx + c$ for $a > 0$ and different values of $b^2 - 4ac$

The three cases can be understood by inspecting equation (9), which involves the quantity $b^2 - 4ac$.

- If $b^2 - 4ac > 0$, we obtain a positive value for $\sqrt{b^2 - 4ac}$, leading to two distinct solutions.

- If $b^2 - 4ac = 0$, it follows that $\sqrt{b^2 - 4ac} = 0$, leading to just one solution. (Although, as you will see below, this one solution is sometimes regarded as two solutions with equal values.)

In Section 4, you will see that complex numbers enable us to write down square roots of negative numbers, and hence to produce (complex) solutions of a quadratic equation even when $b^2 - 4ac < 0$.

- If $b^2 - 4ac < 0$, there are no real values for $\sqrt{b^2 - 4ac}$, leading to no real solutions.

The quantity $b^2 - 4ac$ is often referred to as the **discriminant** of the quadratic equation because it *discriminates* between these three cases.

Exercise 4

Solve the following equations for x.

(a) $2x^2 + 7x - 4 = 0$ (b) $x^2 + x - 6 = 0$

Sometimes, you may find that you need to solve a quadratic equation where the coefficients are letters rather than numbers.

Exercise 5

ω is the Greek letter omega. The Greek alphabet is given in the Handbook.

If K and ω are constants with $K \geq \omega$, show that the solutions (for x) of

$$x^2 + 2Kx + \omega^2 = 0$$

are $x = -K \pm \sqrt{K^2 - \omega^2}$.

The solutions of a quadratic equation correspond to a **factorisation** of the corresponding quadratic function. For example, $x^2 + x - 6 = 0$ has solutions $x = 2$ and $x = -3$, and this corresponds to the factorisation

You may like to check this by multiplying out $(x - 2)(x + 3)$.

$$x^2 + x - 6 = (x - 2)(x + 3).$$

With experience, you may find that such factorisations provide a convenient way of solving some quadratic equations, but the formula in equation (9) provides a reliable method that can be used in all cases.

One point of caution: if you want to factorise a quadratic function, you can do this by first solving the equation (e.g. by using equation (9)), but you need to be careful to match the coefficient of x^2 in the factorisation with that in the original quadratic function. For example, $2x^2 + 7x - 4 = 0$ has solutions $x = \frac{1}{2}$ and $x = -4$, but to factorise $2x^2 + 7x - 4$ we write

$$2x^2 + 7x - 4 = 2\left(x - \tfrac{1}{2}\right)(x + 4) = (2x - 1)(x + 4),$$

where the 2 is needed to ensure that the coefficients of x^2 are the same on each side.

It is helpful to recognise some particular factorisations. Two useful ones are

$$x^2 + 2Ax + A^2 = (x + A)^2 \quad \text{and} \quad x^2 - 2Ax + A^2 = (x - A)^2.$$

So, for example, $x^2 - 6x + 9 = (x - 3)^2$. Such quadratics are called **perfect squares**. Perfect squares correspond to quadratic equations in which the discriminant $b^2 - 4ac$ is equal to zero. (You may like to check this for yourself.) Thus equations in which the discriminant is zero can be written in the form $(x + A)(x + A) = 0$ or $(x - A)(x - A) = 0$, and these factorisations lead us sometimes to consider such equations as having two *equal* roots ($x = -A$ and $x = -A$, or $x = A$ and $x = A$) rather just one root.

Another useful factorisation is

$$x^2 - A^2 = (x + A)(x - A).$$

So, for example, $x^2 - 16 = (x + 4)(x - 4)$. Such a quadratic is called a **difference of two squares**.

You need to be particularly careful when solving a quadratic equation that involves the *same* letters as appear in the standard formula (9), but in a *different* way.

Example 1

Solve for x the equation

$$abx^2 - (a + b)x + 1 = 0,$$

where a and b are non-zero constants.

Solution

You need to keep a cool head here, because the letters in equation (9) are used in a different way in the given equation. In equation (9), we need

$$ab \text{ for } a, \quad -(a + b) \text{ for } b, \quad 1 \text{ for } c.$$

So we obtain the solutions

$$x = \frac{a + b \pm \sqrt{(a + b)^2 - 4ab}}{2ab}.$$

This expression gives the solutions, but it turns out to be possible to express them in a much simpler form. We have $(a + b)^2 = a^2 + 2ab + b^2$, so the discriminant can be written as

$$(a + b)^2 - 4ab = (a^2 + 2ab + b^2) - 4ab = a^2 - 2ab + b^2 = (a - b)^2.$$

So the solutions can be written in the alternative form

$$x = \frac{a + b \pm \sqrt{(a - b)^2}}{2ab} = \frac{a + b \pm (a - b)}{2ab}.$$

Now $(a + b) + (a - b) = 2a$ and $(a + b) - (a - b) = 2b$, so the two solutions are $x = 1/a$ and $x = 1/b$.

This solution also follows from the factorisation $(ax - 1)(bx - 1) = 0$.

Exercise 6

Factorise the following expressions, where $a > 0$.

(a) $x^2 - a$ (b) $2x^2 - 8a$ (c) $x^4 - 6x^2 + 9$

1.4 Powers

In a^n, a is called the **base**, and n may be referred to as the **power**, the **index** or the **exponent**.

You will know that $10^5 = 10 \times 10 \times 10 \times 10 \times 10$. In general, a^n means the product of n copies of a (for any real number a and any positive integer n). In particular, $a^1 = a$.

For positive integers m and n, we have the property

$$a^n \times a^m = a^{n+m}, \tag{10}$$

since each side is the product of $n + m$ copies of a. For example,

$$10^2 \times 10^5 = 10^7.$$

Consequently, if we multiply m copies of a^n, we obtain

$$\underbrace{a^n \times a^n \times a^n \times \cdots \times a^n}_{m \text{ times}} = a^{\overbrace{n+n+n+\cdots+n}^{m \text{ times}}};$$

that is,

$$(a^n)^m = a^{n \times m} = a^{nm}. \tag{11}$$

For example, $(10^2)^3 = 10^6$.

The definition of a^n can be extended to cases where n is not a positive integer by assuming that equations (10) and (11) hold more generally. For $a \neq 0$, this assumption leads to the definition of a^0 as 1, and a^{-n} as $1/a^n$; and, for $a > 0$, to the definition of $a^{1/n}$ as the nth root of a, and $a^{m/n}$ as the nth root of a^m. So, for example:

Recall that the **nth root** of a number a is a number b such that $b^n = a$, and we write $b = \sqrt[n]{a}$.

$$10^{-4} = 1/10^4 = 0.0001;$$

$$27^{1/3} = \sqrt[3]{27} = 3 \quad (\text{since } 3^3 = 27);$$

$$4^{-3/2} = \frac{1}{4^{3/2}} = \frac{1}{\sqrt[2]{4^3}} = \frac{1}{\sqrt{64}} = \frac{1}{8}.$$

The negative square root of 5, for example, would be written as $-5^{1/2}$ or $-\sqrt{5}$.

If a is positive, it is conventional to take the fractional power of a to be positive. So, for example, $9^{1/2} = \sqrt{9}$ means 3 rather than -3. If a is negative, fractional powers of a do not necessarily exist – at least not as real numbers. (The square roots of negative numbers are discussed in Section 4.)

The following properties of powers hold for all real numbers $a > 0$ and all real exponents x and y. These properties are not proved here, but we will make use of them as necessary.

$$a^x > 0, \tag{12}$$

$$a^{-x} = 1/a^x, \tag{13}$$

$$a^{x+y} = a^x \times a^y, \tag{14}$$
$$a^x/a^y = a^{x-y}, \tag{15}$$
$$(a^x)^y = a^{x \times y} = a^{xy}. \tag{16}$$

We also note that $0^x = 0$ for all $x \neq 0$.

Finally, given *positive* numbers a and b, we have the following rules for products and quotients:

$$(ab)^x = a^x \times b^x \quad \text{and} \quad (a/b)^x = a^x/b^x.$$

For example, $15^7 = 3^7 \times 5^7$ and $(5/3)^4 = 5^4/3^4$.

These rules do *not* apply if a or b is negative. For example,
$$\sqrt{(-1) \times (-1)} \neq \sqrt{(-1)}\sqrt{(-1)}.$$

Exercise 7

Use the properties of indices to simplify each of the following, where $a > 0$ and x is real.

(a) $a^3 a^5$ (b) a^3/a^5 (c) $(a^3)^5$ (d) $(2^{-1})^4 \times 4^3$

(e) $8^{-1/3}$ (f) $16^{3/4}$ (g) $\left(\frac{4}{9}\right)^{3/2}$ (h) $(16x^4)^{1/2}$

1.5   Combining functions

> **Diagnostic test**
>
> Try Exercise 8. If your answer agrees with the solution, you may proceed quickly to Section 2.

Consider the following, which leads to an example of the *composition* of two functions. A hiker travels a distance of x kilometres after walking for a time t hours along a path. As he travels, the path rises up a mountain, so that after walking x kilometres along the path, his height (in kilometres) is h.

We might express x as a function of t using a function f, so that $x = f(t)$. As a practical example, the distance might be

$$x = f(t) = 2t - \tfrac{1}{4}t^2 \quad \text{(for } 0 < t < 2\text{)}.$$

Similarly, the height can be expressed as a function of x by another function g, so that $h = g(x)$. For example, the height might be

$$h = g(x) = \tfrac{1}{2}x - \tfrac{1}{8}x^2 \quad \text{(for } 0 < x < 3\text{)}.$$

Now, we might want to determine the hiker's height h as a function of time t. With $h = \tfrac{1}{2}x - \tfrac{1}{8}x^2$ and $x = 2t - \tfrac{1}{4}t^2$, we have

$$h = \tfrac{1}{2}\left(2t - \tfrac{1}{4}t^2\right) - \tfrac{1}{8}\left(2t - \tfrac{1}{4}t^2\right)^2 = \left(t - \tfrac{1}{8}t^2\right) - \tfrac{1}{8}\left(4t^2 - t^3 + \tfrac{1}{16}t^4\right)$$
$$= t - \tfrac{5}{8}t^2 + \tfrac{1}{8}t^3 - \tfrac{1}{128}t^4,$$

so we can write $h = H(t)$, where $H(t)$ is the function

$$H(t) = t - \tfrac{5}{8}t^2 + \tfrac{1}{8}t^3 - \tfrac{1}{128}t^4.$$

It is a very common procedure to express a quantity that is a function of one variable (height as a function of position, in our example) in terms of another variable (in this case, time). There is a shorthand way of describing what is being done in mathematical language. The relation between the function H and the functions f and g is written

$$H(t) = g(f(t)),$$

meaning that to obtain the function H we apply the function f to t, and then the function g to the result. We say that H is the **composition** of the function g with the function f.

In the hiker example above, the function $g(x)$ gives height as a function of position, while the function $H(t)$ gives height as a function of time. These are different functions, and texts in pure mathematics are usually strict about this distinction, and use different symbols for these functions, just as we have done above. When mathematics is used in the physical sciences, however, another approach is frequently used: we write $h(x)$ to denote height as a function of distance, and $h(t)$ to denote height as a function of time. The symbol inside the brackets (x or t) indicates which of the functions $h(x) = \tfrac{1}{2}x - \tfrac{1}{8}x^2$ or $h(t) = t - \tfrac{5}{8}t^2 + \tfrac{1}{8}t^3 - \tfrac{1}{128}t^4$ is intended. If this approach were not adopted, we would have to introduce a different symbol for a quantity every time we make a change of variable, which would make some physics texts impossible to read. The approach works well so long as you do not use $h(x)$ and $h(t)$ in the same equation.

Later on, when doing calculus, you will see that it is useful to be able to recognise a complicated function as the composition of simpler ones. Remember that the composite function $g(f(x))$ tells us to 'apply f first, then g', while $f(g(x))$ tells us to 'apply g first, then f'. The 'inner' function is applied before the 'outer' function, and the order in which the functions are applied matters!

Example 2

Express the function

$$h(x) = \frac{1}{\left(\sqrt{1 + 2x^2}\,\right)^3} \tag{17}$$

as a composite of a quadratic function and a power function.

Solution

Note first that $1 + 2x^2$ is quadratic and that by writing $y = 1 + 2x^2$, the right-hand side of equation (17) becomes $\dfrac{1}{(\sqrt{y})^3} = y^{-3/2}$ (a power).

So we can obtain $h(x)$ in two steps.

Step 1   Calculate $y = 1 + 2x^2$.

Step 2   Apply $\dfrac{1}{(\sqrt{y})^3} = y^{-3/2}$ to the result of Step 1.

So if $f(x) = 1 + 2x^2$ and $g(y) = y^{-3/2}$, then $h(x) = g(f(x))$.

Here, the domain of g is $x > 0$, but since $f(x) = 1 + 2x^2$ is always greater than 0, there is no problem.

Exercise 8

(a) If $f(x) = x^2$ and $g(x) = 1/(x-1)$, with $x > 1$, find the following.

   (i) $f(g(x))$ (ii) $g(f(x))$

(b) Express $h(x) = \sin(1 + x^2)$ as a composition of three basic functions.

2   The exponential and logarithm functions

Diagnostic test

Try Exercise 11. If your answer agrees with the solution, you may proceed quickly to Section 3.

This diagnostic test covers both the subsections in this section.

2.1   The exponential function

The exponential function plays a central role in mathematics. Here its definition is given, followed by two of its most significant properties, before we examine some of their consequences.

The exponential function $\exp(x)$ can be defined by writing an infinite series

$$\exp(x) = 1 + x + \frac{x^2}{2!} + \frac{x^3}{3!} + \cdots + \frac{x^n}{n!} + \cdots, \tag{18}$$

where $n!$ is the factorial of n, that is,

$$n! = n \times (n-1) \times (n-2) \times \cdots \times 3 \times 2 \times 1.$$

You may have met other definitions of $\exp(x)$. These can be shown to be equivalent to equation (18).

For example, $2! = 2$, $3! = 6$ and $4! = 24$.

This definition involves adding an infinite number of terms together. In general, dealing with infinite series can be a source of difficulties; for example, there will be problems if the terms keep growing as you go to larger and larger values of n. There is no problem with the series for the exponential function: as you add more terms in equation (18), their sum eventually approaches a definite number $\exp(x)$, which depends on x. The infinite series in equation (18) is called the **Taylor series** for $\exp(x)$. A graph of the exponential function is shown in Figure 9.

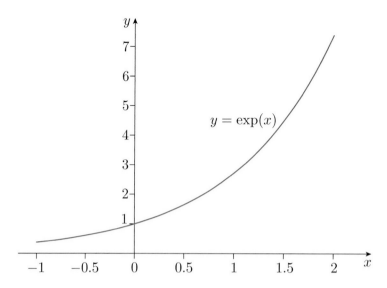

Figure 9   Graph of the exponential function

Exercise 9

With the help of a calculator, add together the first six terms in equation (18) for $x = 1/2$. Repeat your calculation for $x = 1$ using seven terms, and for $x = 2$ using eight terms. Hence obtain estimates for $\exp(1/2)$, $\exp(1)$ and $\exp(2)$.

Now for the two important properties of the exponential function. The first is that

$$\frac{d\exp(x)}{dx} = \exp(x). \tag{19}$$

Differentiation is discussed in Section 5.

That is, when you differentiate the exponential function, the result is just the function you started from.

The second property is that

$$\exp(x + y) = \exp(x)\exp(y). \tag{20}$$

These two properties (equations (19) and (20)) touch on so many aspects of mathematics that their power will become clear only as you progress through the module.

Equation (19) makes the exponential function a powerful tool for dealing with differential equations, as you will see later in this book. In order to see that this expression is correct, apply the rule for differentiating x^n to each term in the definition, equation (18). This gives

$$\frac{d}{dx}\exp(x) = 0 + 1 + \frac{2x}{2!} + \frac{3x^2}{3!} + \cdots + \frac{nx^{n-1}}{n!} + \cdots$$

Note that $\dfrac{n}{n!} = \dfrac{1}{(n-1)!}$.

$$= 1 + x + \frac{x^2}{2!} + \frac{x^3}{3!} + \cdots + \frac{x^{n-1}}{(n-1)!} + \cdots$$

$$= \exp(x).$$

Equation (20) is more difficult to derive directly from the definition, but the following exercise checks that it is correct in particular cases.

Exercise 10

Use the numerical values of $\exp(1/2)$, $\exp(1)$ and $\exp(2)$ quoted in the solution to Exercise 9 to provide a numerical check that $\exp(1/2) \times \exp(1/2) = \exp(1)$ and $\exp(1) \times \exp(1) = \exp(2)$, as predicted by equation (20).

An alternative notation

The property $\exp(x + y) = \exp(x)\exp(y)$ is analogous to the property noted earlier for powers:

$$a^{x+y} = a^x a^y \quad \text{(for } a > 0\text{)}.$$

This suggests that it is sensible to regard $\exp(x)$ as the power of some positive number. We write

$$\exp(x) = e^x, \tag{21}$$

where e is known as **Euler's number**. The value of e is easily found by putting $x = 1$ in equation (21). This gives

$$e = \exp(1) = 2.718\,281\,828\ldots,$$

using a numerical result from Exercise 9. We then have $\exp(2) = e^2$, $\exp(3) = e^3$, and so on.

Writing the exponential function in the form $\exp(x) = e^x$, equation (20) takes the form

$$e^{x+y} = e^x e^y$$

for any numbers x and y, and this is a special case of the equation $a^{x+y} = a^x a^y$ for powers. The exponential function shares other properties with powers of positive numbers. In particular,

$$e^x > 0, \tag{22}$$

$$e^{-x} = \frac{1}{e^x}, \tag{23}$$

$$\frac{e^x}{e^y} = e^{x-y}, \tag{24}$$

$$(e^x)^y = e^{xy}. \tag{25}$$

This value is correct to only ten significant figures; in fact, e is an irrational number, with a never-ending and never-repeating decimal representation.

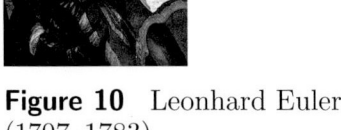

Figure 10   Leonhard Euler (1707–1783)

The number e

The number e is named after Leonhard Euler (Figure 10), who explored many properties of the exponential function, but the discovery of the number e is credited to Jacob Bernoulli (Figure 11), who used it to solve a problem involving the repayment of interest. (Euler and Bernoulli are pronounced as 'oiler' and 'ber-noo-lee'.)

Figure 11   Jacob Bernoulli (1654–1705)

2.2 The natural logarithm

It is useful to have a function that does the opposite of the exponential function. This function is called the **natural logarithm** function, and is given the symbol $\ln(x)$. The natural logarithm is the inverse function of the exponential function, so if $y = \exp(x)$, then $x = \ln(y)$.

When x is a single symbol, we may also write $\ln x$ rather than $\ln(x)$.

Some texts give other notations for $\ln(x)$, such as $\log_e(x)$ and $\log(x)$. We often refer to $\ln(x)$ as *the* **logarithm** function (although other less useful functions are also logarithms!). 'Take the logarithm of x', for example, generally means 'apply the natural logarithm function to x, to give $\ln(x)$'.

Because the exponential of a real number is always positive (see Figure 9), the natural logarithm function $\ln(x)$ is defined only for $x > 0$. Its domain is the set of real positive numbers, $x > 0$. A graph of the natural logarithm function is shown in Figure 12.

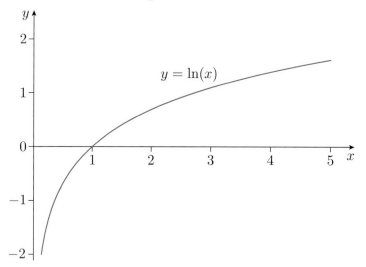

Figure 12   Graph of the natural logarithm function

The logarithm function obeys the important property

$$\ln(XY) = \ln X + \ln Y \tag{26}$$

for all $X > 0$ and $Y > 0$. To see why this is true, let $X = \exp(x)$ and $Y = \exp(y)$. Then, substituting in the left-hand side of equation (26) and using equation (20) gives

$$\ln(XY) = \ln(\exp(x)\exp(y)) = \ln(\exp(x + y)).$$

Because the logarithm and exponential are inverse functions of one another, the right-hand side becomes simply $x + y$. By replacing $x = \ln(X)$ and $y = \ln(Y)$, we obtain the fundamental property of the logarithm function given in equation (26).

Log tables and slide rules

Before electronic calculators became inexpensive, equation (26) was used to multiply or divide numbers. One converted numbers to their logarithms using a book of tables (log tables), added them (which is easier than multiplying), and used another table to find the answer.

An application of this idea is the slide rule, a mechanical calculator marked with logarithmic scales, where the addition step is performed by moving one scale past the other. Pilot training still requires knowledge of this device, partly because it still works when every electrical circuit has failed!

Common log tables (e.g. Figure 13) were based on another logarithm function, $\log_{10}$, defined so that if $10^y = x$, then $y = \log_{10} x$. This function is rarely used in advanced mathematics.

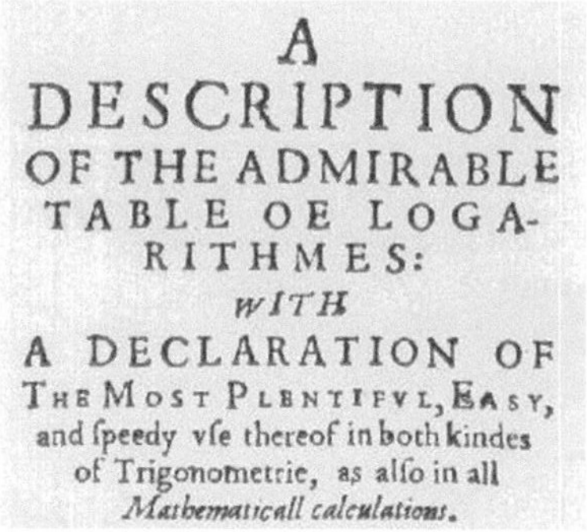

Several properties of the exponential function were listed in equations (22)–(25). By taking logarithms on both sides of these equations, we obtain the following results for the natural logarithm function:

$$\ln(1/u) = -\ln u, \tag{27}$$

$$\ln(u/v) = \ln u - \ln v, \tag{28}$$

$$\ln(u^v) = v \ln u. \tag{29}$$

A
DESCRIPTION
OF THE ADMIRABLE
TABLE OE LOGA-
RITHMES:
WITH
A DECLARATION OF
THE MOST PLENTIFVL, EASY,
and speedy vſe thereof in both kindes
of Trigonometrie, as alſo in all
Mathematicall calculations.

Figure 13 Part of the title page of a 1616 translation of John Napier's *A Description of the Admirable Table of Logarithmes.*

Exercise 11

Simplify each of the following (where a, b and x are positive, and x and y are real).

(a) $\ln 7 + \ln 4 - \ln 14$ (b) $\ln a + 2\ln b - \ln(a^2 b)$

(c) $\ln(e^x \times e^y)$ (d) $e^{2\ln x}$ (e) $e^{-2\ln x}$

(f) $\exp(2\ln x + \ln(x+1))$

We sometimes want to calculate the value of

$$y = a^x$$

where $a > 0$ and x is not an integer or a simple fraction. For example, we may need to evaluate 5^π. The exponential and natural logarithm functions allow us to do this. We write

$$a = \exp(\ln(a)) = e^{\ln a},$$

and then

$$a^x = \left(e^{\ln a}\right)^x = e^{x\ln a}, \tag{30}$$

which can be evaluated using the ln and exp functions.

This calculation of a^x is built into most modern calculators.

Exercise 12

Use equation (30) to determine the values of $A = 5^\pi$ and $B = 10^{-4.315}$ to four significant figures.

Distinguish carefully between a function of the form x^a, and a function of the form a^x, where a is a constant. A function of the form x^a is called a **power function**. Examples include x^2, $x^{1/2}$ and $x^{-5/2}$. By contrast, a function of the form a^x, where $a > 0$, can be written as $a^x = e^{kx}$, where $k = \ln a$. We say that this describes an **exponential dependence**, although e^{kx} is only the *exponential function*, e^x, if $k = 1$.

3 Trigonometric functions

This section adds another class of functions to the 'library' developed in Sections 1 and 2. These are the trigonometric functions. They originate in the geometry of right-angled triangles, but in this module we are equally often concerned with their use in describing repetitive or oscillatory behaviour. In particular, they arise as solutions of certain differential equations.

Differential equations are equations involving derivatives. They are the subject of the next two units.

3.1 Introducing the trigonometric functions

> **Diagnostic test**
>
> Try Exercise 13. If your answer agrees with the solution, you may proceed quickly to Subsection 3.2.

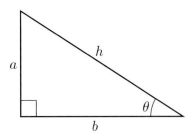

Figure 14   Trigonometric ratios: $\sin\theta = a/h$, $\cos\theta = b/h$, $\tan\theta = a/b$

You will have met $\sin\theta = a/h$, $\cos\theta = b/h$ and $\tan\theta = a/b$ as ratios in a right-angled triangle (see Figure 14). However, these definitions of the sine, cosine and tangent functions work only for $0 < \theta < \pi/2$, where θ is in radians.

> Note that many of the formulas in this module are valid only in radians, and angles will almost always be expressed in radians.

Recall that $180° = \pi$ radians.

To define the **sine** and **cosine** functions for a general value of θ, we can use Figure 15, which shows a circle of radius 1. Imagine that the line OA started along the x-axis, and was then rotated anticlockwise through an angle θ. Then the point A has coordinates $(\cos\theta, \sin\theta)$. Here θ may have *any* value, and this *defines* the cosine and sine functions for all values of θ (positive, zero or negative). A negative value of θ corresponds to a rotation *clockwise*.

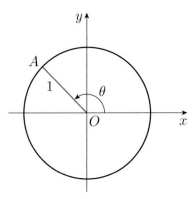

Figure 15   The point A has coordinates $(\cos\theta, \sin\theta)$

If we rotate through 2π radians ($360°$), then we go round a full circle. So rotations of θ and $\theta + 2\pi$ leave A in exactly the same place. This leads to the repetitive nature of the graphs of sin and cos: we have

$$\sin(\theta + 2\pi) = \sin\theta \quad \text{and} \quad \cos(\theta + 2\pi) = \cos\theta, \quad \text{for any } \theta$$

(see Figure 16). Functions like this, which repeat their values every 2π, are said to be **periodic**, with period 2π.

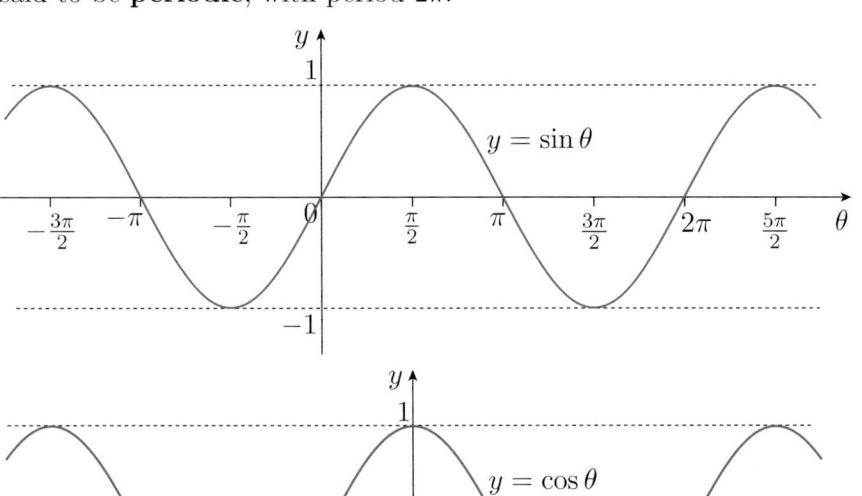

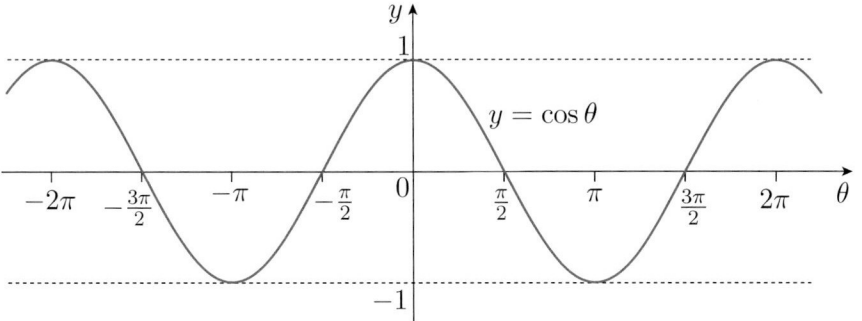

Figure 16   Graphs of the sine and cosine functions

You should also note that the graph of the cosine function is the same as that of the sine function, shifted to the left by $\pi/2$. We can express this mathematically as

$$\cos\theta = \sin(\theta + \pi/2).$$

Other trigonometric functions can be defined in terms of sin and cos. You will have met the **tangent** function $\tan\theta = \sin\theta/\cos\theta$. This is defined for all real θ except where $\cos\theta = 0$ (i.e. at $\theta = \pm\pi/2$, $\pm 3\pi/2$, and so on). You may also have met

$$\sec\theta = \frac{1}{\cos\theta}, \quad \operatorname{cosec}\theta = \frac{1}{\sin\theta} \quad \text{and} \quad \cot\theta = \frac{1}{\tan\theta} = \frac{\cos\theta}{\sin\theta}.$$

These functions are referred to as **secant**, **cosecant** and **cotangent**.

We need to restrict the domains of cosec and cot to exclude points where $\sin\theta = 0$, and the domains of sec and tan to exclude points where $\cos\theta = 0$.

Exercise 13

(a) Use Figure 15 to find the values of $\sin\theta$ and $\cos\theta$ for $\theta = 0$ and $\theta = \frac{\pi}{2}$.

(b) Find the values of $\tan\theta$, $\sec\theta$, $\operatorname{cosec}\theta$ and $\cot\theta$ at $\theta = 0$ and $\theta = \frac{\pi}{2}$ in all cases where these values exist.

(c) Two right-angled triangles are shown in Figure 17. Use these to calculate the values of $\sin\theta$, $\cos\theta$, $\tan\theta$ and $\cot\theta$ for θ equal to each of $\frac{\pi}{4}$, $\frac{\pi}{3}$ and $\frac{\pi}{6}$.

(d) For what values of θ is $\sin\theta = 0$? (Refer to Figure 16.)

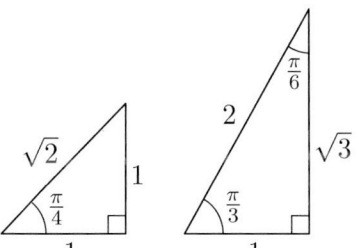

Figure 17   Two right-angled triangles

The graphs of sec, cosec and cot are given in the Handbook (as well as those of sin, cos and tan).

The function tan has the graph shown in Figure 18. Notice that $\tan\theta$ actually repeats its values every π. (This is because $\sin(\theta + \pi) = -\sin\theta$ and $\cos(\theta + \pi) = -\cos\theta$, so that $\tan(\theta + \pi) = \tan\theta$.)

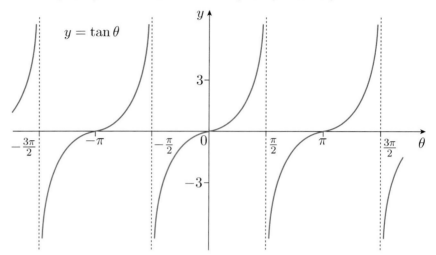

Figure 18   Graph of $y = \tan\theta$

3.2   Inverse trigonometric functions

Diagnostic test

Try Exercise 14. If your answer agrees with the solution, you may proceed quickly to Subsection 3.3.

Suppose that you need to solve for x the equation

$$\cos x = \tfrac{1}{2}.$$

What solutions are there? You have seen (in Exercise 13(c)) that $\cos\frac{\pi}{3} = \frac{1}{2}$, so one solution is certainly $x = \frac{\pi}{3}$. There are others, however. For instance, since cos repeats its values every 2π, another solution is $x = \frac{\pi}{3} + 2\pi$. We can find an infinite number of solutions by adding or subtracting multiples of 2π to/from $\frac{\pi}{3}$. There are even more solutions. If you look at the graph of cos in Figure 16, you can see that a horizontal line at $y = \frac{1}{2}$ would cut it twice between 0 and 2π: we also have $\cos\frac{5\pi}{3} = \frac{1}{2}$. And more solutions can be found by adding or subtracting multiples of 2π to/from $\frac{5\pi}{3}$.

In general, an equation of the form

$$\cos x = y \tag{31}$$

is solved for x by finding a value of the **inverse trigonometric function** arccos:

$$x = \arccos y.$$

However, we need to be careful here. Solutions of equation (31) are not unique, as we saw for $y = \frac{1}{2}$. If we reverse the roles of the axes for the cosine curve in Figure 16, we obtain the curve shown in Figure 19. However, this is *not* the graph of a *function*: a vertical line may meet the curve in many places, reflecting the fact that for a given y, equation (31) may have multiple solutions x. To ensure that $\arccos y$ has a unique value, we need to restrict the range in which values of arccos can lie. The *restricted values* of arccos are given in Table 1, together with those of two other inverse trigonometric functions, arcsin and arctan. In Figure 19, when the values taken by arccos are restricted, we obtain just the part of the curve shown in blue, which *is* a valid graph for a function.

Some texts use $\sin^{-1}$, $\cos^{-1}$ and $\tan^{-1}$ rather than arcsin, arccos and arctan.

Graphs of arcsin and arctan, as well as arccos, are given in the Handbook.

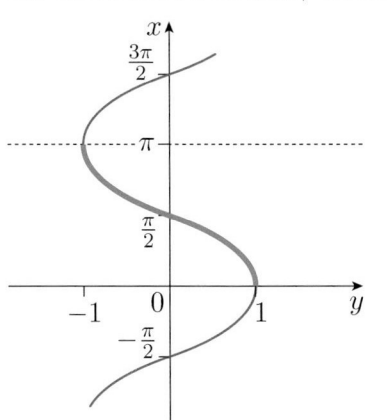

Figure 19   The graph of $x = \arccos y$ is just the blue part of the curve

Table 1   Domains and values of inverse trigonometric functions

Function	Inverse function	Domain of inverse function	Restricted values of inverse function
$y = \sin x$	$x = \arcsin y$	$-1 \leq y \leq 1$	$-\frac{\pi}{2} \leq x \leq \frac{\pi}{2}$
$y = \cos x$	$x = \arccos y$	$-1 \leq y \leq 1$	$0 \leq x \leq \pi$
$y = \tan x$	$x = \arctan y$	$\mathbb{R}$	$-\frac{\pi}{2} < x < \frac{\pi}{2}$

Calculators and computer software can be expected to give values of the inverse trigonometric functions drawn from suitably restricted values, usually those in Table 1. However, these values are not always appropriate in particular real-world problems. It is therefore important to be alert to the fact that an equation such as $\cos x = y$ actually has infinitely many solutions: if $|y| < 1$, there are two solutions in the range 0 to 2π, together with infinitely many others obtained by shifting these two by multiples of 2π.

For $|y| > 1$, $\cos x = y$ has no solutions.

Exercise 14

(a) Find all the solutions of $\sin\theta = 0.8$ in the range 0 to 6π.

(b) Find all the solutions of $\tan\theta = 1$.

You will need a calculator in order to get started.

3.3 Some useful trigonometric identities

Figure 20 shows the relation between a clockwise rotation through θ (regarded as a rotation through $-\theta$) and an anticlockwise rotation through θ. Notice that such rotations lead to equal x-coordinates but to y-coordinates of opposite signs. So we have

$$\cos(-\theta) = \cos\theta \quad \text{and} \quad \sin(-\theta) = -\sin\theta.$$

These relations hold for all values of θ, and are examples of **trigonometric identities**. Such identities can be useful in a variety of contexts, such as simplifying expressions involving trigonometric functions or evaluating integrals.

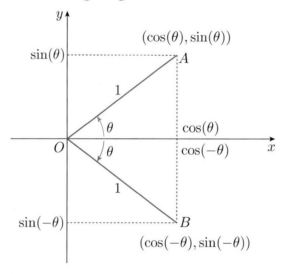

Figure 20   The effects of positive (anticlockwise) and negative (clockwise) rotations

There are three particularly useful trigonometric identities that you should remember.

$$\cos^2\theta + \sin^2\theta = 1, \tag{32}$$
$$\sin(\theta \pm \phi) = \sin\theta\cos\phi \pm \cos\theta\sin\phi, \tag{33}$$
$$\cos(\theta \pm \phi) = \cos\theta\cos\phi \mp \sin\theta\sin\phi. \tag{34}$$

Other useful trigonometric identities are given below. You should be aware of these identities, but there is no need to remember them, as they can all be very easily derived from equations (32)–(34) in one or two lines (see Exercise 15).

$$1 + \tan^2 \theta = \sec^2 \theta, \tag{35}$$

$$\cot^2 \theta + 1 = \operatorname{cosec}^2 \theta; \tag{36}$$

All the trigonometric identities discussed in this subsection are included in the module Handbook for easy reference.

$$\tan(\theta \pm \phi) = (\tan \theta \pm \tan \phi)/(1 \mp \tan \theta \tan \phi)); \tag{37}$$

$$\sin \theta \sin \phi = \tfrac{1}{2}[\cos(\theta - \phi) - \cos(\theta + \phi)], \tag{38}$$

$$\cos \theta \cos \phi = \tfrac{1}{2}[\cos(\theta - \phi) + \cos(\theta + \phi)], \tag{39}$$

$$\sin \theta \cos \phi = \tfrac{1}{2}[\sin(\theta + \phi) + \sin(\theta - \phi)]; \tag{40}$$

$$\sin(2\theta) = 2 \sin \theta \cos \theta, \tag{41}$$

$$\cos(2\theta) = \cos^2 \theta - \sin^2 \theta = 2 \cos^2 \theta - 1 = 1 - 2 \sin^2 \theta, \tag{42}$$

$$\tan(2\theta) = (2 \tan \theta)/(1 - \tan^2 \theta). \tag{43}$$

Exercise 15

Use equations (32)–(34) to derive the following identities.

(a) Equation (35)   (b) Equation (37)

(c) Equation (38)   (d) Equation (41)

Exercise 16

Use equations (33) and (34), and particular values of sin and cos, to simplify each of the following.

(a) $\sin(2\pi - \theta)$ (b) $\sin\left(\frac{\pi}{2} - \theta\right)$ (c) $\sin(\pi - \theta)$

(d) $\cos(\pi - \theta)$ (e) $\cos(2\pi - \theta)$ (f) $\cos\left(\frac{\pi}{2} - \theta\right)$ (g) $\cos\left(\frac{3\pi}{2} + x\right)$

Taylor series for trigonometric functions

The sine and cosine functions can be expressed as infinite series:

$$\sin x = x - \frac{x^3}{3!} + \frac{x^5}{5!} - \frac{x^7}{7!} + \frac{x^9}{9!} - \cdots, \tag{44}$$

Note that these equations are valid only in radians.

$$\cos x = 1 - \frac{x^2}{2!} + \frac{x^4}{4!} - \frac{x^6}{6!} - \frac{x^8}{8!} + \cdots. \tag{45}$$

Because the factorial $n!$ becomes very large as n increases, these series sum to a finite number, no matter how large x is. They are the **Taylor series for the sine and cosine functions**. A frequent use of these expressions is to approximate $\sin \theta$ and $\cos \theta$ when θ is small.

$$\sin \theta \simeq \theta \quad (\text{for } \theta \ll 1 \text{ in radians}), \tag{46}$$

$$\cos \theta \simeq 1 - \tfrac{1}{2}\theta^2 \quad (\text{for } \theta \ll 1 \text{ in radians}). \tag{47}$$

The symbols $\ll$ and $\gg$ mean 'much smaller than' and 'much larger than', respectively.

4 Complex numbers

Diagnostic test

Try Exercises 17(a), 17(b), 17(e) and 18. If your answers agree with the solutions, you may proceed quickly to Subsection 4.2.

Complex numbers provide a system within which we can solve any quadratic equation (and, indeed, any polynomial equation). They are used in many of the mathematical techniques introduced in this module.

There is no *real* number x satisfying the equation

$$x^2 = -1.$$

However, there are circumstances where it is convenient to have a system of 'numbers' in which such an equation can be solved. Such a system is provided by the complex numbers. A **complex number** is one of the form

Engineers commonly use j to represent $\sqrt{-1}$.

$$z = a + bi \quad \text{(or equivalently, } z = a + ib\text{)},$$

where $i = \sqrt{-1}$, and a and b are real numbers. We refer to a as the **real part** of z, written $\text{Re}(z)$, and to b as the **imaginary part** of z, written $\text{Im}(z)$. A complex number of the form $a + 0i$ is, in effect, just the real number a; so the real numbers are seen as a subset of the complex numbers.

$\text{Im}(z)$ is the *real* number b; it is *not* equal to bi.

The set of all complex numbers is denoted by $\mathbb{C}$. Within $\mathbb{C}$, we can solve any quadratic equation. For example, the equation $x^2 - 2x + 2 = 0$ has the solutions

$$x = \frac{2 \pm \sqrt{2^2 - 4 \times 2}}{2} = \frac{2 \pm \sqrt{-4}}{2} = \frac{2 \pm \sqrt{4} \times \sqrt{-1}}{2} = \frac{2 \pm 2i}{2} = 1 \pm i,$$

and the equation $x^2 = -1$ has the solutions $x = \pm i$.

An nth-order polynomial is sometimes referred to as a **polynomial of degree n**.

An ***nth-order polynomial*** with real coefficients is a function of the form

$$p(x) = a_n x^n + a_{n-1} x^{n-1} + \cdots + a_1 x + a_0,$$

where $a_n \neq 0$ and each coefficient a_k $(k = 0, 1, \ldots, n)$ is a constant in $\mathbb{R}$.

In fact, this result also holds if the coefficients a_k are complex.

If x is allowed to be complex, any such polynomial can be written as a product of the form

$$p(x) = a_n(x - c_1)(x - c_2) \ldots (x - c_n),$$

where each c_k $(k = 1, 2, \ldots, n)$ is a complex number. Remember that real numbers are included in the complex numbers, so this does not prevent some (or all) of the c_k being real. The equation $p(x) = 0$ then has n solutions: $x = c_1$, $x = c_2$, $\ldots$, $x = c_n$. These are called the **roots** of the polynomial. If a factor $x - c$ occurs more than once, then the root c is a **repeated root**. For example, the polynomial $x^2 - 2cx + c^2 = (x - c)^2$ has the repeated root c.

Repeated roots are sometimes referred to as **equal roots** or **coincident roots**.

Why are complex numbers important?

Complex numbers are an abstract construct, seemingly far removed from what you can measure with laboratory apparatus. Their mystical air of unreality is scarcely helped by calling $\sqrt{-1}$ an *imaginary* number! It is true that you cannot use complex numbers to count sheep, but complex numbers describe other aspects of reality and are used in numerous descriptions of physical phenomena.

One reason why complex numbers are important is that their exponentials (discussed below) are closely linked to the oscillating functions that describe vibrations and waves. But beyond this, it seems that complex numbers are woven deeply into fundamental scientific laws. In fact, the laws of quantum mechanics, our most fundamental theory of Nature, are expressed in terms of complex numbers.

4.1 The arithmetic of complex numbers

We can perform arithmetic with complex numbers, and this follows all the familiar rules for real numbers, such as

$$u(v + w) = uv + uw \quad \text{and} \quad u \times v = v \times u.$$

To add, subtract or multiply complex numbers, just manipulate brackets in the usual way, and remember that $i^2 = -1$. For example,

$$(2 + 3i) + (4 - 7i) = 2 + 4 + 3i - 7i = 6 - 4i$$

and

$$\begin{aligned}
(2 + 3i) \times (4 - 7i) &= 2 \times (4 - 7i) + 3i \times (4 - 7i) \\
&= 8 - 14i + 12i - 21i^2 \\
&= 8 + 21 - 2i \\
&= 29 - 2i.
\end{aligned}$$

Division of complex numbers is a little more complicated. It is best described in terms of the **complex conjugate**, which is defined as follows: if $z = a + bi$ is a complex number, then the complex conjugate of z is

$$\overline{z} = a - bi.$$

Then, to divide one complex number by another, as in u/v, we multiply top and bottom by the complex conjugate $\overline{v}$ of the denominator. For example, to simplify

$$\frac{2 + 3i}{4 - 7i},$$

we multiply top and bottom by $4 + 7i$, the complex conjugate of the denominator, to obtain

You will see the notation z^* for the complex conjugate of z in many textbooks.

$$\frac{2+3i}{4-7i} = \frac{(2+3i) \times (4+7i)}{(4-7i) \times (4+7i)}$$

$$= \frac{8+14i+12i-21}{16+28i-28i+49}$$

$$= \frac{-13+26i}{65}$$

$$= -\tfrac{1}{5} + \tfrac{2}{5}i.$$

This process always reduces the denominator to a real number because the product of a complex number $a + bi$ and its complex conjugate $a - bi$ is always real:

$$(a+bi) \times (a-bi) = a^2 + b^2.$$

Note that $a^2 + b^2$ is always positive, unless $a = b = 0$.

Given any complex number $z = a + bi$, its **modulus** $|z|$ is defined to be $\sqrt{a^2 + b^2}$, so we have

$$|z|^2 = a^2 + b^2 = z\bar{z}.$$

The process of dividing one complex number, $u = a + bi$, by another, $v = c + di$, is then summarised by

$$\frac{u}{v} = \frac{u\bar{v}}{v\bar{v}} = \frac{u\bar{v}}{|v|^2} = \frac{(a+bi) \times (c-di)}{c^2 + d^2}. \tag{48}$$

Exercise 17

Let $v = 3 - 4i$ and $w = 2 - i$. Evaluate each of the following.

(a) $\bar{v}$ (b) $|v|$ (c) $v - w$ (d) vw

(e) w/v (f) $1/w$ (g) w^2 (h) $2w - 3v$

Exercise 18

Solve (for x in $\mathbb{C}$) the quadratic equation $2x^2 + 2x + 1 = 0$.

Notice that the solutions obtained in Exercise 18 are complex conjugates of one another. This is not accidental: any quadratic function with real coefficients has roots that are a pair of complex conjugates (of the form $a \pm bi$). This follows directly from equation (9) for the solution of a quadratic equation.

4.2 Polar form of complex numbers

Diagnostic test

Try Exercises 21(a), 21(c) and 21(f). If your answers agree with the solutions, you may proceed quickly to Subsection 4.3.

Before discussing the polar form of a complex number, here is a brief review of polar coordinates.

Polar coordinates

Polar coordinates provide an alternative way of representing points in the plane. Figure 21 shows a point A with Cartesian coordinates (x, y) and polar coordinates (r, θ). The quantity r is the distance from the origin to A, so $r \geq 0$. The angle θ is measured anticlockwise from the positive x-axis. (Negative angles correspond to measuring clockwise from the positive x-axis.)

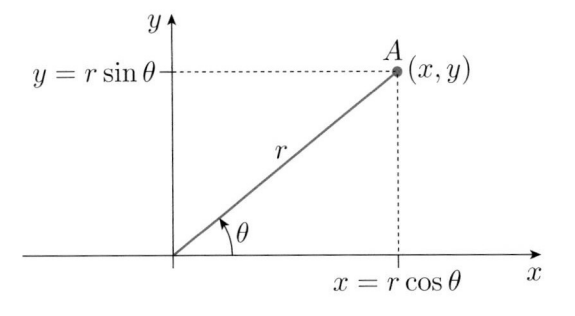

Figure 21 Cartesian (x, y) and polar (r, θ) coordinates of a point A

It is convenient to allow θ to take any real value, but this has the consequence that the polar representation of a point is not unique. For example, (r, θ) and $(r, \theta + 2\pi)$ provide polar coordinates of the same point. We can see from Figure 21 that if a point has polar coordinates (r, θ) and Cartesian coordinates (x, y), then

$$x = r \cos \theta \quad \text{and} \quad y = r \sin \theta. \tag{49}$$

These equations allow us to translate from polar to Cartesian coordinates. To translate from Cartesian to polar coordinates, we can use (see Figure 21)

$$r = \sqrt{x^2 + y^2}, \quad \cos \theta = x/r, \quad \sin \theta = y/r \quad (r \neq 0). \tag{50}$$

If $r = 0$, then we can choose any value for θ.

Equations (50) do not have a unique solution for θ in $\mathbb{R}$, but they do have a unique solution in the range $-\pi < \theta \leq \pi$.

Exercise 19

Locate each of the following points (x, y) on a diagram like Figure 21.

$$(-2, 0), \quad (1, 1), \quad (-1, -1), \quad (4, 0), \quad (0, 4), \quad (-\sqrt{3}, 1).$$

Hence find the polar coordinates (r, θ) of each point, for θ in the range $-\pi < \theta \leq \pi$.

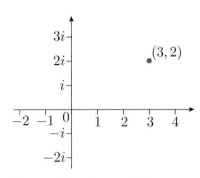

Figure 22 Argand diagram showing the point $3 + 2i$

Polar form of a complex number

A complex number $x + yi$ can be represented geometrically by treating its real and imaginary parts as Cartesian coordinates (x, y) in a plane. This produces a diagram known as an **Argand diagram**. For example, Figure 22 shows on an Argand diagram the point $3 + 2i$, with real part 3 and imaginary part 2.

By combining polar coordinates with the Argand diagram, we obtain the *polar form* of a complex number. For a complex number $z = x + yi$, we take the Cartesian coordinates (x, y) and convert them to the corresponding polar coordinates (r, θ). Then, using the relation between polar and Cartesian coordinates, we have

$$z = x + yi = x + iy = r\cos\theta + ir\sin\theta = r(\cos\theta + i\sin\theta). \tag{51}$$

This is the **polar form** of z. Here, $r = \sqrt{x^2 + y^2} = |z|$ is the **modulus** of z, and θ is an **argument** of z. As noted above, θ is not unique, but there *is* a unique value of θ in the range $-\pi < \theta \leq \pi$. This is called the **principal value** of the argument, and is written as $\mathrm{Arg}(z)$. When there is no possibility of confusion, we often write (r, θ) as shorthand for the polar form $r(\cos\theta + i\sin\theta)$.

Exercise 20

If a complex number z has polar form $\left(2, -\frac{\pi}{4}\right)$, what is its Cartesian form?

Exercise 21

Express each of the following complex numbers in polar form, choosing the principal value of the argument.

(a) -2 (b) $1 + i$ (c) $-1 - i$ (d) 4 (e) $4i$ (f) $-\sqrt{3} + i$

4.3 Euler's formula

> **Diagnostic test**
>
> Try Exercises 23 and 24. If your answers agree with the solutions, you may proceed quickly to Section 5.

The definition of the exponential function, equation (18), remains valid even when x is a complex number. There is a remarkable result that connects the exponential function and trigonometric functions, known as Euler's formula. If x is a real number, **Euler's formula** states that

$$\exp(ix) = \cos x + i\sin x. \tag{52}$$

To see why this is true, replace x in equation (18) by ix. This gives the Taylor series for $\exp(ix)$:

$$\exp(ix) = 1 + ix - \frac{x^2}{2!} - i\frac{x^3}{3!} + \frac{x^4}{4!} + i\frac{x^5}{5!} - \frac{x^6}{6!} - \cdots. \qquad (53)$$

Note that the definition $i^2 = -1$ gives $i^3 = -i$, $i^4 = 1$, $i^5 = i$, $i^6 = -1$, etc.

Collecting together the real and imaginary parts, we see that they correspond to the Taylor expansions of $\cos x$ and $\sin x$ (equations (44) and (45)) introduced at the end of Subsection 3.3:

$$\exp(ix) = \left(1 - \frac{x^2}{2!} + \frac{x^4}{4!} - \frac{x^6}{6!} + \cdots\right) + i\left(x - \frac{x^3}{3!} + \frac{x^5}{5!} - \cdots\right).$$

So

$$\exp(ix) = \cos x + i\sin x, \quad \text{or equivalently,} \quad e^{ix} = \cos x + i\sin x.$$

'Our jewel'

Euler's formula is a very interesting result because it connects exponential functions, which are easy to deal with mathematically, with trigonometric functions, which occur in descriptions of waves, oscillations and vibrations. Richard Feynman (Figure 23), who was a noted educator as well a Nobel prizewinner for his work on quantum electrodynamics, referred to Euler's formula as 'our jewel'.

One of the most common uses of Euler's formula is in the description of wave motion (Figure 24). A wave, such as an undulation of the height h of the surface of some water at position x and time t, might be described by a function such as

$$h(x,t) = A\cos(kx - \omega t),$$

where k, ω and A are real constants. In advanced calculations involving wave motion (including the ones that made Richard Feynman famous), a wave is often represented by a complex function of the form

$$H(x,t) = A\exp[i(kx - \omega t)],$$

whose real part is given by the equation for $h(x,t)$ above. It is often convenient to use this exponential form, and then take the real part at the end of the calculation.

Figure 23 Richard Feynman (1918–1988), Nobel laureate and bongo player

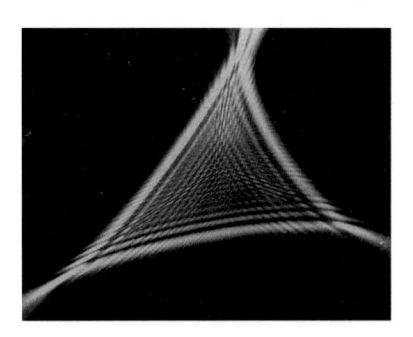

Figure 24 Euler's formula can help us to understand subtle phenomena involving wave motion, such as this pattern caused by the partial focusing of light waves

Exponential form of complex numbers

Combining equation (51) for the polar form of a complex number with Euler's formula, equation (52), it follows that any complex number can be written as

$$z = x + iy = r\exp(i\theta),$$

where r and θ have the same values as in the polar form. This alternative way of expressing a complex number, the **exponential form**, is particularly useful when we need to multiply and divide complex numbers.

In this form, r is the modulus of z, and θ is the argument of z. As with the polar form, the value of θ is not unique, but there is a unique choice of θ in the range $-\pi < \theta \leq \pi$.

Exercise 22

Express the following complex numbers as complex exponentials with arguments in the range $-\pi < \theta \leq \pi$.

(a) $z = 3e^{-i7\pi/2}$ (b) $z = e^{i71\pi}$

Exercise 23

A complex number has polar form $z = (r, \theta)$. Use the exponential form of z to find $\mathrm{Re}(ze^{i\omega t})$, i.e. the real part of $ze^{i\omega t}$, where ω and t are real.

Multiplication, division and powers revisited

Multiplication and division of complex numbers is far simpler in exponential and polar forms than in Cartesian form. If $z_1 = x_1 + iy_1 = r_1 e^{i\theta_1}$ and $z_2 = x_2 + iy_2 = r_2 e^{i\theta_2}$, then

$$z_1 z_2 = (r_1 e^{i\theta_1})(r_2 e^{i\theta_2}) = (r_1 r_2)\, e^{i(\theta_1 + \theta_2)}. \tag{54}$$

Note that although $\theta_1 + \theta_2$ is *an* argument of the product, it may not be the principal value of the argument.

So to multiply two numbers in exponential form, we just multiply their moduli and add their arguments. In polar form this rule is written as

$$r_1(\cos\theta_1 + i\sin\theta_1) \times r_2(\cos\theta_2 + i\sin\theta_2)$$
$$= r_1 r_2(\cos(\theta_1 + \theta_2) + i\sin(\theta_1 + \theta_2)),$$

or, in shorthand notation,

$$(r_1, \theta_1) \times (r_2, \theta_2) = (r_1 r_2, \theta_1 + \theta_2).$$

Similarly, for division of complex numbers,

$$\frac{z_1}{z_2} = \frac{r_1 e^{i\theta_1}}{r_2 e^{i\theta_2}} = \frac{r_1}{r_2}\, e^{i(\theta_1 - \theta_2)}. \tag{55}$$

So to divide two numbers in exponential form, we just divide their moduli and subtract their arguments. In shorthand polar form this means that

$$(r_1, \theta_1) \div (r_2, \theta_2) = (r_1/r_2, \theta_1 - \theta_2).$$

Further, if we multiply the complex number $z = re^{i\theta}$ by itself repeatedly, we obtain a formula for an integer power of a complex number:

$$z^n = (re^{i\theta})^n = r^n e^{in\theta} \tag{56}$$

or

$$(r, \theta)^n = (r^n, n\theta).$$

For a complex number of unit modulus (i.e. one with $r = 1$), we have

$$(\cos\theta + i\sin\theta)^n = \cos(n\theta) + i\sin(n\theta). \tag{57}$$

To avoid problems, n must be an integer in de Moivre's theorem.

This result is known as **de Moivre's theorem** (after Abraham de Moivre, 1667–1754).

Exercise 24

Express $1 - i$ in exponential form and hence simplify $(1-i)^{20}$.

Euler's formula also leads to useful expressions for the trigonometric functions in terms of complex exponentials. A complex number of unit modulus can be written as

$$e^{i\theta} = \cos\theta + i\sin\theta,$$

and its complex conjugate is

$$e^{-i\theta} = \cos\theta - i\sin\theta.$$

The complex conjugate is obtained by changing the sign of i wherever it appears.

Adding and subtracting these two equations then gives the results

$$\cos\theta = \frac{1}{2}\big(e^{i\theta} + e^{-i\theta}\big), \tag{58}$$

$$\sin\theta = \frac{1}{2i}\big(e^{i\theta} - e^{-i\theta}\big). \tag{59}$$

These formulas find many applications. As an example, let us derive a trigonometric identity relating $\cos^2\theta$ to $\cos 2\theta$. Using equation (54), we have

$$\begin{aligned}
\cos^2\theta &= \tfrac{1}{4}\big(e^{i\theta} + e^{-i\theta}\big)^2 \\
&= \tfrac{1}{4}\big(e^{i\theta}e^{i\theta} + 2e^{i\theta}e^{-i\theta} + e^{-i\theta}e^{-i\theta}\big) \\
&= \tfrac{1}{4}\big(e^{2i\theta} + 2 + e^{-2i\theta}\big) \\
&= \tfrac{1}{4}\big(e^{2i\theta} + e^{-2i\theta}\big) + \tfrac{1}{2} \\
&= \tfrac{1}{2}[\cos(2\theta) + 1].
\end{aligned}$$

This is a rearranged version of equation (42).

5 Differentiation

The concepts and techniques of calculus are central to many of the mathematical methods discussed in this module. This section considers differentiation.

Differentiation is fundamental to mechanics: if an object moving in a straight line has position $x(t)$ at time t, then its velocity at time t is given by the derivative

$$v(t) = \frac{dx}{dt},$$

and its acceleration at time t is given by

$$a(t) = \frac{dv}{dt} = \frac{d^2x}{dt^2}.$$

5.1 Derivative as a rate of change

You may use the Handbook to look up standard derivatives.

Differentiation gives the rate of change of one variable with respect to another. For example, consider the function (introduced in Subsection 1.1)

$$V(t) = 2 \times 10^6 - 15t, \tag{60}$$

where $V(t)$ is the volume of water in a reservoir (in cubic metres) at time t (in minutes, from midday on 1 June). In this case, the rate of change of V with respect to t is -15 (in cubic metres per minute). This is negative because the volume is decreasing, and it is constant because the volume of water is falling by the same amount each minute. For linear functions, such as this, the rate of change is always constant. This corresponds to the fact that a linear function has a straight-line graph whose gradient (or slope) is the same everywhere.

Now consider a non-linear function, such as

$$y(t) = -4.9t^2 + 10t + 2 \tag{61}$$

(introduced in Subsection 1.3), which gives the height (y metres at time t seconds) of a ball thrown vertically upwards with an initial speed of 10 metres per second, from an initial height of 2 metres. In this case, the rate of change of height with respect to time is the vertical velocity v of the ball (which is positive when the ball is moving upwards, and negative when it is moving downwards). Differentiation allows us to show that the velocity of the ball (in metres per second) is

$$v(t) = -9.8t + 10. \tag{62}$$

This is a function of time: the velocity of the ball is positive to begin with, and then becomes negative as the ball falls back to the ground. This corresponds to the fact that the quadratic function in equation (61) has a parabolic graph (Figure 25), with a gradient that varies from point to point. The process that takes us from the function $y(t)$ in equation (61) to the function $v(t)$ in equation (62) is called **differentiation**. The function $v(t)$ is called the **derivative** or **derived function** of $y(t)$. This function is denoted by dy/dt or $y'(t)$, so in the present case

$$\frac{dy}{dt} = y'(t) = -9.8t + 10.$$

At each value of t, this derivative gives the gradient of the graph of y against t.

More generally, given a function $f(x)$, the gradient of the graph of $f(x)$ against x at a particular point $x = x_0$ is equal to the derivative $f'(x)$ of the function f at that point. This leads to a definition of the derivative, based on Figure 26.

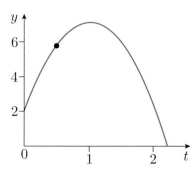

Figure 25 A graph of height y against time t for a ball thrown upwards

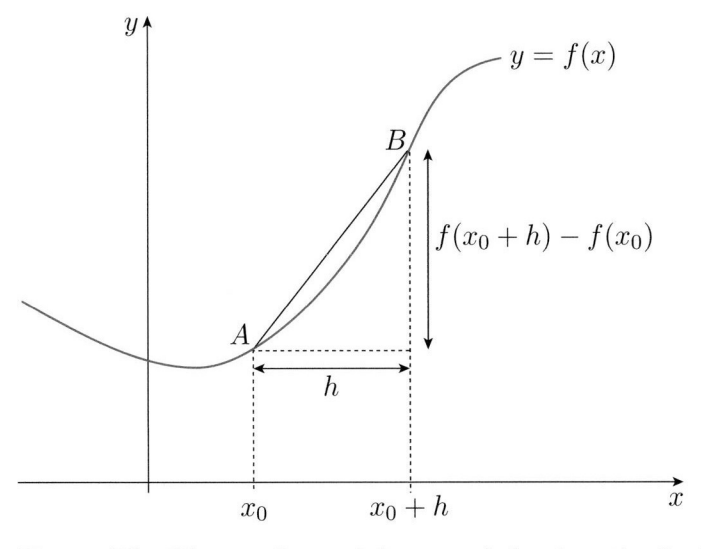

Figure 26 The gradient of f at x_0, defined as the limiting value of the gradient of the chord AB

The **gradient** of the graph $y = f(x)$ at $x = x_0$ is defined as the limiting value of the gradient of the chord AB in Figure 26, as B approaches A. The gradient of this chord is $(f(x_0 + h) - f(x_0))/h$, and the process of allowing B to approach A corresponds to h tending to 0, often written as $h \to 0$. Hence the derivative of f at x_0 may be formally defined as follows.

This definition assumes that the limit exists and is the same whether h approaches 0 through positive or negative values. When these conditions are not met, the function cannot be differentiated at x_0.

Definition

The **derivative of a function** $f(x)$ at $x = x_0$ is

$$f'(x_0) = \lim_{h \to 0} \left(\frac{f(x_0 + h) - f(x_0)}{h} \right).$$

Working from this definition, it is possible to obtain formulas for the derivatives of standard functions. You need not be concerned with the sometimes lengthy details. For our purposes, it is enough to know that all the basic derivatives that we need are tabulated in the module Handbook, and can be used as required. As usual, it helps to remember the most frequently used results, such as the derivatives of x^a, $\sin x$, $\exp(x)$ and $\ln x$, but this generally comes with practice rather than rote memorisation. Note that the *basic* derivatives are tabulated. The Handbook does not give the derivative of every function that you might encounter. Generally, you need to combine two elements:

- derivatives of standard functions

- rules for differentiating combinations of functions of various types, in sums, products, quotients and compositions.

The skill in differentiation lies mostly in applying the rules. The simplest rule concerns constant multiples and sums. In general, the derivative of a combination $a\,f(x) + b\,g(x)$, where a and b are constants, is given by

$$\frac{d}{dx}[a\,f(x) + b\,g(x)] = a\,\frac{df}{dx} + b\,\frac{dg}{dx}. \tag{63}$$

To illustrate this, let us return to equation (61):

$$y(t) = -4.9t^2 + 10t + 2.$$

Applying patterns for derivatives given in the Handbook, we see that

$$\frac{d}{dt}(t^2) = 2t, \quad \frac{d}{dt}(t) = 1 \quad \text{and} \quad \frac{d}{dt}(\text{constant}) = 0.$$

Hence, applying the rule in equation (63), we get

$$\begin{aligned}
\frac{dy}{dt} &= -4.9\,\frac{d}{dt}(t^2) + 10\,\frac{d}{dt}(t) + \frac{d}{dt}(2)\\
&= -4.9(2t) + 10(1) + 0\\
&= -9.8t + 10.
\end{aligned}$$

A similar process applied to the function in equation (60) gives $dV/dt = -15$, a constant negative value corresponding to the fact that V decreases at a constant rate.

Notation for derivatives

There are various notations for derivatives, some of which we have used above. We will use whichever is convenient in a particular context.

In text, $\dfrac{dy}{dt}$ may be written as dy/dt, to save space.

Notation expressed purely in terms of variables, such as dy/dt, is referred to as *Leibniz notation* (after its inventor, Gottfried Wilhelm Leibniz (1646–1716)). This notation is extended to write, for example,

$$\frac{d}{dt}(3t + 5\sin 2t) \quad \text{or} \quad \frac{d}{dx}(ax + bx^2).$$

It is implicit that, in general, dy/dt is a function of t, but this fact may sometimes be emphasised by writing $\dfrac{dy}{dt}(t)$. In Leibniz notation, the value of a derivative at a particular point, such as $t = 3$, is written as $\left.\dfrac{dy}{dt}\right|_{t=3}$.

The alternative to Leibniz notation is *function notation*, where differentiation is indicated by adding a prime ($'$) to the function name. So the derivative of $f(x)$ is $f'(x)$. This clearly shows that the derivative is a function of x, and the value of the derivative at $x = 3$ is written as $f'(3)$. To give another example, the derivative of $h(t)$ is $h'(t)$, and the value of this derivative at $t = 4$ is $h'(4)$. We must take care to use this notation correctly. The symbol y', for example, means the derivative of the function y, but could lead to confusion if y is being used for both $y(t)$ and $y(x)$.

Because the derivative of a function is itself a function, it can be differentiated again. For example, if $y(x) = x^3 + 5x$, then

$$\frac{dy}{dx} = y'(x) = 3x^2 + 5. \tag{64}$$

This derivative is itself a function of x, and can be differentiated again to obtain the **second derivative** of $y(x)$. In Leibniz notation, we write the second derivative as d^2y/dx^2. In function notation, it is written with two primes, as $y''(x)$. So the derivative of equation (64) is

The derivative dy/dx is sometimes referred to as the **first derivative**.

$$\frac{d}{dx}\left(\frac{dy}{dx}\right) = \frac{d^2y}{dx^2} = y''(x) = 6x.$$

The value of this derivative at $x = 4$ is then denoted by

$$\left.\frac{d^2y}{dx^2}\right|_{x=4} = 24 \quad \text{or} \quad y''(4) = 24.$$

Differentiating again gives the **third derivative**, written $\dfrac{d^3y}{dx^3}$ or $y'''(x)$, which may also be written $y^{(3)}(x)$. For equation (64), $y'''(x) = 6$. The process can be continued, and a general **nth derivative** is written as $\dfrac{d^ny}{dx^n}$ or $y^{(n)}(x)$, where n is referred to as the **order** of the derivative.

There is one final piece of notation to mention. Time (habitually denoted by t) is so often the independent variable that there is a separate notational convention for differentiation with respect to it. A dot is placed over the dependent variable to indicate a first derivative with respect to t, and two dots to indicate a second derivative. So if $x(t)$ is the position of an object as a function of time t, then $\dot{x}$ means the same as dx/dt or $x'(t)$, while $\ddot{x}$ means the same as d^2x/dt^2 or $x''(t)$. As noted at the beginning of this section, these derivatives represent the velocity and acceleration of a particle in straight-line motion.

This notation is attributed to Isaac Newton (1642–1727), so is sometimes referred to as *Newtonian notation.*

The following exercises offer practice in differentiating standard functions, and constant multiples and sums of these. Refer to the Handbook for standard derivatives if necessary.

It will be helpful later on, especially in integration, if you can remember the derivatives of polynomials, exponentials, natural logarithms and trigonometric functions.

Exercise 25

Suppose that an object is moving in a straight line so that its position x (measured from a chosen origin) is related to time t by the equation

$$x = 5 + 7\cos(3t).$$

Find expressions in terms of t for the velocity $\dot{x}$ and acceleration $\ddot{x}$ of the object.

Exercise 26

The weekly wage bill of a company, t years in the future, is projected to be B pounds sterling, where

$$B = 10^5 \exp(0.04t).$$

Find an expression for the rate at which the wage bill will be rising in t years' time. What will this rate of rise be as a percentage of the wage bill at that time?

Exercise 27

Calculate the following derivatives.

(a) $\dfrac{dy}{dx}$, where $y = 1 - 9\exp(-5x)$.

(b) $F'(2)$, where $F(x) = 3x^4 - 4x + 1$.

(c) $\dfrac{d^2y}{dt^2}$, where $y = \ln t \ (t > 0)$.

(d) $g''(0)$, where $g(t) = a\cos(3t) + b\sin(3t)$ (and a and b are constants).

(e) $F'\!\left(\frac{\pi}{6}\right)$, where $F(x) = 3\sec(2x) - 4\cos(-3x)$.

We sometimes need to differentiate a **complex-valued** function of the form

$$f(t) = g(t) + i\,h(t),$$

where g and h are real functions. Differentiation of such a function follows the usual rule for constant multiples and sums. So

$$f'(t) = g'(t) + i\,h'(t).$$

For example, if $f(t) = \cos(3t) + i\sin(3t)$, then

$$f'(t) = -3\sin(3t) + 3i\cos(3t).$$

Exercise 28

Find the second derivative $d^2 f/dt^2$ of the function $f(t) = \cos(2t) + i\sin(2t)$. Do this in two ways: first by differentiating the real and imaginary parts, and then by using Euler's formula to express this function as a complex exponential, which you can differentiate using equation (19). Check that you obtain the same result in both cases.

5.2 Differentiating combinations of functions

> **Diagnostic test**
>
> Try Exercises 31 and 32(b). If your answers agree with the solutions, you may proceed quickly to Subsection 5.3.

The rule for differentiating constant multiples and sums is natural and easy to apply. Rules for products, quotients and compositions of functions are also very important. They are given below and in the Handbook, but you will be much better off if you remember them through practice of use. We begin with the rules for products and quotients.

The product rule

The derivative of the product of two functions is given by

$$(fg)' = f'g + fg', \tag{65}$$

or, in Leibniz notation,

$$\frac{d}{dx}(uv) = \frac{du}{dx}v + u\frac{dv}{dx}. \tag{66}$$

The quotient rule

The derivative of the quotient of two functions is given by

$$\left(\frac{f}{g}\right)' = \frac{f'g - fg'}{g^2}, \tag{67}$$

or, in Leibniz notation,

$$\frac{d}{dx}\left(\frac{u}{v}\right) = \frac{\dfrac{du}{dx}v - u\dfrac{dv}{dx}}{v^2}. \tag{68}$$

Example 3

(a) Find $h'(x)$, where $h(x) = x^3\cos(2x)$.

(b) Find $w'(x)$, where $w(x) = x^2/(3x^2 + 1)$.

Solution

(a) $h(x)$ is a product $f(x)\,g(x)$, with $f(x) = x^3$ and $g(x) = \cos(2x)$.

We have

$$f'(x) = 3x^2 \quad \text{and} \quad g'(x) = -2\sin(2x).$$

So the product rule gives

$$h'(x) = 3x^2\cos(2x) - 2x^3\sin(2x).$$

(b) $w(x)$ is a quotient $u(x)/v(x)$, with $u(x) = x^2$ and $v(x) = 3x^2 + 1$.

We have

$$u'(x) = 2x \quad \text{and} \quad v'(x) = 6x.$$

So the quotient rule gives

$$w'(x) = \frac{2x(3x^2 + 1) - x^2 \times 6x}{(3x^2 + 1)^2} = \frac{2x}{(3x^2 + 1)^2}.$$

(a) Find $\dfrac{dy}{dx}$, where $y(x) = \dfrac{\ln x}{x^2 + 1}$.

(b) Find $f'(t)$, where $f(t) = t^5 \ln(3t)$ and $t > 0$.

(c) Find $g'(0)$ (in terms of the constants A, B and C), where
$g(t) = (At + B)\sin(Ct)$.

(d) If the position of an object at time t is given by $e^{-3t}\sin(4t)$, find its velocity and acceleration as functions of time.

The rule for composite functions is a little more complicated to use.

The composite rule

If h is the composition of two functions g and u, so that $h(x) = g(u(x))$, then

$$h'(x) = g'(u(x))\, u'(x). \tag{69}$$

Expressed in Leibniz notation, this rule looks rather different: if $u = u(x)$ is a function of x, and $h = h(u)$, then

$$\frac{dh}{dx} = \frac{dh}{du}\frac{du}{dx}. \tag{70}$$

In this form, the composite rule is often called the **chain rule**.

The essential point is that the derivative of a composite function is found by differentiating the outer function and then multiplying by the derivative of the inner function. For example, consider differentiating $h(x) = \sin(x^3 + 2x)$. First, you should recognise that $h(x)$ is the composition of two functions: $h(x) = g(u(x))$. The inner function is $u(x) = x^3 + 2x$, and the outer function is $g(u) = \sin(u)$. To apply the composite rule, we first find the derivatives of these: $u'(x) = 3x^2 + 2$ and $g'(u) = \cos(u)$. Multiplying these then gives

$$h'(x) = g'(u(x)) \times u'(x) = \cos(x^3 + 2x) \times (3x^2 + 2).$$

Alternatively, we can use the chain rule by writing $u = x^3 + 2x$ so that $h(u) = \sin(u)$. Then

$$\frac{dh}{dx} = \frac{dh}{du}\frac{du}{dx} = \cos(u) \times (3x^2 + 2) = \cos(3x^2 + 2) \times (3x^2 + 2).$$

Example 4

Find df/dx, where $f(x) = \sin^3 x = (\sin x)^3$.

Solution

If we let $u = \sin x$, then we have $f(x) = [u(x)]^3$.

The chain rule then gives

$$\frac{df}{dx} = \frac{df}{du}\frac{du}{dx} = 3u^2 \cos x = 3\sin^2 x \cos x,$$

where we have replaced the variable u by $\sin x$ in the last step.

> The recognition of $\sin^3 x$ as a composite function, and of how to break it down into two parts, each consisting of a standard function, is the key to differentiating it.

Exercise 30

Use the composite rule (or chain rule) to differentiate each of the following.

(a) $y(t) = \exp(t^2)$ (b) $f(x) = (3x^3 + 4)^6$ (c) $z(v) = \tan(3v + 4)$

(d) $g(z) = \sqrt{4 - z^2}$ (e) $f(x) = 1/\left(\sqrt{1 + 2x^2}\,\right)^3$

Exercise 31

Differentiate the following functions.

> These differentiations involve more than one rule.

(a) $y = \sec\left(\dfrac{x}{x^2 + 1}\right)$ (b) $z = t^2 \exp(t^3 + 1)$

Implicit differentiation

Suppose that we want to find the gradient at the point $(x, y) = (2, 1)$ of the tangent to the ellipse with equation

$$x^2 + 4y^2 = 8. \tag{71}$$

We want dy/dx at $x = 2$ and $y = 1$. We could start by expressing y as a function of x, but a more convenient approach is to differentiate the equation as it stands. To differentiate y^2 with respect to x, we use the composite rule, and obtain

$$\frac{d(y^2)}{dx} = \frac{d(y^2)}{dy}\frac{dy}{dx} = 2y\frac{dy}{dx}.$$

So, differentiating both sides of equation (71) with respect to x, we obtain

$$2x + 4 \times 2y\frac{dy}{dx} = 0.$$

When $x = 2$ and $y = 1$, this gives $4 + 8\,dy/dx = 0$, so $dy/dx = -\frac{1}{2}$. Therefore the tangent to this ellipse at $(2, 1)$ has gradient $-\frac{1}{2}$.

Differentiation with respect to x of an expression such as $x^2 + 4y^2$, where y is a function of x, is known as **implicit differentiation**.

Exercise 32

(a) Use the product and composite rules to find the following in terms of x, y and dy/dx.

(i) $\dfrac{d}{dx}(x^2 y)$ (ii) $\dfrac{d}{dx}(y^3)$ (iii) $\dfrac{d}{dx}(x + \sin(xy))$

(b) Find the gradient at the point $(-1, 1)$ of the tangent to the curve

$$x^3 + x^2 y + y^3 = 1.$$

5.3   Investigating functions

Diagnostic test

Try Exercise 33. If your answer agrees with the solution, you may proceed quickly to Section 6.

Faced with an expression made up of some combination of standard functions, how might you investigate its behaviour? As an example, consider the function

$$f = \frac{v}{4 + 1.5v + 0.008v^2},$$

where we would like to see how f varies as v varies.

A sketch graph of f against v helps with this, and a computer package or graphics calculator will provide such a graph. However, it is not always obvious for what range of values to plot the graph, so it is helpful to be able to deduce some information about the general behaviour of a function 'by hand', without recourse to a machine. Such information can also be used to cross-check results obtained from a machine, and to flesh out the picture more fully. This example will be continued in Exercise 34, but first consider some general remarks about sketching graphs.

Example 5 below illustrates ways of answering these questions.

Questions that you might consider before sketching the graph of a function $f(x)$ include the following:

1.   Are there any points where $f(x)$ is not defined?

2.   Where does the graph of $f(x)$ cross the axes?

3.   How does $f(x)$ behave for large and small values of x (or at the endpoints of its domain if this is finite)?

4.   Are there any stationary points of $f(x)$? If so, are there any local maximum or minimum values?

5.   Where does the graph of $f(x)$ have a positive gradient, and where does it have a negative gradient?

The last two questions can be answered using differentiation.

Definition

A **stationary point** of a function $f(x)$ is a value of x where $f'(x) = 0$.

Local maxima and local minima occur at stationary points, although a stationary point need not necessarily be either. Figure 27 illustrates stationary points of various kinds.

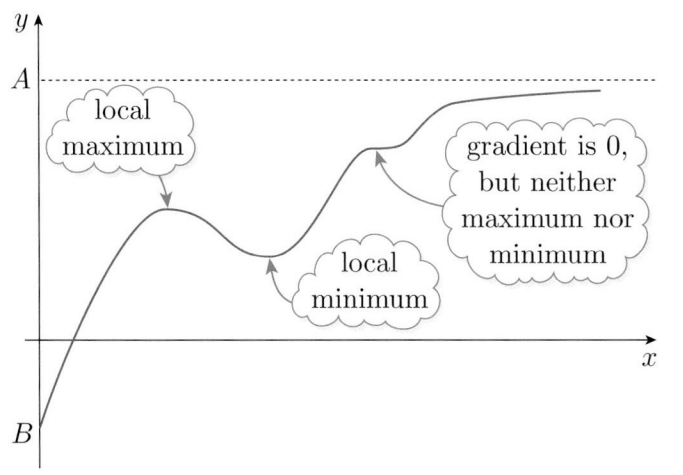

Figure 27   Stationary points of a hypothetical function $f(x)$

There is a **local maximum** at x_0 if $f(x_0) > f(x)$ for all points x in the immediate vicinity of x_0, and there is a **local minimum** at x_0 if $f(x_0) < f(x)$ for all points x in the immediate vicinity of x_0. Figure 27 also shows a stationary point that is neither a local maximum nor a local minimum: such a point is called a **point of inflection**.

To classify a given stationary point of $f(x)$, we can use a test based on the second derivative, $f''(x)$.

Classifying stationary points using second derivatives

A stationary point x_0 of a function $f(x)$ is:

- a local maximum if $f''(x_0) < 0$
- a local minimum if $f''(x_0) > 0$
- a point of inflection if $f''(x_0) = 0$ *and* $f''(x)$ changes sign as x increases through x_0.

Note that the condition $f''(x_0) = 0$ is insufficient *by itself* to determine the nature of the stationary point.

An alternative strategy is sometimes preferred; it is useful in cases where evaluation of the second derivative is messy.

Classifying stationary points using first derivatives

A stationary point x_0 of a function $f(x)$ is:

- a local maximum if, for all x in the immediate vicinity of x_0, we have $f'(x) > 0$ for $x < x_0$ and $f'(x) < 0$ for $x > x_0$

- a local minimum if, for all x in the immediate vicinity of x_0, we have $f'(x) < 0$ for $x < x_0$ and $f'(x) > 0$ for $x > x_0$.

We often wish to find the overall maximum or overall minimum of some function, usually referred to as the **global maximum** or **global minimum**, respectively. The global minimum or global maximum of a function may well occur at a stationary point; but caution is needed, for it need not necessarily do so. For example, if the function $f(x)$ in Figure 27 is defined in the domain $0 \le x < \infty$, then its global minimum occurs at the endpoint $x = 0$, which is not a stationary point. In fact, a function need not have a global maximum or global minimum. For example, the function in Figure 27 exceeds the local maximum value when x is large, but it never reaches a global maximum. Notice that the value of $f(x)$ does not grow without limit. Instead, it gets arbitrarily close to the value A as x increases, but it always remains smaller than A, and never actually reaches this limiting value. The line $y = A$ is called an **asymptote** of the graph of $f(x)$. Such behaviour is sometimes indicated by writing $f \to A$ as $x \to \infty$, which is read as 'f tends to the value A as x tends to infinity'.

Exercise 33

(a) Find any stationary points of the function

$$y(x) = 5 - 2(x + 1)e^{-x/2} \quad (x \ge 0).$$

(b) Classify these as local minima or local maxima or neither, and evaluate $y(x)$ at these points.

Example 5

Suppose that

$$(x^2 - 3)y = x - 2.$$

Sketch a graph of y against x.

Solution

We address some of the questions listed at the beginning of this subsection.

(1) *Points where y is not defined.* We have

$$y = \frac{x - 2}{x^2 - 3}.$$

This is not defined when $x^2 - 3 = 0$, i.e. at $x = \pm\sqrt{3}$.

(2) *Points where $y(x)$ crosses the axes.* We can see that $y = 0$ if (and only if) $x = 2$, so the graph crosses the x-axis at this one point.

(3) *Behaviour for large values of x.* If x is large (positive or negative), then y will be close to zero.

(4) *Stationary points and their classification.* To look for stationary points, we use the quotient rule to calculate

$$\frac{dy}{dx} = \frac{(1)(x^2 - 3) - (x - 2)(2x)}{(x^2 - 3)^2}$$
$$= \frac{-x^2 + 4x - 3}{(x^2 - 3)^2} = -\frac{(x - 1)(x - 3)}{(x^2 - 3)^2}.$$

This is zero if $(x - 1)(x - 3) = 0$. So the function has stationary points at $x = 1$ and $x = 3$.

In this case, the second derivative is a bit messy to calculate, and it is easier to look at the sign of the first derivative near $x = 1$ and $x = 3$ to check whether these stationary points are local maxima or minima. If x is just less than 1, then dy/dx is negative, while if x is just greater than 1, then dy/dx is positive. Hence $x = 1$ is a local minimum. For x just below 3, dy/dx is positive, while for x just above 3, it is negative, so $x = 3$ is a local maximum. The values of the function at these points are: $y = 1/2$ at $x = 1$, and $y = 1/6$ at $x = 3$.

Try $x = 0.9$ and $x = 1.1$.

Try $x = 2.9$ and $x = 3.1$.

(5) *Regions of positive and negative gradient.* Just below the local minimum, and just above the local maximum, the function has a negative gradient. Just above the local minimum, and just below the local maximum, it has a positive gradient. Because there are no other local minima or maxima, we can make further deductions: for example, the gradient remains positive everywhere between the local minimum at $x = 1$ and the point $x = \sqrt{3}$, where the function is not defined.

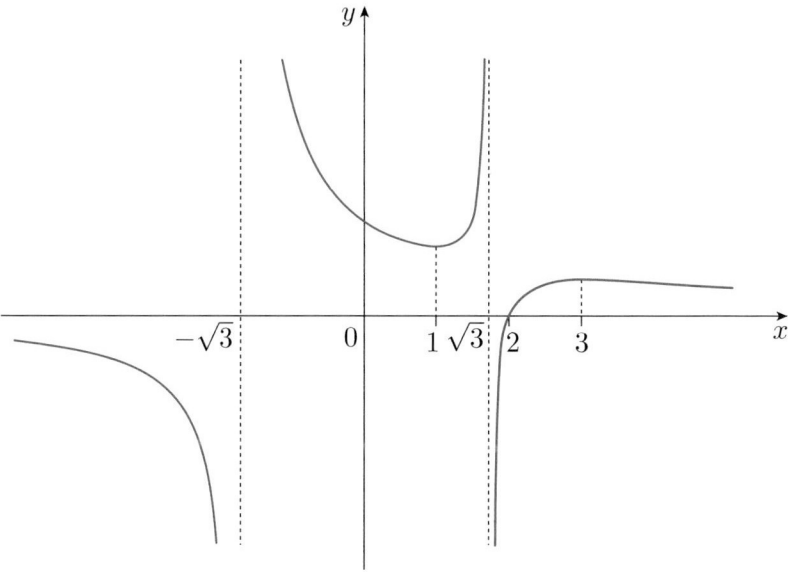

Figure 28 A graph of $y = (x - 2)/(x^2 - 3)$

Incorporating all this information (plus other information, such as the behaviour of y near $x = \pm\sqrt{3}$), we can produce a sketch graph of the function. Figure 28 exhibits all the main features.

Exercise 34

Consider the function
$$f(v) = \frac{v}{4 + 1.5v + 0.008v^2} \quad (v \geq 0).$$

(a) (i) Find any values of v for which $f(v)$ is not defined.

  (ii) Find any values of v for which $f(v)$ is zero.

  (iii) Indicate how $f(v)$ behaves as v becomes large.

  (iv) Find any local maxima or minima of $f(v)$, and evaluate $f(v)$ at these points.

(b) Sketch a graph of $f(v)$, and use it to deduce the global maximum and global minimum of the function.

---

6 Integration

Integration arises in two different contexts. First, it 'reverses the process of differentiation'. Subsection 6.1 provides a reminder of this basic idea, and Subsection 6.2 discusses how to find relatively simple integrals, referring to the Handbook for standard results if necessary. Subsection 6.3 looks at two special techniques for finding more complicated integrals by hand.

Integration also arises as a kind of summation. For example, the mass of an object can be expressed as the integral of a function that describes how the object's density varies from point to point. Such *definite integrals* are discussed in Subsection 6.4.

6.1 Reversing differentiation

> **Diagnostic test**
>
> Try Exercise 35. If your answer agrees with the solution, you may proceed quickly to Subsection 6.2.

In the rest of this book, and elsewhere in the module, you will meet a variety of *differential equations*. These are equations involving the derivative of a function.

For example, if x is the position of a particle and t is time, then the velocity ($v = dx/dt$) might be given by the equation

$$\frac{dx}{dt} = 5t + 7. \tag{72}$$

The objective is usually to 'solve' the equation, so in this case we want to find the position x as a function of time t. To do this involves 'reversing' the differentiation, and this process is referred to as **integration**. In the above example we **integrate** both sides of the equation with respect to t, obtaining

$$x = \int (5t + 7)\, dt. \tag{73}$$

To evaluate this integral, you can use a table of standard integrals in the Handbook. The result is

$$x = \tfrac{5}{2}t^2 + 7t + C, \tag{74}$$

where C can be any constant. To confirm that equation (74) really is the solution of equation (72), we can differentiate it, obtaining

$$\frac{dx}{dt} = \frac{d}{dt}(\tfrac{5}{2}t^2 + 7t + C) = 5t + 7,$$

as required. The constant C is often referred to as an **arbitrary constant** or a **constant of integration**. Its presence means that the differential equation (72) does not have a *unique* solution.

Note that the arbitrary constant is included once the expression has been integrated (as in equation (74)), not before.

More generally, suppose that $f(x)$ is a known function, and $F(x)$ is an unknown function satisfying the differential equation

$$F'(x) = f(x).$$

Then we write the solution of this equation as

$$F(x) = \int f(x)\, dx,$$

where the right-hand side, $\int f(x)\, dx$, is called the **indefinite integral** of $f(x)$, and the function to be integrated, $f(x)$, is called the **integrand**.

For example, the differential equation

$$F'(x) = \frac{1}{1 + x^2} \tag{75}$$

has solution

$$F(x) = \int \frac{1}{1 + x^2}\, dx.$$

We now need to find the integral. In this case we are lucky, since the table of standard derivatives in the Handbook gives

$$\frac{d}{dx}(\arctan x) = \frac{1}{1 + x^2}.$$

Any function that differentiates to $1/(1 + x^2)$, such as $F(x) = \arctan x + 5$, is referred to as an **integral** (or *antiderivative*) of $1/(1 + x^2)$.

Hence we have

$$\int \frac{1}{1 + x^2}\, dx = \arctan x + C,$$

where C is an arbitrary constant.

By contrast, consider finding the integral

$$\int \exp(-x^2)\, dx.$$

At first sight, this might seem no harder a problem to solve than equation (75). In fact, however, it is impossible! To be more precise, there is no simple combination of the elementary functions (polynomials, sin, cos, exp and ln) that when differentiated gives $\exp(-x^2)$.

Finding explicit expressions for integrals is a much harder task than finding derivatives. The rules of differentiation ensure that we can, in principle, find an explicit expression for the derivative of any combination of elementary functions. The equivalent is not true for integrals. What is more, even when integrals can be found, the working needed can be messy. The art of integration often relies on recognising patterns and knowing what works in particular cases.

There is a table of standard integrals in the Handbook. An integral will be readily found if it fits into one of the patterns listed there (such as $\int e^{ax}\, dx$ or $\int x^a\, dx$ for $a \neq -1$). Note that the table in the Handbook does not include arbitrary constants – you must supply these yourself. There are also simple rules for integrating constant multiples and sums. More complicated integrals can often be found using two techniques that will be introduced later: *integration by substitution* and *integration by parts*.

The table of standard integrals in the Handbook contains quite a wide selection of integrals. Some of these integrals are deduced from the table of standard derivatives, others by using integration by parts or substitution. You can regard them all as the fruit of others' experience, and draw on them as needed. The correctness of an integral obtained by using the Handbook can always be verified by differentiation.

Exercise 35

Use differentiation to verify that the following integrals are correct (where $a \neq 0$ is a constant and C is an arbitrary constant).

(a) $\displaystyle\int x \sin(ax)\, dx = -\frac{x}{a}\cos(ax) + \frac{1}{a^2}\sin(ax) + C$

(b) $\displaystyle\int \tan(ax)\, dx = -\frac{1}{a}\ln(\cos(ax)) + C \quad \left(-\frac{\pi}{2} < ax < \frac{\pi}{2}\right)$

6.2 Evaluating integrals

Your first recourse for finding an integral by hand is the table of standard integrals in the Handbook. If the integrals of functions f and g are known, then the integral of $af + bg$, where a and b are constants, is readily found, using the rule

$$\int \left(a\, f(x) + b\, g(x)\right) dx = a \int f(x)\, dx + b \int g(x)\, dx. \tag{76}$$

So, for example (referring to the Handbook for $\int e^{2x}\, dx$ and $\int x^7\, dx$),

$$\int (4e^{2x} + 9x^7)\, dx = 4 \int e^{2x}\, dx + 9 \int x^7\, dx$$
$$= 4\left(\tfrac{1}{2}e^{2x}\right) + 9\left(\tfrac{1}{8}x^8\right) + C$$
$$= 2e^{2x} + \tfrac{9}{8}x^8 + C.$$

Or, preferably, use your memory!

Each of the integrals introduces an arbitrary constant, but the sum of these is also an arbitrary constant, so we need only one.

Sometimes algebraic manipulation can transform an expression to be integrated into a more amenable form. For example, the manipulation

$$\frac{3x^2 + 2x}{\sqrt{x}} = \frac{3x^2}{\sqrt{x}} + \frac{2x}{\sqrt{x}} = 3x^{3/2} + 2x^{1/2}$$

transforms the expression on the left into a sum of constant multiples of integrals tabulated in the Handbook. Less obvious transformations can be achieved using trigonometric formulas. For example, equation (42) can be rearranged to give

$$\cos^2 x = \tfrac{1}{2}(1 + \cos 2x),$$

which enables us to integrate $\cos^2 x$.

Exercise 36

Use the identity

$$\cos^2(ax) = \tfrac{1}{2}[1 + \cos(2ax)]$$

(where $a \neq 0$ is a constant) to obtain $\displaystyle\int \cos^2(ax)\, dx$.

At times, attention needs to be paid to domains, to avoid giving, as integrals, expressions that are not defined. For example, if $x > 0$, then there is no difficulty in writing

$$\int \frac{1}{x}\, dx = \ln x + C \quad (x > 0), \tag{77}$$

but the right-hand side of this expression makes no sense if $x < 0$ because $\ln x$ is not defined in this case. (The domain of $\ln x$ is $x > 0$.) For $x < 0$ we have instead

$$\int \frac{1}{x}\, dx = \ln(-x) + C \quad (x < 0). \tag{78}$$

Equations (77) and (78) are both valid, because

$$\frac{d}{dx}\ln(x) = \frac{1}{x} \quad \text{and} \quad \frac{d}{dx}\ln(-x) = \frac{1}{-x} \times (-1) = \frac{1}{x}.$$

The results in equations (77) and (78) are sometimes combined in the formula

$$\int \frac{1}{x}\, dx = \ln(|x|) + C \quad (x \neq 0),$$

where $|x|$ is the modulus of x, equal to $+x$ if $x \geq 0$, and to $-x$ if $x < 0$.

Exercise 37

Use the standard integrals given in the Handbook as necessary.

Find the following integrals.

(a) $\displaystyle\int e^{5x}\, dx$ 　　(b) $\displaystyle\int 6\sec^2(3t)\, dt$ 　　(c) $\displaystyle\int \frac{1}{36 + 4v^2}\, dv$

(d) $\displaystyle\int \frac{1}{3 - 2y}\, dy \quad \left(y < \tfrac{3}{2}\right)$ 　　(e) $\displaystyle\int \frac{1}{3 - 2y}\, dy \quad \left(y > \tfrac{3}{2}\right)$

Exercise 38

Use the standard integrals given in the Handbook as necessary.

Find the following integrals.

(a) $\displaystyle\int (6\cos(-2t) + 8\sin(4t))\, dt$ 　　(b) $\displaystyle\int \frac{1}{\sqrt{9 - t^2}}\, dt \quad (-3 < t < 3)$

(c) $\displaystyle\int \frac{5t^3 + 7}{t}\, dt \quad (t < 0)$ 　　(d) $\displaystyle\int \left(2\ln(4t) - \frac{2}{t}\right) dt \quad (t > 0)$

(e) $\displaystyle\int \frac{1}{(x - 1)(x + 1)}\, dx \quad (-1 < x < 1)$

The next example again uses a standard integral from the Handbook, but requires careful matching of parameters and attention to domains.

Example 6

For $x > \dfrac{1}{A} > 0$, find $I = \displaystyle\int \frac{1}{x(1 - Ax)}\, dx$.

Solution

The Handbook contains the standard integral

$$\int \frac{1}{(x - a)(x - b)}\, dx = \frac{1}{a - b}\ln\left|\frac{x - a}{x - b}\right| + C.$$

The given integral I can be expressed in the form

$$I = \frac{-1}{A(x-0)\left(x-\frac{1}{A}\right)},$$

which matches the Handbook integral with $a = 1/A$ and $b = 0$.

Hence

$$I = -\frac{1}{A} \int \frac{1}{(x-0)\left(x-\frac{1}{A}\right)} \, dx = -\frac{1}{A} \left(\frac{1}{\frac{1}{A}-0} \ln \left| \frac{x-\frac{1}{A}}{x-0} \right| \right) + C$$

$$= -\ln \left| \frac{x-\frac{1}{A}}{x} \right| + C.$$

The modulus signs can be removed because $x > 1/A$ and $x > 0$. Hence

$$I = \ln \left(\frac{x}{x-\frac{1}{A}} \right) + C = \ln \left(\frac{Ax}{Ax-1} \right) + C.$$

Exercise 39

For $k > 0$ and $-k < v < k$, find $\displaystyle\int \frac{1}{v^2 - k^2} \, dv$.

(*Hint*: Remember that $v^2 - k^2 = (v-k)(v+k)$.)

6.3   Integration by substitution and by parts

Diagnostic test

Try Exercises 40(a), 40(b) and 42(a). If your answers agree with the solutions, you may proceed quickly to Subsection 6.4.

This subsection looks at two useful methods for finding more complicated integrals. Deciding which method to use in any particular case comes through experience.

Integration by substitution

Many integrals are of the form

$$\int f(u(x)) \frac{du}{dx} \, dx,$$

or are constant multiples of such an expression. For example, the integral

$$\int \cos(2 + 3x^2) \times 6x \, dx \tag{79}$$

is of this form, with

$$u(x) = 2 + 3x^2, \quad f(u) = \cos(u) \quad \text{and} \quad \frac{du}{dx} = 6x.$$

In this case, $f(u(x)) = \cos(2 + 3x^2)$ is the composition of an 'inner function' $u(x) = 2 + 3x^2$ and an 'outer function' $f(u) = \cos(u)$. But $f(u(x))$ is only part of the integrand because it is multiplied by the derivative $du/dx = 6x$ of the inner function, $u(x) = 2 + 3x^2$.

This method is also referred to as **integration by change of variable**.

Integrals like this can be found using the method of **integration by substitution**, based on the following formula.

Formula for integration by substitution

$$\int f(u(x))\, u'(x)\, dx = \int f(u)\, du, \tag{80}$$

or, in Leibniz notation,

$$\int f(u(x))\, \frac{du}{dx}\, dx = \int f(u)\, du. \tag{81}$$

In equation (81), the expression $\dfrac{du}{dx}\, dx$ in the integral on the left is effectively replaced by du in the integral on the right. This is worth remembering, and will be used later on.

Example 7

Find $\displaystyle\int 6x \cos(2 + 3x^2)\, dx$.

Solution

We try the substitution $u(x) = 2 + 3x^2$. Then $f(u) = \cos(u)$ and $du/dx = 6x$. So

$$\int \cos(2 + 3x^2)\, 6x\, dx = \int \cos(u)\, \frac{du}{dx}\, dx = \int \cos(u)\, du.$$

The integral over u is now easy. It is $\sin(u) + C$, so we have

$$\int \cos(2 + 3x^2)\, 6x\, dx = \sin(2 + 3x^2) + C,$$

where we have substituted for u in terms of x.

The rule for integration by substitution can be thought of as the reverse of the rule for differentiating a composite function.

The answer can be checked by differentiation:

$$\frac{d}{dx}(\sin(2 + 3x^2) + C) = \cos(2 + 3x^2) \times 6x.$$

Sometimes a rearrangement is needed to coax the integrand into a suitable form. For example, given the integral $\int x \cos(2 + 3x^2)\, dx$, we need to recognise that this is essentially the same as the integral that we have just considered, but with $6x$ replaced by x. Such a constant multiple is easily dealt with by writing

$$\int x \cos(2 + 3x^2)\, dx = \tfrac{1}{6} \int \cos(2 + 3x^2) \times 6x\, dx.$$

We then proceed just as before to obtain $\frac{1}{6}\sin(2 + 3x^2) + C$.

The key to using this method is recognising when the integrand has a suitable form: be on the lookout for an inner function $u(x)$ whose derivative du/dx appears as a multiplicative factor in the integrand.

One form of integral comes up sufficiently often to be worth special mention. If $g(x) \neq 0$, integration by substitution gives

$$\int \frac{g'(x)}{g(x)}\,dx = \ln|g(x)| + C. \tag{82}$$

To see why this is so, make the substitution $u = g(x)$. Then $du/dx = g'(x)$, so

$$\int \frac{g'(x)}{g(x)}\,dx = \int \frac{1}{u}\frac{du}{dx}\,dx = \int \frac{1}{u}\,du.$$

Finding the integral of $1/u$ requires some care with domains (see the text following Exercise 36). For $u > 0$ it is $\ln(u) + C$, and for $u < 0$ it is $\ln(-u) + C$. These cases correspond to $g(x) > 0$ and $g(x) < 0$, respectively. Both cases are included by using the modulus sign in equation (82).

Exercise 40

Find the following integrals by making suitable substitutions.

(a) $\displaystyle\int y^2 \exp(2 + 4y^3)\,dy$ (b) $\displaystyle\int \cos y \sin^2 y\,dy$

(c) $\displaystyle\int t\sqrt{1 - t^2}\,dt$ $(-1 < t < 1)$ (d) $\displaystyle\int \frac{x}{1 + x^2}\,dx$

(e) $\displaystyle\int \frac{\sin 2t}{1 + \sin^2 t}\,dt$ (f) $\displaystyle\int \frac{y}{1 - y^2}\,dy$ $(y \neq \pm 1)$

One advantage of knowing your derivatives is that you can adjust your tactics, choosing $u(x)$ so that $u'(x)$ appears where needed in the integrand.

The identity $\sin(2t) = 2\sin t \cos t$ may be useful in part (e).

All the integrals considered in Exercise 40 have integrands that can be expressed as a constant times $f(u(x))\,u'(x)$ for some choice of $u(x)$. We are not always so fortunate. The integral in the following example is not of this pattern, but we can still use a substitution to help find it.

Example 8

Find the integral $I = \displaystyle\int \frac{x^2}{\sqrt{2x - 1}}\,dx$ for $x > 1/2$.

Solution

We try the substitution $u = 2x - 1$. Then $du/dx = 2$ and the denominator in the integrand becomes $\sqrt{u} = u^{1/2}$. We still need to express the numerator x^2 in terms of u, and the element of integration dx in terms of du. The first task is easily achieved. Rearranging our equation for u, we get $x = (u + 1)/2$, so $x^2 = (u + 1)^2/4$.

To express dx in terms of du, we can use the fact noted earlier that within the integral in equation (81), we can effectively make the replacement $(du/dx)\,dx = du$. Since $du/dx = 2$, we have $2\,dx = du$, so we can make the replacement $dx = \frac{1}{2}\,du$.

Putting all this together, we get

$$I = \int \frac{x^2}{\sqrt{2x-1}}\,dx = \int \frac{1}{4}\frac{(u+1)^2}{u^{1/2}}\,\frac{1}{2}\,du.$$

Now we are in business! A straightforward calculation gives

$$
\begin{aligned}
I &= \frac{1}{8}\int \frac{u^2 + 2u + 1}{u^{1/2}}\,du\\
&= \frac{1}{8}\int \left(u^{3/2} + 2u^{1/2} + u^{-1/2}\right)du\\
&= \frac{1}{8}\left(\frac{2}{5}u^{5/2} + \frac{4}{3}u^{3/2} + 2u^{1/2}\right) + C\\
&= \frac{1}{20}(2x-1)^{5/2} + \frac{1}{6}(2x-1)^{3/2} + \frac{1}{4}(2x-1)^{1/2} + C.
\end{aligned}
$$

Exercise 41

Use the substitution $u = 3x + 1$ to find $\displaystyle\int \frac{9x^2 + 1}{3x + 1}\,dx$ for $x > -1/3$.

Integration by parts

The method of **integration by parts** is based on the following formula.

> **Formula for integration by parts**
>
> $$\int f(x)\,g'(x)\,dx = f(x)\,g(x) - \int f'(x)\,g(x)\,dx, \tag{83}$$
>
> or, in Leibniz notation,
>
> $$\int f(x)\,\frac{dg}{dx}\,dx = f(x)\,g(x) - \int \frac{df}{dx}\,g(x)\,dx. \tag{84}$$

Note that an arbitrary constant need not be included in the expression for $g(x)$ here, and it is usually omitted.

As with integration by substitution, this formula transforms an integral into a different one, and the key to success is to ensure that the 'new' integral is easier to evaluate than the original.

Example 9

Find $\displaystyle\int xe^{-2x}\,dx$.

Solution

Take $f(x) = x$ and $g'(x) = e^{-2x}$. Then $f'(x) = 1$ and $g(x) = -\frac{1}{2}e^{-2x}$, so

$$\int xe^{-2x}\,dx = x\left(-\tfrac{1}{2}e^{-2x}\right) - \int 1 \times \left(-\tfrac{1}{2}e^{-2x}\right)\,dx$$
$$= -\tfrac{1}{2}xe^{-2x} + \tfrac{1}{2}\int e^{-2x}\,dx$$
$$= -\tfrac{1}{2}xe^{-2x} - \tfrac{1}{4}e^{-2x} + C$$
$$= -\tfrac{1}{4}(2x+1)e^{-2x} + C.$$

Our motive for splitting the integrand into $x \times e^{-2x}$ in this way, is that x becomes simpler when it is differentiated, while e^{-2x} at least gets no more complicated when it is integrated. So we end up with an integral that is easier to perform.

Exercise 42

(a) Use integration by parts to find $\int xe^{-x}\,dx$.

(b) Use integration by parts and the result of part (a) to find $\int x^2 e^{-x}\,dx$.

(c) Use integration by parts to find $\int e^x \sin x\,dx$. You will need to integrate by parts twice, and compare your answer with the original integral.

6.4 Definite integrals

Diagnostic test

Try Exercises 43, 45 and 46. If your answers agree with the solutions, you may proceed quickly through this subsection.

An indefinite integral is a *function* (or, to be exact, a family of functions containing an arbitrary constant). A different, though closely related, integral is the **definite integral**, whose value is a *number*.

If $F(x)$ is the integral of $f(x)$, so that

$$\int f(x)\,dx = F(x),$$

then the definite integral of $f(x)$ between $x = a$ and $x = b$ is written as $\int_a^b f(x)\,dx$, and is defined by

$$\int_a^b f(x)\,dx = F(b) - F(a). \tag{85}$$

The value $x = a$ is called the **lower limit of integration**, and the value $x = b$ is called the **upper limit of integration**. A particular expression for $F(x)$ will contain an arbitrary constant, but this does not affect the value of the definite integral because the constant cancels out in equation (85). The difference $F(b) - F(a)$ is commonly written as $\left[F(x)\right]_a^b$ or $F(x)\big|_a^b$. So, for example,

$$\int_0^1 \frac{1}{\sqrt{4 - \theta^2}} \, d\theta = \left[\arcsin\left(\tfrac{1}{2}\theta\right)\right]_0^1 = \arcsin \tfrac{1}{2} - \arcsin 0 = \tfrac{\pi}{6} - 0 = \tfrac{\pi}{6}.$$

A useful way of thinking of a definite integral $\int_a^b f(x)\,dx$ is as an accumulation of small quantities as x varies from a to b. For example, suppose that a straight rod lies along the x-axis and has a density per unit length given by the function $f(x)$, which varies along the length of the rod. The mass of a small segment of this rod, of length δx, centred on x, is approximated by $f(x)\,\delta x$. Some approximation is involved because the density varies inside the segment, but this variation is very slight if the segment is short enough. If we add up the masses of all the segments, we obtain the total mass of the rod. We can do this in the limit where the length of each segment approaches zero and the number of segments becomes huge. This improves the approximation mentioned above, and *in the limit* gives the *exact* total mass of the rod as the definite integral

$$M = \int_a^b f(x)\,dx,$$

where $x = a$ and $x = b$ mark the ends of the rod.

Example 10

A straight rod lies along the x-axis between $x = 2$ and $x = 4$ (measured in metres). The density of the rod per unit length depends on x, and is given by the function $f(x) = 3x^2 - x$ (measured in kilograms per metre). What is the total mass of the rod?

Solution

The total mass of the rod is

$$M = \int_2^4 f(x)\,dx = \int_2^4 (3x^2 - x)\,dx = \left[x^3 - \tfrac{1}{2}x^2\right]_2^4 = 56 - 6 = 50.$$

So the rod has mass 50 kilograms.

Exercise 43

Calculate each of the following definite integrals.

(a) $\displaystyle\int_0^1 (x^3 - 2)\,dx$

(b) $\displaystyle\int_1^2 (x^3 - 2)\,dx$

(c) $\displaystyle\int_0^2 (x^3 - 2)\, dx$

How is this integral related to those in parts (a) and (b)?

Exercise 44

Evaluate $\displaystyle\int_0^{3/2} \frac{1}{9 + 4z^2}\, dz$.

Definite integrals can be evaluated by finding the corresponding indefinite integral, and then using the limits of integration. When using integration by substitution, there is an extra step involving conversion of the limits.

Example 11

Suppose that we wish to evaluate the integral

$$I = \int_{1/2}^{3/2} \frac{1}{\sqrt{4 - (2x-1)^2}}\, dx.$$

The closest integral to this one in the table of standard integrals in the Handbook is

$$\int \frac{1}{\sqrt{a^2 - x^2}}\, dx = \arcsin\left(\frac{x}{a}\right).$$

To convert I into this form, we change the variable of integration to $u = 2x - 1$. Then $du/dx = 2$. This allows us to write $du = (du/dx)\, dx = 2\, dx$, so we can make the replacement $dx = \frac{1}{2}\, du$. Consequently, our integral becomes

$$I = \frac{1}{2} \int_{x=1/2}^{x=3/2} \frac{1}{\sqrt{4 - u^2}}\, du. \tag{86}$$

Here the limits are written as $x = 1/2$ and $x = 3/2$ to explicitly show that they refer to the variable x rather than u. We can easily convert to the appropriate limits for u, using the relationship between u and x. If $x = 1/2$, then $u = 0$, and if $x = 3/2$, then $u = 2$. Hence, using the integral from the Handbook, the integral I becomes

$$I = \frac{1}{2} \int_{u=0}^{u=2} \frac{1}{\sqrt{4 - u^2}}\, du = \frac{1}{2}\left[\arcsin\left(\frac{u}{2}\right)\right]_{u=0}^{u=2} = \frac{\pi}{4}.$$

Exercise 45

Suppose that we are told that for any positive integer n,

$$J_n = \int_0^{n\pi} u^2 \sin^2 u\, du = \frac{n^3\pi^3}{6} - \frac{n\pi}{4}.$$

Use this integral to evaluate

$$I = \int_0^1 x^2 \sin^2(3\pi x)\, dx.$$

Areas and the use of symmetry

Another way of thinking about a definite integral is in terms of an area. If $f(x) \geq 0$ for $a \leq x \leq b$, then the definite integral $\int_a^b f(x)\,dx$ is equal to the area under the graph of $f(x)$ between $x = a$ and $x = b$ (see Figure 29(a)). There is one point to be careful about here. If $f(x) < 0$, corresponding to a region *below* the x-axis, then we have a *negative* contribution to the integral, whereas area is always a *positive* quantity. Thus for a function f as pictured in Figure 29(b), $\int_a^b f(x)\,dx = $ area $A_1 - $ area A_2.

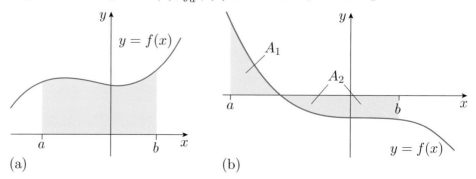

(a)   (b)

Figure 29 $\int_a^b f(x)\,dx$ as an area: (a) with $f(x) > 0$; (b) in general

It is possible for the positive contribution to an definite integral to exactly cancel the negative contribution, giving a zero result. This leads to a useful shortcut in some cases. Recall the following definitions:

- A function $f(x)$ is said to be **odd** if $f(-x) = -f(x)$ for all x.
- A function $f(x)$ is said to be **even** if $f(-x) = +f(x)$ for all x.

If a definite integral is over a range from $-a$ to a, where a is a constant, it is worth checking whether the integrand is an odd function, as you will now see.

Suppose that you are asked to calculate the following definite integrals:

$$I_1 = \int_{-\pi}^{\pi} \sin(x)\,dx, \quad I_2 = \int_{-2}^{2} \sin(x^3)\,dx.$$

You could set about evaluating these, using the methods that you have learned. And you might conclude that the second integral is a real challenge, because you don't know how to find an indefinite integral for $\sin(x^3)$. But there is an alternative approach that is very valuable. Figures 30 and 31 show plots of the integrands over their ranges of integration.

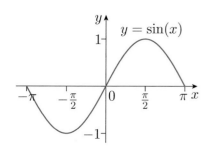

Figure 30   Graph of $\sin(x)$ over the interval $[-\pi, \pi]$

From Figure 30 we see that $\sin(x)$ is an odd function (that is, $\sin(-x) = -\sin(x)$). Because the limits of integration are equally spaced either side of the origin, the contribution to the definite integral coming from any positive value of x is exactly cancelled by a contribution from $-x$. By symmetry, we see that the integral must be equal to zero: $I_1 = 0$. This argument can be generalised as follows.

Definite integral of an odd function over a symmetric range

The integral of an odd function over a range $-a \leq x \leq a$ vanishes:

$$\int_{-a}^{a} f(x)\, dx = 0.$$

Similarly, Figure 31 shows that $\sin(x^3)$ is an odd function. This can be confirmed by noticing that if $f(x) = \sin(x^3)$, then

$$f(-x) = \sin((-x)^3) = \sin(-x^3) = -\sin(x^3) = -f(x).$$

In I_2, $\sin(x^3)$ is integrated over a range centred on the origin, so we can immediately say that $I_2 = 0$ – in spite of being unable to find the corresponding indefinite integral!

Evaluating definite integrals can be tedious and a source of errors when performing calculations by hand. Looking out for opportunities to use symmetries to show that integrals are equal to zero, or else equal to others that you have already calculated, is a valuable skill that will save you time.

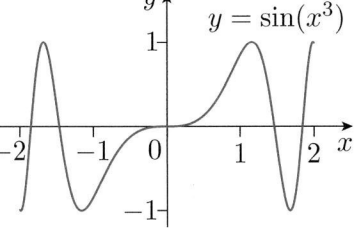

Figure 31   Graph of $\sin(x^3)$ over the interval $[-2, 2]$

Exercise 46

Use symmetry to evaluate (or help to evaluate) the following integrals.

(a) $\displaystyle\int_{-\pi}^{\pi} e^{-x^2} \sin x \, dx$ (b) $\displaystyle\int_{-1}^{1} x \sin(1 + x^4) \, dx$

(c) $\displaystyle\int_{-1}^{1} (x^2 + x^3) \cos(x^3) \, dx$

Spectral lines and symmetry

Atoms emit light at certain definite frequencies (corresponding to 'spectral lines' of definite colours, e.g. Figure 32(a)). The frequencies fall into well-defined patterns, but with certain frequencies in the pattern missing. It turns out that the brightness of each predicted frequency is related to a definite integral. The missing frequencies correspond to integrals that are equal to zero, and this often happens for reasons of symmetry similar to those discussed above.

The fact that many frequencies are missing means that spectra are much simpler than they would otherwise be, and this gives us the chance to analyse complicated spectra, and find what mixture of substances is responsible for them. Such understanding is vital in fields as diverse as nuclear physics, astronomy, medicine and atmospheric science (see Figure 32(b)).

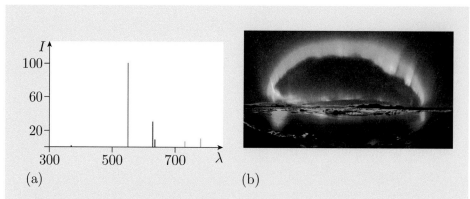

Figure 32   (a) A graph of intensity I against wavelength λ for the visible spectral lines emitted by oxygen atoms. These spectral lines are limited in number because certain integrals vanish for reasons of symmetry. The green line is by far the most intense, and this is responsible for the magnificent green glow of (b) the Aurora Borealis.

Learning outcomes

After studying this unit, you should be able to do the following.

- Understand the following terms: variable, dependent variable, independent variable, parameter; domain and image set of a function; inverse function, linear function, quadratic function.

- Solve two simultaneous linear equations by Gaussian elimination.

- Solve quadratic equations, using a formula or by factorisation.

- Compose functions and recognise compositions of functions.

- Recognise, sketch graphs of and manipulate the power, exponential and (natural) logarithm functions.

- Recognise, sketch graphs of and manipulate trigonometric functions and their inverses.

- Be aware of the series expansions of sin, cos and exp.

- Add, subtract, multiply and divide complex numbers, and move between Cartesian, polar and exponential forms of a complex number. Express sin and cos in terms of complex exponentials.

- Differentiate functions, using a table of standard derivatives and the rules for differentiating products, quotients and compositions of functions.

- Identify stationary points, local maxima and minima, and asymptotes; use such information to sketch graphs of functions.

- Find indefinite integrals, using a table of standard integrals and (in simple cases) rules for integration by substitution and by parts.

- Find definite integrals, using substitution and symmetry arguments where appropriate.

Solutions to exercises

Solution to Exercise 1

(a) The domain of $f(x)$ is given in the question as $x \geq 0$. Since $f(0) = 6$, and $f(x)$ increases indefinitely as x increases, the image set of $y = f(x)$ is $y \geq 6$. This can also be written as $6 \leq y < \infty$.

(b) Setting $y = 2x^2 + 6$ and solving for x gives $x = \pm\sqrt{\frac{1}{2}(y-6)}$. However, we are told that $x \geq 0$, so we can ignore the negative solution. The inverse function is therefore $x = g(y) = \sqrt{\frac{1}{2}(y-6)}$.

The domain of the inverse function $g(y)$ is equal to the image set of the original function, and so is $y \geq 6$. The image set of the inverse function $x = g(y)$ is equal to the domain of the original function, and so is $x \geq 0$.

Solution to Exercise 2

(a) For $Y = 2000$ at $t = -3600$, we have

$$2000 = 5(-3600) + c = -18\,000 + c.$$

Hence $c = 2000 + 18\,000 = 20\,000$.

(b) (i) The coastguard vessel catches the smuggler's boat when $X = Y$, i.e. when

$$7t = 5t + 20\,000.$$

This gives $2t = 20\,000$, so $t = 10\,000$.

$10\,000$ seconds is 2 hours, 46 minutes and 40 seconds. So the smuggler's boat is caught at about 2.47 am.

(ii) At $t = 10\,000$, both X and Y are equal to $70\,000$. So the smuggler's boat is caught $70\,\text{km}$ from A, which *is* inside territorial waters.

Solution to Exercise 3

Multiplying the first equation by $\frac{3}{2}$ gives

$$3u - \tfrac{15}{2}v = \tfrac{57}{2}.$$

Subtracting this from the second equation gives

$$\left(4 + \tfrac{15}{2}\right)v = -29 - \tfrac{57}{2},$$

i.e. $\frac{23}{2}v = -\frac{115}{2}$, so $v = -\frac{115}{23} = -5$.

Substituting this into the first equation gives

$$2u - 5(-5) = 19,$$

so $u = (19 - 25)/2 = -3$.

Thus the solution is $u = -3$, $v = -5$.

(It is good practice to check solutions where you can, and this is easily done here. With $u = -3$ and $v = -5$, we have

$$2u - 5v = 2(-3) - 5(-5) = -6 + 25 = 19,$$
$$3u + 4v = 3(-3) + 4(-5) = -9 - 20 = -29,$$

so these values of u and v do satisfy the given equations.)

Solution to Exercise 4

(a) Using equation (9), we obtain

$$\begin{aligned} x &= \frac{-7 \pm \sqrt{7^2 - 4 \times 2 \times (-4)}}{2 \times 2} \\ &= \frac{-7 \pm \sqrt{49 + 32}}{4} \\ &= \frac{-7 \pm 9}{4} = \tfrac{1}{2} \text{ or } -4. \end{aligned}$$

(These solutions can be checked by substitution into the quadratic equation. For example, with $x = -4$,

$$2x^2 + 7x - 4 = 32 - 28 - 4 = 0,$$

as required.)

(b) Using equation (9), we obtain

$$\begin{aligned} x &= \frac{-1 \pm \sqrt{1^2 - 4 \times 1 \times (-6)}}{2 \times 1} \\ &= \frac{-1 \pm \sqrt{1 + 24}}{2} \\ &= \frac{-1 \pm 5}{2} = -3 \text{ or } 2. \end{aligned}$$

Solution to Exercise 5

Using equation (9), we obtain

$$\begin{aligned} x &= \frac{-2K \pm \sqrt{4K^2 - 4\omega^2}}{2} \\ &= \frac{-2K \pm 2\sqrt{K^2 - \omega^2}}{2} \\ &= -K \pm \sqrt{K^2 - \omega^2}, \end{aligned}$$

as required.

Solution to Exercise 6

(a) We could use equation (9); however, in these cases it is easier to factorise by hand.

This is a difference of two squares:

$$x^2 - a = (x - \sqrt{a})(x + \sqrt{a}).$$

(b) This can also be expressed in terms of a difference of two squares:
$$2x^2 - 8a = 2(x^2 - 4a) = 2(x - 2\sqrt{a})(x + 2\sqrt{a}).$$

(c) This is a perfect square. Let $y = x^2$. Then
$$x^4 - 6x^2 + 9 = y^2 - 6y + 9 = (y - 3)^2 = (x^2 - 3)^2.$$

Solution to Exercise 7

(a) $a^3 a^5 = a^{3+5} = a^8$.

(b) $a^3/a^5 = a^{3-5} = a^{-2}$ (or $1/a^2$).

(c) $(a^3)^5 = a^{3 \times 5} = a^{15}$.

(d) $(2^{-1})^4 \times 4^3 = 2^{-4} \times (2^2)^3 = 2^{-4} \times 2^6 = 2^2 = 4$.

(e) $8^{-1/3} = 1/8^{1/3} = 1/\sqrt[3]{8} = \frac{1}{2}$.

(f) $16^{3/4} = (16^{1/4})^3 = (\sqrt[4]{16})^3 = 2^3 = 8$.

(g) $\left(\frac{4}{9}\right)^{3/2} = \left(\sqrt{\frac{4}{9}}\right)^3 = \left(\frac{2}{3}\right)^3 = \frac{8}{27}$.

(h) $(16x^4)^{1/2} = 16^{1/2}(x^4)^{1/2} = \sqrt{16}x^{4 \times 1/2} = 4x^2$.

Solution to Exercise 8

(a) With $f(x) = x^2$ and $g(x) = 1/(x - 1)$ we have the following.

    (i) $f(g(x)) = (1/(x - 1))^2 = (1/(x - 1)^2)$.

    (ii) $g(f(x)) = 1/(x^2 - 1)$.

            Note that $g(f(x))$ is not the same as $f(g(x))$.

(b) We can obtain $h(x)$ in three steps.

    Step 1   Apply the square function to x.

    Step 2   Add 1 to the result of Step 1.

    Step 3   Apply the sine function to the result of Step 2.

    Then $h(x) = r(q(p(x)))$, where
$$p(x) = x^2, \quad q(x) = x + 1, \quad r(x) = \sin(x).$$

Solution to Exercise 9

For $x = 1/2$ the sum is
$$1 + \tfrac{1}{2} + \tfrac{(1/2)^2}{2} + \tfrac{(1/2)^3}{6} + \tfrac{(1/2)^4}{24} + \tfrac{(1/2)^5}{120} \simeq 1.649.$$

For $x = 1$ the sum is
$$1 + 1 + \tfrac{1^2}{2} + \tfrac{1^3}{6} + \tfrac{1^4}{24} + \tfrac{1^5}{120} + \tfrac{1^6}{720} \simeq 2.718.$$

For $x = 2$ the sum is
$$1 + 2 + \tfrac{2^2}{2} + \tfrac{2^3}{6} + \tfrac{2^4}{24} + \tfrac{2^5}{120} + \tfrac{2^6}{720} + \tfrac{2^7}{5040} \simeq 7.381.$$

These answers can be compared with those obtained by entering $\exp(1/2)$, $\exp(1)$ and $\exp(2)$ directly into a calculator:

$\exp(1/2) = 1.648\,721\,271\ldots,$

$\exp(1) = 2.718\,281\,828\ldots,$

$\exp(2) = 7.389\,056\,099\ldots.$

Our first two answers are correct to four significant figures. The last answer is correct to only two significant figures, but it could be made as accurate as we wish by adding more terms in the series. Note that as x increases, we need more terms in the sum to get an accurate answer for $\exp(x)$.

Solution to Exercise 10

Using a calculator we find

$$\exp(1/2) \times \exp(1/2) = 1.648\,721\,271\ldots \times 1.648\,721\,271\ldots$$
$$= 2.718\,281\,829\ldots,$$

which agrees with $\exp(1) = 2.718\,281\,828$. (Any discrepancy in the last decimal place is insignificant because of rounding.)

Similarly,

$$\exp(1) \times \exp(1) = 2.718\,281\,828\ldots \times 2.718\,281\,828\ldots$$
$$= 7.389\,056\,096\ldots,$$

which agrees with $\exp(2) = 7.389\,056\,099\ldots$.

Solution to Exercise 11

(a) $\ln 7 + \ln 4 - \ln 14 = \ln(7 \times 4/14) = \ln 2.$

(b) $\begin{aligned}[t] \ln a + 2\ln b - \ln(a^2 b) &= \ln a + \ln(b^2) - \ln(a^2 b) \\ &= \ln\big(a \times b^2 \div (a^2 b)\big) \\ &= \ln(b/a) \quad (\text{or } \ln b - \ln a). \end{aligned}$

(c) To simplify $\ln(e^x \times e^y)$, we first rearrange it in the form $\ln(e^{something})$, which just equals *something*:

$\ln(e^x \times e^y) = \ln(e^{x+y}) = x + y.$

An alternative argument gives

$\ln(e^x \times e^y) = \ln(e^x) + \ln(e^y) = x + y.$

(d) In parts (d)–(f), we first rearrange the expression as $e^{\ln(something)}$, which also just equals *something*.

Here, $e^{2\ln x} = e^{\ln(x^2)} = x^2.$

(e) $e^{-2\ln x} = e^{\ln(x^{-2})} = x^{-2}$ (or $1/x^2$).

(f) $\exp\big(2\ln x + \ln(x+1)\big) = \exp\big(\ln(x^2 \times (x+1))\big) = x^2(x+1).$

An alternative argument gives

$\exp\big(2\ln x + \ln(x+1)\big) = \exp\big(\ln(x^2)\big) \times \exp\big(\ln(x+1)\big) = x^2(x+1).$

Solution to Exercise 12

Using equation (30) we have

$$A = e^{\pi \ln 5} = e^{5.0562} = 157.0$$

and

$$B = e^{-4.315 \ln 10} = e^{-9.9357} = 4.842 \times 10^{-5},$$

to four significant figures.

Solution to Exercise 13

(a) Note that the question asks us to use Figure 15, not read off values from Figure 16! The figure given here shows a circle of radius 1. The point A corresponds to a rotation through 0, and the point B corresponds to a rotation through $\frac{\pi}{2}$.

We see from the figure that A has coordinates $(1,0) = (\cos 0, \sin 0)$, and B has coordinates $(0,1) = \left(\cos \frac{\pi}{2}, \sin \frac{\pi}{2}\right)$. Therefore

$$\sin 0 = 0, \quad \cos 0 = 1, \quad \sin \tfrac{\pi}{2} = 1, \quad \cos \tfrac{\pi}{2} = 0.$$

(b) Since $\sin 0 = 0$, $\operatorname{cosec} 0$ and $\cot 0$ are not defined. We have

$$\tan 0 = 0 \quad \text{and} \quad \sec 0 = 1.$$

Since $\cos \frac{\pi}{2} = 0$, $\tan \frac{\pi}{2}$ and $\sec \frac{\pi}{2}$ are not defined. We have

$$\cot \tfrac{\pi}{2} = 0 \quad \text{and} \quad \operatorname{cosec} \tfrac{\pi}{2} = 1.$$

(c) Using the triangles in Figure 17, we obtain

$$\sin \tfrac{\pi}{4} = \tfrac{1}{\sqrt{2}}, \quad \sin \tfrac{\pi}{3} = \tfrac{\sqrt{3}}{2}, \quad \sin \tfrac{\pi}{6} = \tfrac{1}{2},$$
$$\cos \tfrac{\pi}{4} = \tfrac{1}{\sqrt{2}}, \quad \cos \tfrac{\pi}{3} = \tfrac{1}{2}, \quad \cos \tfrac{\pi}{6} = \tfrac{\sqrt{3}}{2},$$
$$\tan \tfrac{\pi}{4} = 1, \quad \tan \tfrac{\pi}{3} = \sqrt{3}, \quad \tan \tfrac{\pi}{6} = \tfrac{1}{\sqrt{3}},$$
$$\cot \tfrac{\pi}{4} = 1, \quad \cot \tfrac{\pi}{3} = \tfrac{1}{\sqrt{3}}, \quad \cot \tfrac{\pi}{6} = \sqrt{3}.$$

(d) From Figure 16, $\sin \theta = 0$ for $\theta = 0$ and $\theta = \pi$, and for any value of θ that differs from 0 or π by any integer multiple of 2π. Hence we conclude that $\sin \theta = 0$ if $\theta = n\pi$, where $n = 0, \pm 1, \pm 2, \ldots$ (i.e. n is any integer). This can be written as $n \in \mathbb{Z}$, where $\mathbb{Z}$ is the set of all integers.

The symbol $\in$ means 'is a member of'.

Solution to Exercise 14

(a) Using a calculator, one solution is $\arcsin 0.8 = 0.93$ (to two decimal places). Looking at the graph of $y = \sin \theta$ shown below, we see that it is symmetric about $\theta = \frac{\pi}{2}$. So there is also a solution of $\sin \theta = 0.8$ at $\theta = \pi - 0.93 = 2.21$ (to two decimal places). These are the only solutions with θ between 0 and 2π. (If θ is between π and 2π, then $\sin \theta$ is negative.)

The other solutions are obtained by adding multiples of 2π to these two. The solutions in the required range are (to two decimal places)

$$0.93, \ 2.21, \ 7.21, \ 8.50, \ 13.49, \ 14.78.$$

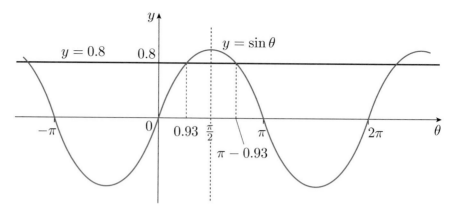

(b) We saw in Exercise 13(c) that $\tan \frac{\pi}{4} = 1$, so $\theta = \frac{\pi}{4}$ is one solution. We can see from the graph of tan (Figure 18) that there is one solution of this equation in the range $-\frac{\pi}{2}$ to $\frac{\pi}{2}$, and that other solutions are obtained by adding multiples of π to this. We can express the full set of solutions as

$$\tfrac{\pi}{4} + n\pi,$$

where n is any integer (positive, zero or negative).

Solution to Exercise 15

(a) Dividing equation (32) by $\cos^2 \theta$ gives equation (35).

(b) Dividing equation (33) by equation (34) gives

$$\tan(\theta \pm \phi) = \frac{\sin\theta\cos\phi \pm \cos\theta\sin\phi}{\cos\theta\cos\phi \mp \sin\theta\sin\phi}.$$

Then dividing each term in the numerator and denominator of the right-hand side by $\cos\theta\cos\phi$ gives equation (37).

(c) Using equation (34) we obtain

$$\cos(\theta - \phi) - \cos(\theta + \phi) = 2\sin\theta\sin\phi,$$

which establishes the result in equation (38).

(d) Setting $\phi = \theta$ in equation (33) and taking the upper signs gives equation (41).

Solution to Exercise 16

(a) $\sin(2\pi - \theta) = \sin 2\pi\cos\theta - \cos 2\pi\sin\theta$

$$= 0 \times \cos\theta - 1 \times \sin\theta = -\sin\theta.$$

(b) $\sin\left(\frac{\pi}{2} - \theta\right) = \sin\frac{\pi}{2}\cos\theta - \cos\frac{\pi}{2}\sin\theta$

$$= 1 \times \cos\theta - 0 \times \sin\theta = \cos\theta.$$

For $0 < \theta < \frac{\pi}{2}$, this result can be confirmed by examination of a right-angled triangle.

(c) $\sin(\pi - \theta) = \sin \pi \cos \theta - \cos \pi \sin \theta$
$$= 0 \times \cos \theta - (-1) \times \sin \theta = \sin \theta.$$

(d) $\cos(\pi - \theta) = \cos \pi \cos \theta + \sin \pi \sin \theta$
$$= (-1) \times \cos \theta + 0 \times \sin \theta = -\cos \theta.$$

(e) $\cos(2\pi - \theta) = \cos 2\pi \cos \theta + \sin 2\pi \sin \theta$
$$= 1 \times \cos \theta + 0 \times \sin \theta = \cos \theta.$$

(f) $\cos\left(\frac{\pi}{2} - \theta\right) = \cos \frac{\pi}{2} \cos \theta + \sin \frac{\pi}{2} \sin \theta$
$$= 0 \times \cos \theta + 1 \times \sin \theta = \sin \theta.$$

For $0 < \theta < \frac{\pi}{2}$, this result can be confirmed by examination of a right-angled triangle.

(g) $\cos\left(\frac{3\pi}{2} + x\right) = \cos \frac{3\pi}{2} \cos x - \sin \frac{3\pi}{2} \sin x$
$$= 0 \times \cos x - (-1) \times \sin x = \sin x.$$

Solution to Exercise 17

(a) $\overline{v} = 3 + 4i$.

(b) $|v| = \sqrt{3^2 + 4^2} = 5$.

(c) $v - w = (3 - 4i) - (2 - i) = 1 - 3i$.

(d) $vw = (3 - 4i)(2 - i) = 6 - 8i - 3i + 4i^2 = 2 - 11i$.

(e) $\dfrac{w}{v} = \dfrac{w\overline{v}}{|v|^2} = \dfrac{(2 - i)(3 + 4i)}{3^2 + 4^2}$
$$= \dfrac{6 - 3i + 8i - 4i^2}{25}$$
$$= \tfrac{10}{25} + \tfrac{5}{25}i = \tfrac{2}{5} + \tfrac{1}{5}i.$$

(f) $\dfrac{1}{w} = \dfrac{\overline{w}}{|w|^2} = \dfrac{2 + i}{2^2 + 1^2} = \tfrac{2}{5} + \tfrac{1}{5}i.$

(g) $w^2 = (2 - i)(2 - i) = 4 - 2i - 2i + i^2 = 3 - 4i$.

(h) $2w - 3v = 4 - 2i - (9 - 12i) = -5 + 10i$.

Solution to Exercise 18

We obtain
$$x = \frac{-2 \pm \sqrt{4 - 8}}{4} = \frac{-2 \pm 2i}{4} = -\tfrac{1}{2} \pm \tfrac{1}{2}i.$$

Solution to Exercise 19

The points are illustrated in the figure below.

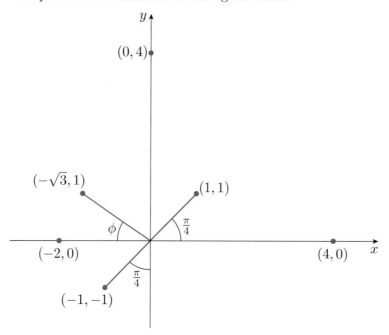

Using trigonometry in this diagram, the polar coordinates of these points are as follows:

$$(x, y) = (-2, 0) \text{ corresponds to } (r, \theta) = (2, \pi),$$
$$(x, y) = (1, 1) \text{ corresponds to } (r, \theta) = \left(\sqrt{2}, \tfrac{\pi}{4}\right),$$
$$(x, y) = (-1, -1) \text{ corresponds to } (r, \theta) = \left(\sqrt{2}, -\tfrac{3\pi}{4}\right),$$
$$(x, y) = (4, 0) \text{ corresponds to } (r, \theta) = (4, 0),$$
$$(x, y) = (0, 4) \text{ corresponds to } (r, \theta) = \left(4, \tfrac{\pi}{2}\right),$$
$$(x, y) = (-\sqrt{3}, 1) \text{ corresponds to } (r, \theta) = (2, \pi - \phi),$$
$$\text{where } \phi \text{ is as shown in the figure.}$$

Now $\tan \phi = \frac{1}{\sqrt{3}}$, so $\phi = \frac{\pi}{6}$ (see the solution to Exercise 13(c)). So $(x, y) = (-\sqrt{3}, 1)$ has polar coordinates $(r, \theta) = \left(2, \tfrac{5\pi}{6}\right)$.

Solution to Exercise 20

$$z = 2\left(\cos\left(-\tfrac{\pi}{4}\right) + i\sin\left(-\tfrac{\pi}{4}\right)\right) = 2\left(\tfrac{1}{\sqrt{2}} - \tfrac{1}{\sqrt{2}}i\right) = \sqrt{2}(1 - i).$$

Solution to Exercise 21

(a) For all these numbers, we can use the diagram accompanying the solution to Exercise 19.

-2 has polar coordinates $(r, \theta) = (2, \pi)$. (Note that r must be positive, and the principal value of the argument must be in the range $-\pi < \theta \leq \pi$.)

Writing the polar form in full, we get $-2 = 2(\cos \pi + i \sin \pi)$.

(b) $1 + i$ has polar coordinates $(r, \theta) = \left(\sqrt{2}, \frac{\pi}{4}\right)$.

So $1 + i = \sqrt{2}\left(\cos\left(\frac{\pi}{4}\right) + i\sin\left(\frac{\pi}{4}\right)\right)$.

(c) $-1 - i$ has polar coordinates $(r, \theta) = \left(\sqrt{2}, -\frac{3\pi}{4}\right)$.

So $-1 - i = \sqrt{2}\left(\cos\left(-\frac{3\pi}{4}\right) + i\sin\left(-\frac{3\pi}{4}\right)\right)$.

(d) 4 has polar coordinates $(r, \theta) = (4, 0)$.

So $4 = 4(\cos(0) + i\sin(0))$.

(e) $4i$ has polar coordinates $(r, \theta) = \left(4, \frac{\pi}{2}\right)$.

So $4i = 4\left(\cos\left(\frac{\pi}{2}\right) + i\sin\left(\frac{\pi}{2}\right)\right)$.

(f) $-\sqrt{3} + i$ has polar coordinates $(r, \theta) = \left(\sqrt{3+1}, \pi - \frac{\pi}{6}\right) = \left(2, \frac{5\pi}{6}\right)$.

So $-\sqrt{3} + i = 2\left(\cos\left(\frac{5\pi}{6}\right) + i\sin\left(\frac{5\pi}{6}\right)\right)$.

Solution to Exercise 22

(a) The modulus of z is 3, and the argument is $-7\pi/2$. We need to find the principal value of the argument, which means that we need to add some multiple of 2π to it so that it lies in the range $-\pi < \theta \leq \pi$. Clearly $-7\pi/2 + 4\pi = \pi/2$ lies in this range, so

$$z = 3e^{-i7\pi/2} = 3e^{i\pi/2}.$$

(b) The argument is 71π, which is equivalent to $71\pi - 70\pi = \pi$. So

$$z = e^{i71\pi} = e^{i\pi}.$$

Solution to Exercise 23

The exponential form of z is $z = re^{i\theta}$, so

$$ze^{i\omega t} = re^{i\theta}e^{i\omega t} = re^{i(\omega t + \theta)}.$$

Taking the real part of this expression, we obtain

$$\mathrm{Re}\left(ze^{i\omega t}\right) = \mathrm{Re}\left(re^{i(\omega t + \theta)}\right) = r\cos(\omega t + \theta).$$

Solution to Exercise 24

The polar coordinates of $z = 1 - i$ are $(r, \theta) = \left(\sqrt{2}, -\frac{\pi}{4}\right)$, so the exponential form of z is

$$z = \sqrt{2}e^{-i\pi/4}.$$

Hence

$$\begin{aligned}
z^{20} &= \left(\sqrt{2}e^{-i\pi/4}\right)^{20} \\
&= (\sqrt{2})^{20}e^{-i20\pi/4} \\
&= 2^{10}e^{-5i\pi} \\
&= 1024\, e^{i\pi},
\end{aligned}$$

where we have added 6π to the argument of the exponential to obtain the principal value in the last line. Returning to Cartesian form by using Euler's formula, we obtain

$$(1 - i)^{20} = 1024(\cos\pi + i\sin\pi) = -1024.$$

Solution to Exercise 25

Using the Handbook result

$$\frac{d}{dx}(\cos(ax)) = -a\sin(ax)$$

with $a = 3$ and x replaced by t, we get

$$\dot{x} = \frac{dx}{dt} = -21\sin(3t).$$

To differentiate again, we use

$$\frac{d}{dx}(\sin(ax)) = a\cos(ax)$$

to obtain

$$\ddot{x} = \frac{d^2x}{dt^2} = -63\cos(3t).$$

Solution to Exercise 26

We need the Handbook result

$$\frac{d}{dx}(e^{ax}) = ae^x.$$

The rate at which the wage bill will be rising is

$$\frac{dB}{dt} = 10^5(0.04)\exp(0.04t) = 4000\exp(0.04t).$$

As a fraction of the future wage bill B, the rate of rise dB/dt is

$$\frac{1}{B}\frac{dB}{dt} = \frac{10^5(0.04)\exp(0.04t)}{10^5\exp(0.04t)} = 0.04.$$

So the rate of rise is 4% per year.

Solution to Exercise 27

(a) $\dfrac{dy}{dx} = (-9)(-5)\exp(-5x) = 45\exp(-5x).$

(b) $F'(x) = 12x^3 - 4$, so putting $x = 2$ gives

$$F'(2) = 12 \times 2^3 - 4 = 92.$$

(c) $\dfrac{dy}{dt} = \dfrac{1}{t}$, so $\dfrac{d^2y}{dt^2} = -\dfrac{1}{t^2}.$

(d) $g'(t) = -3a\sin(3t) + 3b\cos(3t)$, and then

$$g''(t) = -9a\cos(3t) - 9b\sin(3t),$$

so

$$g''(0) = -9a.$$

(e) $F'(x) = 6\sec(2x)\tan(2x) - 12\sin(-3x)$. Hence

$$F'\left(\tfrac{\pi}{6}\right) = 6\sec\tfrac{\pi}{3}\tan\tfrac{\pi}{3} - 12\sin\left(-\tfrac{\pi}{2}\right)$$
$$= 6 \times 2 \times \sqrt{3} - 12 \times (-1) = 12\sqrt{3} + 12.$$

Solution to Exercise 28

Given $f(t) = \cos(2t) + i\sin(2t)$, we have $f'(t) = -2\sin(2t) + 2i\cos(2t)$
then

$$f''(t) = -4\cos(2t) - 4i\sin(2t).$$

Writing $f(t) = \exp(2it)$, we have $f'(t) = 2i\exp(2it)$ and

$$f''(t) = (2i)^2 \exp(2it) = -4\exp(2it) = -4\cos(2t) - 4i\sin(2t),$$

as before.

Solution to Exercise 29

(a) The function $y = (\ln x)/(x^2 + 1)$ is a quotient. Using standard derivatives from the Handbook, we obtain

$$\frac{dy}{dx} = \frac{\left(\frac{1}{x}\right)(x^2 + 1) - (\ln x)(2x)}{(x^2 + 1)^2}$$

$$= \frac{x + x^{-1} - 2x\ln x}{(x^2 + 1)^2}.$$

This can be simplified by multiplying the numerator and denominator by x:

$$\frac{dy}{dx} = \frac{x^2 + 1 - 2x^2 \ln x}{x(x^2 + 1)^2}.$$

(b) The function $f(t) = t^5 \ln(3t)$ is a product. Recalling that

$$\frac{d}{dx}(\ln(ax)) = 1/x \quad \text{for } ax > 0,$$

we get

$$f'(t) = 5t^4 \ln(3t) + t^5 \times \frac{1}{t} = 5t^4 \ln(3t) + t^4.$$

(c) The function $g(t) = (At + B)\sin(Ct)$ is a product. We get

$$g'(t) = A\sin(Ct) + (At + B)C\cos(Ct),$$

so $g'(0) = BC$.

(d) Given $x(t) = e^{-3t}\sin(4t)$, we want to find $\dot{x}(t)$ and $\ddot{x}(t)$. Using the product rule:

$$\dot{x}(t) = -3e^{-3t}\sin(4t) + e^{-3t}(4\cos(4t))$$
$$= e^{-3t}(4\cos(4t) - 3\sin(4t)).$$

Using the product rule again:

$$\ddot{x}(t) = -3e^{-3t}(4\cos(4t) - 3\sin(4t)) + e^{-3t}(-16\sin(4t) - 12\cos(4t))$$
$$= -e^{-3t}(7\sin(4t) + 24\cos(4t)).$$

Solution to Exercise 30

(a) In each case, we indicate the split into inner and outer functions but (except in this part) omit details. It is perfectly acceptable to do the differentiation in your head, using the product of the derivatives of outer and inner functions.

Taking the inner function to be $u = t^2$, the outer function is $y(u) = \exp(u)$. We have $dy/du = \exp(u)$ and $du/dt = 2t$, so

$$\frac{dy}{dt} = \frac{dy}{du}\frac{du}{dt} = \exp(u)\,2t = 2t\exp(t^2).$$

(b) Taking the inner function to be $u = 3x^3 + 4$, the outer function is $f(u) = u^6$, so

$$f'(x) = 6(3x^3 + 4)^5 \times (9x^2) = 54x^2(3x^3 + 4)^5.$$

(c) Taking the inner function to be $u = 3v + 4$, the outer function is $z(u) = \tan u$, so

$$\frac{dz}{dv} = \sec^2(3v + 4) \times 3 = 3\sec^2(3v + 4).$$

(d) Taking the inner function to be $u = 4 - z^2$, the outer function is $g(u) = u^{1/2}$, so

$$g'(z) = \tfrac{1}{2}(4 - z^2)^{-1/2} \times (-2z) = \frac{-z}{\sqrt{4 - z^2}}.$$

(e) Taking the inner function to be $u = 1 + 2x^2$, the outer function is $f(u) = u^{-3/2}$ (see Example 2), so

$$f'(x) = -\tfrac{3}{2}\left(1 + 2x^2\right)^{-5/2} \times (4x) = \frac{-6x}{\left(\sqrt{1 + 2x^2}\,\right)^5}.$$

Solution to Exercise 31

(a) $\sec(x/(x^2 + 1))$ is a composite function, with

$$y = \sec u, \quad u = \frac{x}{x^2 + 1}.$$

Here u is a quotient, and

$$\frac{du}{dx} = \frac{1(x^2 + 1) - x(2x)}{(x^2 + 1)^2} = \frac{1 - x^2}{(x^2 + 1)^2}.$$

Then, using the chain rule,

$$\frac{dy}{dx} = \frac{dy}{du}\frac{du}{dx} = \sec u \tan u \,\frac{1 - x^2}{(x^2 + 1)^2}$$

$$= \frac{1 - x^2}{(x^2 + 1)^2} \sec\left(\frac{x}{x^2 + 1}\right) \tan\left(\frac{x}{x^2 + 1}\right).$$

(b) $t^2 \exp(t^3 + 1)$ is a product of $u = t^2$ and $v = \exp(t^3 + 1)$. The second part of the product is a composite function with inner function $g = t^3 + 1$ and outer function $f = \exp g$. The chain rule gives

$$\frac{dv}{dt} = \exp(t^3 + 1) \times 3t^2 = 3t^2\exp(t^3 + 1).$$

Then, using the product rule,

$$\frac{dz}{dt} = 2t \exp(t^3 + 1) + t^2(3t^2 \exp(t^3 + 1))$$
$$= (3t^4 + 2t) \exp(t^3 + 1).$$

Solution to Exercise 32

(a) (i) The product rule gives

$$\frac{d}{dx}(x^2 y) = 2xy + x^2 \frac{dy}{dx}.$$

(ii) The composite rule gives

$$\frac{d}{dx}(y^3) = 3y^2 \frac{dy}{dx}.$$

(iii) The composite rule gives

$$\frac{d}{dx}(x + \sin(xy)) = 1 + \cos(xy)\frac{d}{dx}(xy)$$
$$= 1 + \cos(xy)\left(y + x\frac{dy}{dx}\right).$$

(b) Using implicit differentiation, we obtain

$$3x^2 + 2xy + x^2\frac{dy}{dx} + 3y^2\frac{dy}{dx} = 0.$$

When $x = -1$ and $y = 1$, this gives

$$3 - 2 + \frac{dy}{dx} + 3\frac{dy}{dx} = 0.$$

Hence $dy/dx = -\frac{1}{4}$, and the required gradient is $-\frac{1}{4}$.

Solution to Exercise 33

(a) To test for stationary points, use the product rule to find

$$y'(x) = -2e^{-x/2} - (2(x+1)) \times \left(-\tfrac{1}{2}e^{-x/2}\right)$$
$$= (-2 + (x+1))e^{-x/2}$$
$$= (x-1)e^{-x/2}.$$

So $y'(x) = 0$ only at $x = 1$. This is the only stationary point.

(b) To classify the stationary point, we differentiate again:

$$y''(x) = e^{-x/2} + (x-1)\left(-\tfrac{1}{2}\right)e^{-x/2} = \tfrac{1}{2}(3-x)e^{-x/2}.$$

At the stationary point, $y''(1) = e^{-1/2} > 0$, so the stationary point is a local minimum.

Alternatively, we see that the first derivative y' is negative if $x < 1$ and positive if $x > 1$, so the first derivative test confirms that it is a local minimum.

The value of the function at the stationary point is
$y(1) = 5 - 4e^{-1/2} = 2.574$ (to four significant figures).

Solution to Exercise 34

(a) (i) The denominator $4 + 1.5v + 0.008v^2$ is positive for all $v \geq 0$, so $f(v)$ is defined for all $v \geq 0$.

(ii) $f(v) = 0$ only when $v = 0$.

(iii) As $v \to \infty$, $f(v) \to 0$.

(iv) To find any stationary points, differentiate $f(v)$ using the quotient rule, to obtain

$$f'(v) = \frac{(4 + 1.5v + 0.008v^2) - v(1.5 + 0.016v)}{(4 + 1.5v + 0.008v^2)^2}$$

$$= \frac{4 - 0.008v^2}{(4 + 1.5v + 0.008v^2)^2}.$$

The stationary points occur when $4 - 0.008v^2 = 0$, i.e. at $v = \pm\sqrt{500} = \pm 22.36$ (to two decimal places). The negative stationary point is outside the domain ($v \geq 0$), so we need consider only $v = 22.36$.

For $v < 22.36$, $f'(v) > 0$, while for $v > 22.36$, $f'(v) < 0$. Therefore $v = 22.36$ is a local maximum. At this point, $f(22.36) = 0.538$ (to three decimal places).

(b) A graph of f is shown below.

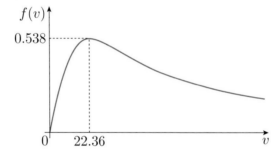

From the graph we see that the global maximum of f occurs at the local maximum, i.e. at $v = \sqrt{500} = 22.36$. The global minimum occurs at the endpoint of the domain, i.e. at $v = 0$.

Solution to Exercise 35

(a) Using the product rule for derivatives,

$$\frac{d}{dx}\left(-\frac{x}{a}\cos(ax) + \frac{1}{a^2}\sin(ax) + C\right)$$

$$= -\frac{1}{a}\cos(ax) + \left(-\frac{x}{a}\right)[-a\sin(ax)] + \frac{a}{a^2}\cos(ax)$$

$$= x\sin(ax).$$

Therefore

$$\int x\sin(ax)\,dx = -\frac{x}{a}\cos(ax) + \frac{1}{a^2}\sin(ax) + C,$$

so verifying the given integral.

(b) Using the composite rule for derivatives, and noting that $\cos(ax) > 0$ for $-\pi/2 < ax < \pi/2$, we have

$$\frac{d}{dx}\left(-\frac{1}{a}\ln(\cos(ax)) + C\right) = \left(-\frac{1}{a}\right)\frac{1}{\cos(ax)}\frac{d}{dx}(\cos(ax))$$
$$= \left(-\frac{1}{a}\right)\frac{-a\sin(ax)}{\cos(ax)}$$
$$= \tan(ax).$$

Therefore

$$\int \tan(ax)\,dx = -\frac{1}{a}\ln(\cos(ax)) + C,$$

so verifying the given integral.

Solution to Exercise 36

Using the given identity, we have

$$\int \cos^2(ax)\,dx = \frac{1}{2}\int[1 + \cos(2ax)]\,dx = \frac{1}{2}\left(x + \frac{1}{2a}\sin(2ax)\right) + C$$
$$= \frac{1}{2}x + \frac{1}{4a}\sin(2ax) + C.$$

Solution to Exercise 37

(a) $\displaystyle\int e^{5x}\,dx = \frac{1}{5}e^{5x} + C.$

(b) $\displaystyle\int 6\sec^2(3t)\,dt = 6 \times \frac{1}{3}\tan(3t) + C = 2\tan(3t) + C.$

(c) This does not quite match a Handbook integral as it stands. We have $36 + 4x^2 = 4(9 + x^2)$, so

$$\int \frac{1}{36 + 4v^2}\,dv = \int \frac{1}{4(9 + v^2)}\,dv = \frac{1}{4}\int \frac{1}{9 + v^2}\,dv$$
$$= \frac{1}{4}\left(\frac{1}{3}\arctan\left(\frac{1}{3}v\right)\right) + C$$
$$= \frac{1}{12}\arctan\left(\frac{1}{3}v\right) + C.$$

(d) For $y < \frac{3}{2}$, the integrand is positive, and we have

$$\int \frac{1}{3 - 2y}\,dy = -\frac{1}{2}\ln(3 - 2y) + C.$$

(e) For $y > \frac{3}{2}$, the integrand is negative, and we have

$$\int \frac{1}{3 - 2y}\,dy = -\frac{1}{2}\ln(-3 + 2y) + C = -\frac{1}{2}\ln(2y - 3) + C.$$

Solution to Exercise 38

(a) $\displaystyle\int (6\cos(-2t) + 8\sin(4t)) = -3\sin(-2t) - 2\cos(4t) + C.$

Note that you can use $\cos\theta = \cos(-\theta)$ to simplify the integrand (or use $\sin\theta = -\sin(-\theta)$ to simplify the result) to obtain $3\sin(2t) - 2\cos(4t) + C.$

(b) For $-3 < t < 3$,

$$\int \frac{1}{\sqrt{9 - t^2}}\, dt = \arcsin\left(\tfrac{1}{3}t\right) + C.$$

(c) For $t < 0$,

$$\int \frac{5t^3 + 7}{t}\, dt = \int \left(5t^2 + \frac{7}{t}\right) dt = \tfrac{5}{3}t^3 + 7\ln(-t) + C.$$

(d) For $t > 0$,

$$\int \left(2\ln(4t) - \frac{2}{t}\right) dt = 2t(\ln(4t) - 1) - 2\ln t + C.$$

(e) Choose $a = 1$, $b = -1$. Then $b < x < a$ and we can use the standard integral

$$\int \frac{1}{(x - a)(x - b)}\, dx = \frac{1}{a - b}\ln\left|\frac{a - x}{x - b}\right| = \frac{1}{a - b}\ln\left(\frac{a - x}{x - b}\right).$$

So

$$\int \frac{1}{(x - 1)(x + 1)}\, dx = \frac{1}{2}\ln\left(\frac{1 - x}{x + 1}\right) + C.$$

Solution to Exercise 39

Using $v^2 - k^2 = (v - k)(v + k)$, and taking $a = k$ and $b = -k$ in the Handbook entry for $\displaystyle\int \frac{1}{(x - a)(x - b)}\, dx$, with $b < x < a$, we obtain

$$\int \frac{1}{v^2 - k^2}\, dv = \int \frac{1}{(v - k)(v + k)}\, dv$$

$$= \frac{1}{2k}\ln\left|\frac{k - v}{v + k}\right| + C$$

$$= \frac{1}{2k}\ln\left(\frac{k - v}{v + k}\right) + C \quad (-k < v < k).$$

Solution to Exercise 40

(a) If $u = 2 + 4y^3$, then $du/dy = 12y^2$. So

$$\int y^2 \exp(2 + 4y^3)\, dy = \tfrac{1}{12}\int e^u \frac{du}{dx}\, du$$

$$= \tfrac{1}{12}\int e^u\, du$$

$$= \tfrac{1}{12}e^u + C = \tfrac{1}{12}e^{2 + 4y^3} + C.$$

(b) If $u = \sin y$, then $du/dy = \cos y$. So

$$\int \cos y \sin^2 y\, dy = \int u^2 \frac{du}{dy}\, dy$$

$$= \int u^2\, du$$

$$= \tfrac{1}{3}u^3 + C = \tfrac{1}{3}\sin^3 y + C.$$

(c) If $u = 1 - t^2$, then $du/dt = -2t$. So

$$\int t\sqrt{1 - t^2}\, dt = -\tfrac{1}{2} \int \sqrt{u}\, \frac{du}{dx}\, dx$$
$$= -\tfrac{1}{2} \int u^{1/2}\, du$$
$$= -\tfrac{1}{2}\left(\tfrac{2}{3} u^{3/2}\right) + C$$
$$= -\tfrac{1}{3}\left(\sqrt{1 - t^2}\right)^3 + C.$$

(d) If $u = 1 + x^2$, then $du/dx = 2x$. So

$$\int \frac{x}{1 + x^2}\, dx = \tfrac{1}{2} \int \frac{1}{u}\, \frac{du}{dx}\, dx$$
$$= \tfrac{1}{2} \int \frac{1}{u}\, du$$
$$= \tfrac{1}{2}\ln(u) + C = \tfrac{1}{2}\ln(1 + x^2) + C.$$

In this case, there is no problem with the domain of the ln function because $u = 1 + x^2 > 0$. The answer can also be obtained directly from equation (82) because the integrand is proportional to $g'(x)/g(x)$ with $g(x) > 0$.

(e) If $u = 1 + \sin^2 t$, then $du/dt = 2\sin t \cos t = \sin 2t$, using the trigonometric identity for $\sin 2t$ (equation (41)). So the integrand is of the form $g'(x)/g(x)$ with $g(x) > 0$. Hence equation (82) gives

$$\int \frac{\sin 2t}{1 + \sin^2 t}\, dt = \ln|1 + \sin^2 t| + C = \ln(1 + \sin^2 t) + C.$$

(f) Using equation (82) with $g(y) = 1 - y^2$, so that $g'(y) = -2y$, we have (for $y \neq \pm 1$)

$$\int \frac{y}{1 - y^2}\, dy = -\tfrac{1}{2} \int \frac{-2y}{1 - y^2}\, dy$$
$$= -\tfrac{1}{2}\ln|1 - y^2| + C.$$

Solution to Exercise 41

Taking $u = 3x + 1$, we have $du/dx = 3$, so we can take $du = (du/dx)\, dx = 3\, dx$, and $dx = du/3$. Also, $x = (u - 1)/3$, so

$$9x^2 + 1 = (u - 1)^2 + 1 = u^2 - 2u + 2.$$

Putting everything together gives

$$I = \int \frac{9x^2 + 1}{3x + 1}\, dx = \int \frac{u^2 - 2u + 2}{u}\, \frac{du}{3}$$
$$= \tfrac{1}{3} \int \left(u - 2 + \frac{2}{u}\right) du$$
$$= \tfrac{1}{3}\left(\tfrac{1}{2} u^2 - 2u + 2\ln u\right) + C$$
$$= \tfrac{1}{6}(3x + 1)^2 - \tfrac{2}{3}(3x + 1) + \tfrac{2}{3}\ln(3x + 1) + C.$$

There is no problem with the domain of the ln function in this case because $3x + 1 > 0$.

Solution to Exercise 42

(a) Take $f(x) = x$ and $g'(x) = e^{-x}$. Then $f'(x) = 1$ and $g(x) = -e^{-x}$. So

$$\int xe^{-x}\,dx = x(-e^{-x}) - \int 1 \times (-e^{-x})\,dx$$

$$= -xe^{-x} + \int e^{-x}\,dx$$

$$= -xe^{-x} - e^{-x} + C$$

$$= -(x+1)e^{-x} + C.$$

(b) Take $f(x) = x^2$ and $g'(x) = e^{-x}$. Then $f'(x) = 2x$ and $g(x) = -e^{-x}$. So

$$\int x^2 e^{-x}\,dx = x^2(-e^{-x}) - \int 2x(-e^{-x})\,dx$$

$$= -x^2 e^{-x} + 2\int xe^{-x}\,dx.$$

Using the result of part (a), we get

$$\int x^2 e^{-x}\,dx = -x^2 e^{-x} + 2(-(x+1)e^{-x} + C)$$

$$= -(x^2 + 2x + 2)e^{-x} + B,$$

where $B = 2C$ is an arbitrary constant.

(c) Take $f(x) = \sin x$ and $g'(x) = e^x$ (the other way around also works). Then $f'(x) = \cos x$ and $g(x) = e^x$. So

$$\int e^x \sin x\,dx = e^x \sin x - \int e^x \cos x\,dx.$$

We now evaluate the integral on the right-hand side by parts, taking $f(x) = \cos x$ and $g'(x) = e^x$. Then $f'(x) = -\sin x$ and $g(x) = e^x$. So

$$\int e^x \cos x\,dx = e^x \cos x + \int e^x \sin x\,dx.$$

Putting the two results together, we get

$$\int e^x \sin x\,dx = e^x \sin x - e^x \cos x - \int e^x \sin x\,dx,$$

and rearranging gives

$$\int e^x \sin x\,dx = \tfrac{1}{2}e^x(\sin x - \cos x).$$

Solution to Exercise 43

(a) $\displaystyle\int_0^1 (x^3 - 2)\,dx = \left[\tfrac{1}{4}x^4 - 2x\right]_0^1 = \left(\tfrac{1}{4} - 2\right) - (0 - 0) = -\tfrac{7}{4}.$

(b) $\displaystyle\int_1^2 (x^3 - 2)\,dx = \left[\tfrac{1}{4}x^4 - 2x\right]_1^2 = \left(\tfrac{16}{4} - 4\right) - \left(\tfrac{1}{4} - 2\right) = \tfrac{7}{4}.$

(c) $\displaystyle\int_0^2 (x^3 - 2)\,dx = \left[\tfrac{1}{4}x^4 - 2x\right]_0^2 = \left(\tfrac{16}{4} - 4\right) - (0 - 0) = 0.$

This integral is the sum of the integrals in parts (a) and (b).

Solution to Exercise 44

$$\int_0^{3/2} \frac{1}{9 + 4z^2}\, dz = \frac{1}{4} \int_0^{3/2} \frac{1}{9/4 + z^2}\, dz$$

$$= \frac{1}{4} \left[\frac{1}{3/2} \arctan\left(\frac{x}{3/2} \right) \right]_0^{3/2}$$

$$= \frac{1}{6} (\arctan 1 - \arctan 0)$$

$$= \frac{1}{6} \left(\frac{\pi}{4} - 0 \right) = \frac{\pi}{24}.$$

Solution to Exercise 45

Make the change of variable $u = 3\pi x$, so that $x = u/3\pi$ and $du = (du/dx)\, dx = 3\pi\, dx$. Expressing the limits of integration in terms of u, we see that the lower limit is $u = 0$, while the upper limit is $u = 3\pi$. Hence

$$I = \int_{u=0}^{u=3\pi} \left(\frac{u}{3\pi} \right)^2 \sin^2 u \left(\frac{du}{3\pi} \right)$$

$$= \left(\frac{1}{3\pi} \right)^3 \int_{u=0}^{u=3\pi} u^2 \sin^2 u\, du.$$

We can then use the given integral to conclude that

$$I = \left(\frac{1}{3\pi} \right)^3 J_3 = \left(\frac{1}{3\pi} \right)^3 \left(\frac{3^3 \pi^3}{6} - \frac{3\pi}{4} \right) = \frac{1}{6} - \frac{1}{36\pi^2}.$$

Solution to Exercise 46

(a) First notice that $f(x) = e^{-x^2} \sin(x)$ is an odd function of x because

$$f(-x) = e^{-(-x)^2} \sin(-x) = -e^{-x^2} \sin(x) = -f(x).$$

Since the range of integration (from $-\pi$ to $+\pi$) is symmetric about the origin, the integral vanishes.

(b) The integrand is odd because

$$f(-x) = -x \sin(1 + (-x)^4) = -f(x).$$

Since the range of integration is symmetric about the origin, the integral vanishes.

(c) We write the integral as

$$I = \int_{-1}^1 x^2 \cos(x^3)\, dx + \int_{-1}^1 x^3 \cos(x^3)\, dx.$$

The second integral vanishes since the integrand is odd and the range of integration is symmetric about the origin.

The first integral can be evaluated by changing the variable to $u = x^3$, so that $du = 3x^2\, dx$, and the two limits become $u = -1$ and $u = 1$.

Hence

$$I = \frac{1}{3} \int_{u=-1}^{u=1} \cos u\, du = \left[\frac{1}{3} \sin u \right]_{u=-1}^{u=1} = \frac{2}{3} \sin(1) \simeq 0.561.$$

Acknowledgements

Grateful acknowledgement is made to the following sources:

Figure 1: NASA.

Figure 2: Taken from www.astro.le.ac.uk/users/gwy/images/nano.

Figure 23: Taken from http://wrongsideofmemphis.com/tag/kepler.

Figure 24: M.V. Berry and S. Klein (1996) *Coloured Diffraction Catastrophes*, National Academy of Sciences.

Figure 32(b): Image Editor / www.flickr.com.

Every effort has been made to contact copyright holders. If any have been inadvertently overlooked, the publishers will be pleased to make the necessary arrangements at the first opportunity.

Unit 2

First-order differential equations

Introduction

This unit introduces differential equations. This topic is of central importance in physics because many physical laws are expressed as differential equations. Differential equations also appear in many other areas of science and applied mathematics. This introduction gives a brief outline of the topic.

We begin by discussing the solution and derivation of a simple differential equation, namely

$$\frac{df}{dx} = -A\,f(x), \tag{1}$$

where $A > 0$ is a constant. This is called a *differential equation* because it contains a *derivative* of an initially unknown function $f(x)$. It is solved by finding a function $f(x)$ that satisfies the equation. You will see how it is solved, and how it arises in two different physical situations. This illustrates several important points about differential equations in quick succession before the body of the unit discusses them at a slower pace.

In some cases differential equations can be solved by guessing the solution. Noting that equation (1) is very similar to equation (19) of Unit 1, we try the function $f(x) = \exp(-Ax)$. The derivative of this function is

Equation (19) of Unit 1 is
$$\frac{d\exp(x)}{dx} = \exp(x).$$

$$\frac{df}{dx} = -A\exp(-Ax).$$

However, we assumed that $\exp(-Ax) = f(x)$, so this shows that our guess satisfies

$$\frac{df}{dx} = -A\,f(x),$$

which is the differential equation that we wished to solve.

The same reasoning works if this **trial solution** is multiplied by any constant: if $f(x) = B\exp(-Ax)$, then $df/dx = -AB\exp(-Ax) = -A\,f(x)$. So we see that

$$f(x) = B\exp(-Ax) \tag{2}$$

is a solution of the differential equation (1) for any value of B. The reason why the trial solution works in this case is easy to understand. The exponential function $\exp(x)$ has the property that when you differentiate it, you get the same function back again. The differential equation (1) describes a function with almost that property, so it is natural to seek a solution of this equation in the form of equation (2).

You have now seen an example of a differential equation and its solution. But how does this differential equation arise in applications? We will discuss two examples.

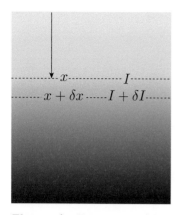

Figure 1   Intensity of light I in the sea at depth x

First, we consider a model for light penetrating into the ocean depths. Sunlight is absorbed in seawater, and almost no light reaches the deepest parts of the oceans. If you were involved with underwater engineering or investigating the behaviour of plankton, which can adjust their depth depending on the light intensity, you might wish to understand how the light intensity decreases as the depth increases. Let the intensity of light be $I(x)$ at depth x below the surface (Figure 1).

We would like to be able to find the function $I(x)$. This is done by finding a differential equation satisfied by $I(x)$. The differential equation is found using the following argument.

Consider what happens as we go from a depth x, passing through a thin layer of seawater of thickness δx to a slightly larger depth $x + \delta x$. (It is conventional to write the small change in any quantity X as δX, where δ is the Greek letter 'delta'). On passing through this thin layer, the intensity of light changes by an amount δI, due to absorption of light. This change is negative because the light intensity is reduced. We might reasonably expect that the amount of light absorbed is proportional to the amount of light entering the layer. Also, the amount of light absorbed by a thin layer is expected to be proportional to the thickness of the layer, so

$$\delta I = -AI \, \delta x,$$

where A is a constant (called the **absorption coefficient**) that describes how effectively seawater absorbs light.

Now divide both sides of this equation by δx, to obtain

$$\frac{\delta I}{\delta x} = -AI.$$

It is assumed that δx is small. If we take the limit as δx tends to zero, we get a differential equation for $I(x)$:

$$\frac{dI}{dx} = -A \, I(x). \tag{3}$$

This is the same as the equation we have already solved, apart from a change in the name of the function from $f(x)$ to $I(x)$. The solution is therefore

$$I(x) = B \exp(-Ax),$$

for some constant B. This solution is plotted in Figure 2 for $A = B = 1$. It has the expected property that the intensity I decreases as the depth x increases. The decrease is rapid in the upper layers but more gradual in the murky lower depths. A function of this type is said to exhibit **exponential decay**.

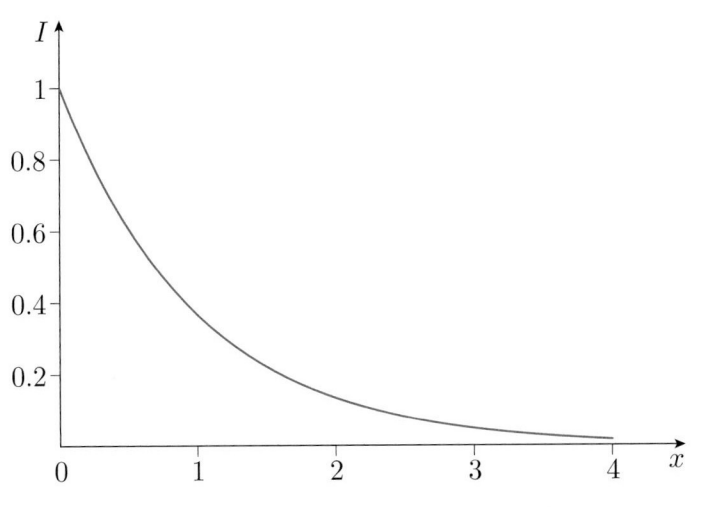

Figure 2 The graph of $I(x) = B\exp(-Ax)$ for $A = B = 1$

Notice that a complicated situation has been made much simpler by considering a very thin layer, in which the absorption of light can be taken to be proportional to the thickness of the layer. This approximation is valid for a thin layer but not for a thick one (as shown by the non-linear shape of the graph in Figure 2). The beauty of this approach emerges when we imagine the layer becoming infinitesimally thin. In this limit, the approximation becomes exact and, at the same time, we obtain an equation involving derivatives, that is, a *differential equation*. So here is mathematical alchemy – we start with an approximation that is reasonable only on a small scale, and use it to obtain a differential equation that avoids this approximation and has solutions that apply on a large scale.

Into the deep

In the ocean, the light that is absorbed least and penetrates furthest beneath the surface is blue in colour. In the clearest ocean water, the absorption coefficient of blue light is $A \simeq 2 \times 10^{-2}\,\mathrm{m}^{-1}$, while that for red light is 100 times greater. At a depth of 200 metres, the intensity of blue light is reduced by a factor $\exp(-4) = 0.018$, while the intensity of red light is reduced by a factor $\exp(-400) = 2 \times 10^{-174}$; essentially no red light is left at this depth. So deep-sea divers see their way around in dim blue light. Most life in the oceans, and all plant life, is concentrated in the top 200 metres of water because deeper waters are too dark to sustain photosynthesis. The ocean floor is generally much further below the surface; it is completely dark, and creatures like the anglerfish (Figure 3) have evolved to make light for themselves via chemical reactions.

Figure 3 An anglerfish creates light to attract its prey

Radioactive decay provides another context in which differential equation (1) appears. In this case, atoms of a radioactive substance 'decay'; that is, they release radiation and are transformed into other types of atom.

The term 'continuous variable' here means that $N \in \mathbb{R}$. We are also assuming that N is large and *positive*.

At time t, a given piece of radioactive material contains N 'parent' atoms (where N is a very large number). Because the number of atoms is very large, we will treat N as a continuous variable, rather than an integer. The radioactive 'parent' atoms are unstable and can break up to produce a 'daughter' atom and an energetic particle. By considering small intervals of time δt, it can be shown that the differential equation for the number of parent atoms as a function of time is

$$\frac{dN}{dt} = -AN,$$

where A is a constant that depends on the parent atom type. This is the same equation as equation (1), with different names for the symbols, and the solution can be found from equation (2) by changing the names of the symbols. The solution is therefore

$$N(t) = B \exp(-At).$$

Setting $t = 0$, we get $N(0) = B$, so we identify the constant B with the number of atoms present at time $t = 0$, i.e. the initial number of parent atoms at $t = 0$, which we denote by N_0. Hence

$$N(t) = N_0 \exp(-At). \tag{4}$$

The constant A is called the *decay constant*. It is large for types of parent atom that decay rapidly. The decay rate is often expressed in terms of the *half-life* of the atoms, $T_{1/2}$, which is the time taken for half of the parent atoms to decay. To determine the relation between the decay constant and the half-life, set

$$\frac{1}{2} = \frac{N(T_{1/2})}{N(0)} = \exp(-AT_{1/2}).$$

Taking the logarithm of this gives $\ln(1/2) = -AT_{1/2}$, so

$$T_{1/2} = \frac{\ln 2}{A}.$$

Figure 4   Skull of a smilodon

Radiocarbon dating

Atoms of carbon-14 are produced in the upper atmosphere by collisions between cosmic rays and molecules. They are unstable, and decay with a half-life of approximately 5644 years. Carbon-14 is absorbed by an organism when it is alive, and decays after the organism has died. By measuring the ratio of the carbon-14 atoms in a dead organism to those in a living one, the number of years since death can be estimated, using equation (4). For example, Figure 4 shows the skull of a smilodon (a sabre-toothed cat that was larger than a modern tiger). Radiocarbon dating of specimens like this reveals that such cats died about 10 000 years ago.

These examples of light intensity and radioactive decay illustrate some significant points.

- The two examples gave rise to essentially the same differential equation, just with different symbols. You need to be able to recognise when a differential equation is of the same form as one that you have seen before.

- In each case, the differential equation was obtained by considering small changes in physical variables (δx and δt). Similar steps are used in the derivation of many differential equations. However, you will not be asked to derive differential equations in this module; instead, we will focus on ways of solving them.

- The solution was obtained by guessing a suitable function. Judicious guesswork can help us to solve some differential equations, but you will see that systematic methods allow us to solve many more.

Study guide

This unit introduces some basic ideas about differential equations, before considering in detail *first-order differential equations*, so called because they involve only derivatives of first order.

Section 1 gives an example of how a differential equation arises in a mathematical model. It also introduces some basic definitions and terminology associated with differential equations and their solutions.

Sections 2 and 3 develop exact methods for solving first-order differential equations of various special types. From the point of view of later studies, these sections contain the most important material in this unit, which will be built on later in the module.

Some integrals cannot be evaluated by hand. In a similar way, many differential equations cannot be solved exactly. This unit therefore ends by looking at *qualitative methods* in Section 4 and *numerical methods* in Section 5. These sections will not be tested in continuous assessment or in the exam, but it is important that you read them in order to gain an insight into what progress can be made when exact solutions of differential equations lie beyond our grasp.

1 Some basics

The Introduction gave a quick and sketchy overview of the subject of differential equations in order to give you some feeling for the scope and significance of this vast topic. Here we start again from the beginning, developing the subject at a slower pace.

An important class of equations that arises in mathematics consists of those that feature the *rates of change* of one or more variables with respect to one or more others. These rates of change are expressed mathematically by *derivatives*, and the corresponding equations are called *differential equations*. Equations of this type crop up in a wide variety of situations. They are found, for example, in models of physical, astronomical, electronic, economic, demographic and biological phenomena.

First-order differential equations, which are the particular topic of this unit, feature derivatives of order one only; that is, if the rate of change of variable y with respect to variable x is involved, the equations feature dy/dx, but not d^2y/dx^2, d^3y/dx^3 or any higher-order derivatives. In many cases we consider the rate of change of a variable with respect to time, but we also discuss differential equations where the independent variable is position, or occasionally some other variable.

When a differential equation arises, it is usually an important aim to *solve* the equation. For an equation that features the derivative dy/dx, this entails expressing the *dependent variable y* directly in terms of the *independent variable x*. The process of solution requires the effect of the derivative to be 'undone'. The reversal of differentiation is achieved by integration, so it is to be expected that integration will feature prominently in the methods for solving differential equations. The solution can be attempted symbolically, to get an exact formula, or numerically, to get approximate numerical values that can be tabulated or graphed.

Subsection 1.1 describes a situation that leads naturally to a first-order differential equation – in this case, one that is slightly more complex than equation (1).

Subsection 1.2 then introduces some important terminology. It explains what is meant by the term 'solution' in the context of first-order differential equations, and brings out the distinction between the *general solution* and the various possible *particular solutions*. The specification of a constraint (in the form of an *initial condition*) usually allows us to find a unique function that is a particular solution of the differential equation and also satisfies the constraint.

1.1   Where do differential equations come from?

To illustrate how differential equations arise, we consider an example drawn from biology.

Suppose that we are interested in the size of a particular population, and in how it varies over time. The first point to make is that the size of any population is measured in integers (whole numbers), so it is not clear how differentiation will be relevant. Nevertheless, if the population is large, say in the hundreds of thousands, a change of one unit will be relatively very small, and in these circumstances we may choose to model the population size by a *continuous* function of time. This function can be written as $P(t)$, and our task is to show how $P(t)$ may be described by a differential equation.

Let us assume a fixed starting time (which we label $t = 0$). If the population is not constant, then there will be 'joiners' and 'leavers'. For example, in a population of humans in a particular country, the former are those who are born, or who immigrate into the country, while the latter are those who die or emigrate. For our simple model we will ignore immigration and emigration, and concentrate solely on births and deaths.

In the small period between t and $t + \delta t$, it is reasonable, as a first approximation, to expect the number of births to be proportional to the population size $P(t)$ at time t, and to the time interval δt. A similar argument applies to the number of deaths, so we can write

$$\text{number of births} \simeq b\, P(t)\, \delta t,$$
$$\text{number of deaths} \simeq c\, P(t)\, \delta t,$$

where b and c are positive constants known as the *proportionate birth rate* and the *proportionate death rate*, respectively.

The *change δP* in the population over the time interval δt is the number of births minus the number of deaths in that interval. So we have

$$\delta P \simeq b\, P(t)\, \delta t - c\, P(t)\, \delta t$$
$$= (b - c)\, P(t)\, \delta t.$$

Births appear with a positive sign because they add to the population; deaths appear with a negative sign because they subtract from the population.

Dividing through by δt, we obtain

$$\frac{\delta P}{\delta t} \simeq (b - c)\, P(t).$$

The approximations involved in deriving this equation become progressively more accurate for shorter time intervals. So, finally, by letting δt tend to zero, we obtain

$$\frac{dP}{dt} = (b - c)\, P(t). \tag{5}$$

This is the step that requires P to be a continuous (rather than discrete) function of t.

This is a *differential* equation because it describes dP/dt rather than the eventual object of our interest (the function $P(t)$ itself).

We can simplify the above equation by introducing the *proportionate growth rate r*, which is defined to be the difference between the proportionate birth and death rates: $r = b - c$. Then our model becomes

$$\frac{dP}{dt} = rP, \tag{6}$$

where r is a constant (which may be positive, negative or zero).

Equation (6) may look familiar: it is essentially the same as the equation discussed in the Introduction (the only difference being the sign on the right-hand side). So it should not surprise you that the solution is of the form

$$P(t) = P_0 \exp(rt), \tag{7}$$

where P_0 is the initial population at time $t = 0$.

For $r > 0$, this leads to the prediction of an exponential growth in population; for $r < 0$, it predicts an exponential decay in population; and for $r = 0$, the population is predicted to remain constant. These three possibilities are sketched in Figure 5.

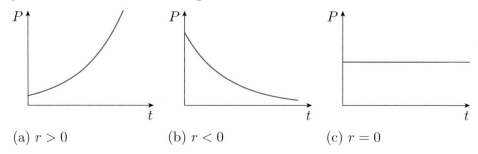

(a) $r > 0$ (b) $r < 0$ (c) $r = 0$

Figure 5 Population models obtained from equation (6), where r is a constant

From equation (6), we see that the proportionate growth rate r is given by

$$r = \frac{1}{P}\frac{dP}{dt},$$

and up to this point, we have assumed this to be constant. However, this is not entirely realistic. For example, if r is a positive constant, then an exponential increase in population may be sustained for a while, but we know that such growth cannot go on forever. When the population is low, we may assume that there is the potential for it to grow (assuming a favourable environment) and the proportionate growth rate r should be high. But when the population becomes too large, competition for basic resources such as food is bound to restrict further growth, and the proportionate growth rate will be lower. We therefore arrive at the conclusion that r will be a function of P, decreasing as P increases. This decline in the proportionate growth rate ensures that unlimited exponential growth will not occur.

A particularly useful model arises from taking $r(P)$ to be a decreasing *linear* function of P, as shown in Figure 6. We write this as

$$r(P) = k\left(1 - \frac{P}{M}\right), \tag{8}$$

where k and M are positive constants. From this formula, you can see that the proportionate growth rate r is modelled as decreasing linearly with P, from the value k (when $P = 0$) to the value 0 (when $P = M$). For $P > M$, the proportionate growth rate is negative.

Using this expression for r, the differential equation satisfied by P becomes

$$\frac{dP}{dt} = kP\left(1 - \frac{P}{M}\right). \tag{9}$$

This is well known to biologists as the **logistic equation**. You will see how to solve this equation exactly in Section 2, and how to analyse its qualitative behaviour in Section 3.

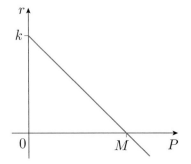

Figure 6 A plot of $r(P)$ as given by equation (8)

It is worth noting that not all differential equations are derived like those above, from first principles using small increments. In science, many differential equations come from physical laws that are framed directly in terms of the rates of change of physical quantities. For example, *Newton's second law* tells us that

$$F = m\,\frac{d^2x}{dt^2},$$

where F is the force acting on a particle of mass m, and d^2x/dt^2 is the acceleration of the particle in the direction of the force. This law produces a large variety of differential equations whose precise form depends on the nature of the force.

The Voyager missions

A spectacular example of the use of Newton's second law is illustrated in Figure 7, which shows the trajectories of the two Voyager spacecraft, launched in 1977.

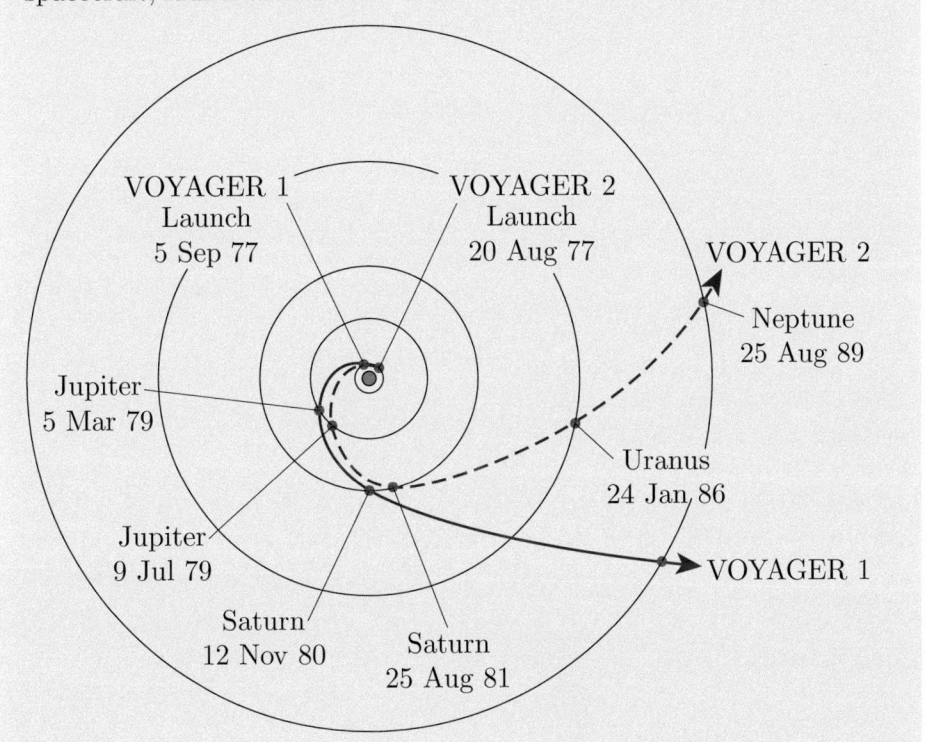

Figure 7 The trajectories of the two Voyager spacecraft were planned by solving differential equations

These trajectories were carefully designed to enable the spacecraft to pass close to various planets and eventually to escape from the Solar System. The trajectories were planned by solving Newton's second law for the position and velocity of each spacecraft. The resulting

Figure 8 A montage of images taken by the two Voyager spacecraft, showing Saturn, its rings and six of its moons

differential equations are complicated by the fact that the forces depend on the positions of the planets, which depend on time. Such equations are much more complicated than the logistic equation, and in practice are solved on computers using numerical methods.

Figure 8 shows a fruit of these labours: close-up views of Saturn and its moons. The moon in the foreground is Dione, which is composed mainly of water ice.

Exercise 1

Suppose that a population obeys the logistic equation (with a proportionate growth rate given by equation (8)), and that you are given the following information. When $P = 10$, the proportionate growth rate is 1, and when $P = 10\,000$, the proportionate growth rate is 0. Find the corresponding values of k and M.

1.2 Differential equations and their solutions

This subsection introduces some of the fundamental concepts associated with differential equations. First, however, you are asked to recall some terminology and notation from your previous exposure to calculus.

Some of this terminology and notation was discussed in Unit 1.

The *derivative* of a variable y with respect to another variable x is denoted in Leibniz notation by dy/dx. In this expression we refer to y as the *dependent variable* and x as the *independent variable*.

Other notations are also used for derivatives. If the relation between variables x and y is expressed in terms of a function f, so that $y = f(x)$, then the derivative may be written in function notation as $f'(x)$. A further notation, attributed to Newton, is restricted to cases in which the independent variable is time, denoted by t. The derivative of $y = f(t)$ can be written in this case as $\dot{y}$, where the dot over the y stands for the d/dt of Leibniz notation.

Thus we may express this derivative in any of the equivalent forms

$$\frac{dy}{dt} = \dot{y} = f'(t).$$

Further derivatives are obtained by differentiating this first derivative. The second derivative of $y = f(t)$ could be represented by any of the forms

$$\frac{d^2y}{dt^2} = \ddot{y} = f''(t).$$

These possible notations have different strengths and weaknesses, and which is most appropriate in any situation depends on the purpose at hand. You will see all of these notations used at various times during the module.

It is common practice in science and applied mathematics to reduce the proliferation of symbols as far as possible. One aspect of this practice is that we often avoid allocating separate symbols to variables and to associated functions. So in place of the equation $y = f(t)$ (where y and t denote variables, and f denotes the function that relates them), we write $y = y(t)$, which is read as 'y is a function of t'. (You saw an example of this in the preceding subsection, where we used P and $P(t)$.)

Strictly speaking, this is an abuse of notation, since there is ambiguity as to exactly what the symbol y represents: it is a variable on the left-hand side of $y = y(t)$, but a function on the right-hand side. However, this is a very convenient abuse!

The following definitions explain just what are meant by a *differential equation*, by the *order* of such an equation, and by a *solution* of it.

Definitions

- A **differential equation** for $y = y(x)$ is an equation that relates the independent variable x, the dependent variable y, and one or more derivatives of y with respect to x.

- The **order** of a differential equation is the order of the highest derivative that appears in the equation. Thus a **first-order differential equation** for $y = y(x)$ features only the first derivative, dy/dx.

- A **solution** of a differential equation is a function $y = y(x)$ that satisfies the equation.

These definitions have been framed in terms of an independent variable x and a dependent variable y. You should be able to translate them to apply to any other independent and dependent variables. Thus equation (9) is a differential equation in which t is the independent variable and P is the dependent variable. It is a first-order equation, since dP/dt appears in it but higher derivatives such as d^2P/dt^2 do not. By contrast, the differential equation

$$3\frac{d^2y}{dx^2} + 2\frac{dy}{dx} + y^2 \sin x = x^2$$

is of second order, since the second derivative d^2y/dx^2 appears in it but higher derivatives do not. Second-order differential equations will be discussed in Unit 3.

The topic of this unit is first-order differential equations. Moreover, it concentrates on first-order equations that can be expressed (possibly after some algebraic manipulation) in the form

$$\frac{dy}{dx} = f(x, y). \tag{10}$$

The right-hand side here stands for an expression involving both, either or neither of the variables x and y, but no other variables and no derivatives.

Equation (9) is of this form, with $f(t, P) = kP\left(1 - \dfrac{P}{M}\right)$.

This substitution includes the requirement that the function should be *differentiable* (i.e. that it should have a derivative) at all points where it is claimed to be a solution.

According to the definition given above, a function has to *satisfy* a differential equation to be regarded as a solution of it. The differential equation is satisfied by the function provided that when the function is substituted into the equation, the left- and right-hand sides of the equation give identical expressions.

In the next exercise you are asked to verify that several functions are solutions of corresponding first-order differential equations. Later in the unit, you will see how all of these differential equations may be solved; but even when a solution has been deduced, it is worth checking by substitution that the supposed solution is indeed valid.

Exercise 2

Verify that each of the following functions is a solution of the corresponding differential equation.

(a) $y = 2e^x - (x^2 + 2x + 2)$; $\dfrac{dy}{dx} = y + x^2$.

(b) $y = \frac{1}{2}x^2 + \frac{3}{2}$; $\dfrac{dy}{dx} = x$.

(c) $u = 2e^{x^2/2}$; $u' = xu$.

The restriction $y \neq 0$ placed on the differential equation in part (d) is necessary to ensure that $-x/3y$ is well defined.

(d) $y = \sqrt{\dfrac{27 - x^2}{3}}$ $(-3\sqrt{3} < x < 3\sqrt{3})$; $\dfrac{dy}{dx} = -\dfrac{x}{3y}$ $(y \neq 0)$.

(e) $y = t + e^{-t}$; $\dot{y} = -y + t + 1$.

(f) $y = t + Ce^{-t}$; $\dot{y} = -y + t + 1$. (Here C is an arbitrary constant.)

In the last two parts of Exercise 2 you were asked to verify that

$$y = t + e^{-t} \quad \text{and} \quad y = t + Ce^{-t}$$

are solutions of the differential equation $\dot{y} = -y + t + 1$, where in the second case C is an *arbitrary constant*. Whatever number is chosen for C, the corresponding expression for $y(t)$ is always a solution of the differential equation. The particular function $y = t + e^{-t}$ is just one example of such a solution, obtained by choosing $C = 1$.

This demonstrates that solutions of a differential equation can exist in profusion; as a result, we need terms to distinguish between the totality of all the solutions for a given equation and an individual solution that is just one of the possibilities.

Definitions

- The **general solution** of a differential equation is the collection of all possible solutions of that equation.

- A **particular solution** of a differential equation is a single solution of the equation, and consists of a solution containing no arbitrary constants.

In many cases it is possible to describe the general solution of a first-order differential equation by a single formula involving one arbitrary constant. For example, $y = t + Ce^{-t}$ is the general solution of the equation $\dot{y} = -y + t + 1$; this means that not only is $y = t + Ce^{-t}$ a solution for all values of C, but also *every* particular solution of the equation may be obtained by giving C a suitable value.

Sometimes the values allowed for the arbitrary constant are restricted in some way. In the above example, if y is real-valued, we should take C to be a real (rather than a complex) number. In other cases, the general solution makes sense only if the arbitrary constant C is restricted to some range, and you will meet examples of this later in this unit. Nevertheless, any arbitrary constant is 'arbitrary' in the sense that it does not have a definite value.

Exercise 3

(a) Verify that, for any value of the constant C, the function $y = C - \frac{1}{3}e^{-3x}$ is a solution of the differential equation

$$\frac{dy}{dx} = e^{-3x}.$$

(b) Verify that, for any value of the constant C, the function $u = Ce^t - t - 1$ is a solution of the differential equation

$$\dot{u} = t + u.$$

(c) Verify that, for any value of the constant C, the function

$$P = \frac{CMe^{kt}}{1 + Ce^{kt}}$$

is a solution of equation (9).

As you have seen, there are many solutions of a differential equation. However, a particular solution of the equation, representing a definite relationship between the variables involved, is often what is needed. This is obtained by using a further piece of information in addition to the differential equation. Often the extra information takes the form of a pair of values for the independent and dependent variables.

For example, in the case of a population model, it would be natural to specify the starting population, P_0 say, and to start measuring time from $t = 0$. We could then write

$$P = P_0 \text{ when } t = 0, \quad \text{or equivalently,} \quad P(0) = P_0.$$

A requirement of this type is called an *initial condition*.

Definitions

- An **initial condition** associated with the differential equation

$$\frac{dy}{dt} = f(t, y)$$

  specifies that the dependent variable y takes some value y_0 when the independent variable t takes some value t_0. This is written either as

$$y = y_0 \text{ when } t = t_0$$

  or as

$$y(t_0) = y_0.$$

  The numbers t_0 and y_0 are referred to as **initial values**.

- The combination of a first-order differential equation and an initial condition is called an **initial-value problem**.

The word 'initial' in these definitions arises from those (frequent) cases in which:

- the independent variable represents time t, and the differential equation describes how a system evolves in time

- the initial condition $y(t_0) = y_0$ describes the way the system is started off at some initial time t_0

- we are interested in how the system behaves at times after the initial time t_0, so we want the solution $y(t)$ for $t > t_0$.

However, this situation is not essential. The term 'initial condition' is used even when we are interested in the solution $y(t)$ for $t < t_0$ or when the independent variable does not represent time.

We usually expect that an initial-value problem should have a *unique* solution, since the outcome is then completely determined by the differential equation that governs the system, and by the configuration that the system had at the start. In fact, all the initial-value problems you will meet in this module have unique solutions, so if you can find a solution to an initial-value problem, then this is *the* solution.

Example 1

Using the result given in Exercise 3(b), find a solution to the initial-value problem

$$\frac{dy}{dx} = x + y, \quad y(0) = 1.$$

Solution

From Exercise 3(b), on replacing the variables t, u by x, y, the differential equation in this question has solutions of the form

$$y = Ce^x - x - 1.$$

The initial condition tells us that $y = 1$ when $x = 0$, and on feeding these values into the above solution we find that

$$1 = Ce^0 - 0 - 1 = C - 1.$$

Hence $C = 2$, and the particular solution of the differential equation that solves the initial-value problem is

$$y = 2e^x - x - 1.$$

Exercise 4

The size P of a population (measured in hundreds of thousands) is modelled by the logistic equation

$$\frac{dP}{dt} = kP\left(1 - \frac{P}{M}\right), \quad P(0) = 1,$$

where $k = 0.15$, $M = 10$, and t is time measured in years.

(a) Use the result given in Exercise 3(c) to find a solution to this initial-value problem.

(b) Use your answer to predict the long-term behaviour of the population size (as $t \to \infty$).

Finally in this subsection, note that we sometimes need to keep an eye on the *domain* of the function solving the differential equation. 'Gaps' in the domain usually show up as some form of restriction on the nature of a solution curve. For example, consider the differential equation

$$\frac{dy}{dx} = \frac{1}{x}. \tag{11}$$

It turns out that there are two distinct families of solutions, illustrated in Figure 9. One family of solutions (given by $y = \ln x + C$) applies for $x > 0$, and another family (given by $y = \ln(-x) + C$) applies for $x < 0$. The right-hand side of the differential equation is not defined for $x = 0$, so there is no solution there, and the two families do not cross the y-axis.

Since $|x| = -x$ if $x < 0$, you can see that this agrees with what we know from Unit 1, namely that

$$\int \frac{1}{x}\, dx = \ln|x| + C.$$

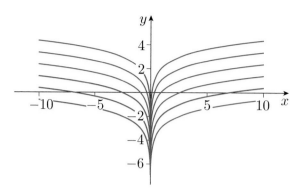

Figure 9　The two families of solutions, for $x > 0$ and $x < 0$, arising from equation (11)

2 Direct integration and separation of variables

This section and the next look at methods for finding *analytic* solutions of first-order differential equations – that is, solutions expressed in terms of exact formulas.

Until now we have considered first-order differential equations of the form

$$\frac{dy}{dx} = f(x,y). \tag{Eq. 10}$$

We now specialise to two important cases where analytic solutions can be found. Each case involves a special technique. The method of *direct integration* applies to first-order differential equations of the form

$$\frac{dy}{dx} = g(x), \tag{12}$$

where the right-hand side is a function of x alone. The method of *separation of variables* applies to first-order differential equations of the form

$$\frac{dy}{dx} = g(x)\,h(y), \tag{13}$$

where the right-hand side is the *product* of a function of x and a function of y. Of course, equation (12) is a special case of equation (13) with $h(y) = 1$. Nevertheless, it is convenient to discuss equation (12) first because it is solved in a very straightforward way.

2.1 Direct integration

An example of a differential equation that can be solved by direct integration is

$$\frac{dy}{dx} = x^2. \tag{14}$$

In order to solve this equation, we need to find functions $y(x)$ whose derivatives are x^2; one such function is $y = \frac{1}{3}x^3$. There are other functions with this same derivative, for example, $y = \frac{1}{3}x^3 + 1$ and $y = \frac{1}{3}x^3 - 2$. In fact, any function of the form

$$y = \tfrac{1}{3}x^3 + C, \tag{15}$$

where C is an arbitrary constant, satisfies differential equation (14), and equation (15) is the general solution of this differential equation.

The values $C = 0$, $C = 1$ and $C = -2$ give the three particular solutions mentioned above.

The expression $\frac{1}{3}x^3 + C$ is also *the indefinite integral* of x^2: that is,

$$\int x^2 \, dx = \tfrac{1}{3}x^3 + C.$$

This is hardly surprising, since integration 'undoes' or reverses the effect of differentiation.

In this case, therefore, the indefinite integral of x^2 is the general solution of differential equation (14), and a similar connection applies more generally, as you will now see.

If we have a differential equation of the form

$$\frac{dy}{dx} = f(x), \tag{16}$$

where the right-hand side, $f(x)$, is a known function of x alone, then we simply integrate both sides with respect to x:

The function $f(x)$ is assumed to be continuous (i.e. its graph has no breaks).

$$\int \frac{dy}{dx} \, dx = \int f(x) \, dx.$$

The left-hand side gives y, so we get

$$y = \int f(x) \, dx = F(x) + C, \tag{17}$$

where $F(x)$ is an integral of $f(x)$, and C is an arbitrary constant.

This means that the *general solution* of equation (16) can be written down directly as an indefinite integral; and if the integration can be performed, then the equation is solved.

Procedure 1   Direct integration

The *general solution* of the differential equation

$$\frac{dy}{dx} = f(x) \tag{Eq. 16}$$

is

$$y = \int f(x) \, dx = F(x) + C, \tag{Eq. 17}$$

where $F(x)$ is an integral of $f(x)$, and C is an arbitrary constant.

Once the general solution has been found, it is possible to single out a particular solution by specifying a value for the constant C. This value can be found by applying an initial condition.

Example 2

(a) Find the general solution of the differential equation

$$\frac{dy}{dx} = e^{-3x}.$$

(b) Find the particular solution of this differential equation that satisfies the initial condition $y(0) = \frac{5}{3}$.

Solution

(a) On applying direct integration, we obtain the general solution

$$y = \int e^{-3x}\, dx = -\tfrac{1}{3}e^{-3x} + C,$$

where C is an arbitrary constant.

(b) The initial condition $y(0) = \frac{5}{3}$ tells us that $y = \frac{5}{3}$ when $x = 0$, so we must have

$$\tfrac{5}{3} = -\tfrac{1}{3}e^0 + C,$$

which gives $C = 2$. The required particular solution is therefore

$$y = -\tfrac{1}{3}e^{-3x} + 2.$$

Procedure 1 uses x for the independent variable and y for the dependent variable. As usual, you should be prepared to translate this into situations where other symbols are used for the variables. But remember that the method of direct integration applies only to first-order differential equations for which the derivative is equal to a function of the *independent* variable alone. Thus direct integration can be applied, for example, to the differential equation

$$\frac{dx}{dt} = \cos t,$$

which has t as the independent variable and x as the dependent variable. In this case, the general solution is

$$x = \int \cos t\, dt = \sin t + C,$$

where C is an arbitrary constant. On the other hand, the differential equation

$$\frac{dx}{dt} = x^2$$

cannot be solved by direct integration because the right-hand side here is a function of the *dependent* variable, x.

Exercise 5

Solve each of the following initial-value problems.

(a) $\dfrac{dy}{dx} = 6x, \quad y(1) = 5.$

(b) $\dfrac{dv}{du} = e^{4u}, \quad v(0) = 2.$

(c) $\dot{y} = 5\sin 2t, \quad y(0) = 0.$

Remember that $\dot{y}$ stands for dy/dt, where t denotes time.

The method of direct integration succeeds in solving a differential equation of the specified type whenever it is possible to carry out the integration that arises – a task that may require you to apply any of the standard techniques of integration, such as the use of tables, integration by parts or integration by substitution (see Unit 1). For more difficult integrals, a computer algebra package may be used.

Exercise 6

Find the general solution of each of the following differential equations.

(a) $\dfrac{dy}{dx} = xe^{-2x}$ (*Hint*: For the integral, try integration by parts.)

(b) $\dot{p} = \dfrac{t}{1+t^2}$ (*Hint*: For the integral, try the substitution $u = 1 + t^2$.)

The solution to Exercise 6(b) can be generalised to any differential equation of the form

$$\frac{dy}{dx} = k\,\frac{f'(x)}{f(x)} \quad (\text{for } f(x) \neq 0),$$

where k is a constant. We get the general solution

$$y = k\ln|f(x)| + C,$$

where C is an arbitrary constant.

This is a simple extension of the result from Unit 1 that
$$\int \frac{f'(x)}{f(x)}\,dx = \ln|f(x)| + C,$$
for $f(x) \neq 0$.

2.2   Separation of variables

Direct integration applies, in an immediate sense, only to the very simplest type of differential equation, as described by equation (16). However, all other analytic methods of solution for first-order equations also eventually boil down to performing integrations. In this subsection, we consider how to solve first-order differential equations of the form

$$\frac{dy}{dx} = g(x)\,h(y), \tag{18}$$

where the right-hand side is a product of a function of x and a function of y. Such first-order differential equations are said to be **separable**.

An easy example

Let us start with the simple example that we solved in the Introduction, namely

$$\frac{dy}{dx} = -Ay, \tag{19}$$

where $y(x) > 0$. This equation is of the required form, with $g(x) = 1$ and $h(y) = -Ay$. In the Introduction we obtained the solution by guesswork, but we will now use a systematic method to find the solution.

Dividing both sides of equation (19) by y, we obtain

Because $y > 0$, division by y causes no problems.

$$\frac{1}{y}\frac{dy}{dx} = -A.$$

Integrating both sides then gives

$$\int \frac{1}{y}\frac{dy}{dx}\,dx = -A\int dx.$$

See equation (81) in Subsection 6.3 of Unit 1.

Applying the rule for integration by substitution to the left-hand side, we obtain

$$\int \frac{1}{y}\,dy = -A\int dx.$$

Integrating both sides (and remembering that $y > 0$) then gives

$$\ln y + C_1 = C_2 - Ax,$$

where C_1 and C_2 are constants of integration. We can rearrange this equation, and combine the constants, to obtain

$$\ln y = C - Ax$$

for some constant $C = C_2 - C_1$. Taking exponentials on both sides, we get

$$y = \exp(C - Ax) = \exp(C)\exp(-Ax) = B\exp(-Ax),$$

where $B = \exp(C)$ is another arbitrary constant. This is the same as the solution obtained (by guesswork) in the Introduction.

In this case, the arbitrary constant B is restricted to positive values because $\exp(C) > 0$ for all C. (This restriction is related to our initial requirement that y is positive.) Note also that B is not simply added to the solution in this case.

A more typical example

Another example of a separable differential equation, as specified in equation (18), is

$$\frac{dy}{dx} = x(1 + y^2). \tag{20}$$

Here, the right-hand side is a product of the functions $g(x) = x$ and $h(y) = 1 + y^2$. You are unlikely to guess the solution in this case. Here we develop the systematic *separation of variables method* for its solution, so-called because we rewrite the equation in a form where only y appears on one side, and only x on the other.

As a first step, we divide both sides of this equation by $1 + y^2$, to obtain

$$\frac{1}{1+y^2}\frac{dy}{dx} = x,$$

Note that $1 + y^2$ is never zero, so it is safe to divide by it.

and then integrate both sides with respect to x, to get

$$\int \frac{1}{1+y^2}\frac{dy}{dx}\,dx = \int x\,dx. \tag{21}$$

The rule for integration by substitution tells us that the left-hand side of this equation can be rewritten as

See Section 6 of Unit 1.

$$\int \frac{1}{1+y^2}\frac{dy}{dx}\,dx = \int \frac{1}{1+y^2}\,dy,$$

so equation (21) becomes

$$\int \frac{1}{1+y^2}\,dy = \int x\,dx.$$

At this point, we have achieved the desired separation: the left-hand side depends only on y, and the right-hand side depends only on x. On performing the two integrations (using the table of standard integrals in the Handbook) we obtain

$$\arctan y = \tfrac{1}{2}x^2 + C, \tag{22}$$

where C is an arbitrary constant. Making y the subject of the equation, we obtain the solution

Note that one arbitrary constant is sufficient here.

$$y(x) = \tan\left(\tfrac{1}{2}x^2 + C\right). \tag{23}$$

General procedure

The approach just demonstrated applies more widely. In principle, it works for any differential equation of the form

$$\frac{dy}{dx} = g(x)\,h(y). \tag{Eq. 18}$$

On dividing both sides of this equation by $h(y)$ (for all values of y other than those where $h(y) = 0$), we obtain

$$\frac{1}{h(y)}\frac{dy}{dx} = g(x).$$

Integration with respect to x on both sides then gives

$$\int \frac{1}{h(y)}\frac{dy}{dx}\,dx = \int g(x)\,dx,$$

and, on applying the rule for integration by substitution to the left-hand side, this becomes

$$\int \frac{1}{h(y)}\,dy = \int g(x)\,dx. \tag{24}$$

This is the form that you need to remember!

If the two integrals can be evaluated at this stage, we obtain an equation that relates x and y, and features an arbitrary constant. This equation is the general solution of the differential equation (for values of y other than those where $h(y) = 0$). Usually, however, y is not the subject of this equation. Such a solution is said to be an **implicit general solution** of the differential equation: an example is provided by equation (22).

Usually, the final aim is to make y the subject of the equation, if possible – that is, to manipulate the equation into the form

$y = \text{function of } x$.

This is called the **explicit general solution** of the differential equation: an example is provided by equation (23).

In either case (implicit or explicit), a particular solution can be obtained from the general solution by applying an initial condition.

The method just described for solving differential equations of the form (18) is called the method of *separation of variables* since, in equation (24), we have separated the variables to either side of the equation, with only the dependent variable appearing on the left, and only the independent variable on the right.

So far, we have assumed that $h(y) \neq 0$. However, the condition $h(y) = 0$ corresponds to $dy/dx = g(x)\,h(y) = 0$ for all x, and so gives extra solutions to the differential equation with $y = \text{constant}$. These exceptional cases should be included in the general solution. The method is summarised below.

Procedure 2   Separation of variables

This method applies to **separable differential equations**, which are of the form

$$\frac{dy}{dx} = g(x)\,h(y). \tag{Eq. 18}$$

1. Assume that $h(y) \neq 0$, and divide both sides of the differential equation by $h(y)$. Integrate both sides with respect to x. The rule for integration by substitution then gives

    $$\int \frac{1}{h(y)}\,dy = \int g(x)\,dx. \tag{Eq. 24}$$

2. If possible, perform the integrations, including an arbitrary constant.

3. If possible, rearrange the formula found in Step 2 to give a family of solutions $y(x)$, including an arbitrary constant.

4. Find any constant values of y for which $h(y) = 0$.

5. The *general solution* is given by the family of solutions in Step 3, supplemented by any constant solutions found in Step 4.

It is a good idea to check, by substitution into the original differential equation, that the function obtained is indeed a solution.

The method of separation of variables is useful, but there may be some difficulties. First, it may not be possible to perform the necessary integrations. Second, it may not be possible to perform the necessary manipulations to obtain an explicit solution.

It is sometimes necessary to be careful about the *domain* of the solution obtained, as the following example illustrates.

Example 3

(a) Find the general solution of the differential equation
$$\frac{dy}{dx} = -\frac{x}{3y} \quad (y > 0).$$

(b) Find the particular solution that satisfies the initial condition $y(0) = 3$.

Solution

(a) The equation is of the form
$$\frac{dy}{dx} = g(x)\,h(y),$$

where the obvious choices for g and h are
$$g(x) = -x \quad \text{and} \quad h(y) = 1/(3y).$$

Notice that $h(y)$ is never equal to zero.

We now apply Procedure 2. On dividing through by $h(y) = 1/(3y)$ (i.e. multiplying through by $3y$) and integrating with respect to x, the differential equation becomes
$$\int 3y\,dy = \int -x\,dx.$$

With practice, you will be able to move directly to this stage, as shown in Procedure 2.

Evaluating the integrals gives
$$\tfrac{3}{2}y^2 = -\tfrac{1}{2}x^2 + C,$$

where C is an arbitrary constant. This is an implicit form of the general solution.

On solving for y and noting the condition $y > 0$ given in the question (which determines the sign of the square root), we obtain
$$y = \sqrt{\tfrac{1}{3}(2C - x^2)}.$$

This can be simplified slightly by writing B in place of $2C$. So
$$y = \sqrt{\tfrac{1}{3}(B - x^2)},$$

where B is an arbitrary constant. In fact, the value of B is somewhat restricted. This is because the condition $y > 0$ implies that y is real, and this requires that $B - x^2 > 0$. Hence $B > x^2 \geq 0$, which tells us that B must be restricted to positive values. At the same time, the condition $B - x^2 > 0$ restricts the possible values of x to lie between $-\sqrt{B}$ and $\sqrt{B}$.

The explicit general solution in this case is therefore

$$y = \sqrt{\tfrac{1}{3}(B - x^2)} \quad (-\sqrt{B} < x < \sqrt{B}),$$

where B is any positive constant.

(b) The initial condition is $y(0) = 3$, so we substitute $x = 0$ and $y = 3$ into the general solution above. This gives $3 = \sqrt{\tfrac{1}{3}B}$, so $B = 27$, and the required particular solution is

You verified in Exercise 2(d) that this function is a solution of the differential equation.

$$y(x) = \sqrt{\tfrac{1}{3}(27 - x^2)} \quad (-3\sqrt{3} < x < 3\sqrt{3}).$$

Here are some exercises on applying the method of separation of variables. Remember the following points:

- The method initially assumes that $h(y) \neq 0$ and then gives a family of solutions containing an arbitrary constant.

- The condition $h(y) = 0$ may give extra solutions $y = $ constant. These should be included in the general solution; they may or may not have the same form as the general family of solutions obtained for $h(y) \neq 0$.

When doing these exercises, try to obtain the *general* solution, including all cases where $h(y) = 0$.

Exercise 7

Find the general solution of each of the following differential equations.

(a) $\dfrac{dy}{dx} = \dfrac{y - 1}{x} \quad (x > 0)$ (b) $\dfrac{dy}{dx} = \dfrac{2y}{1 + x^2}$

Exercise 8

Solve the initial-value problem

$$\frac{dv}{du} = e^{u+v}, \quad v(0) = 0.$$

Exercise 9

Find the general solution of each of the following differential equations.

(a) $u' = xu$ (b) $\dot{x} = 1 + x^2$

Exercise 10

The differential equation here is the logistic equation (equation (9)), which is used to model population sizes.

(a) Solve the initial-value problem

$$\frac{dP}{dt} = kP\left(1 - \frac{P}{M}\right) \quad \text{with } P(0) = 2M,$$

where $P(t) > 0$, and k and M are positive constants.

You may use the fact that

$$\int \frac{1}{x(1-ax)} \, dx = -\ln\left|\frac{1}{x} - a\right| + C \quad \text{for } x \neq 1/a,$$

where C is an arbitrary constant of integration.

(b) Describe what happens to the solution $P(t)$ as t becomes large and positive.

3 Solving linear differential equations

This section presents one final method for finding analytic solutions of first-order differential equations. The method, called the *integrating factor method*, applies only to a particular form of equation known as a *linear* differential equation. The definition and some properties of this type of equation are introduced in Subsection 3.1. Subsection 3.2 shows how to solve a particularly simple type of linear differential equation before we move on to the general method of solution in Subsection 3.3.

3.1 Linear differential equations

This subsection introduces the concept of *linearity* as applied to differential equations. Here the concept is introduced in the context of first-order differential equations, but you should be aware that the idea generalises to higher-order differential equations and is important from a theoretical point of view.

Linear second-order differential equations are considered in Unit 3.

Definitions

- A first-order differential equation for $y = y(x)$ is **linear** if it can be expressed in the form

  $$\frac{dy}{dx} + g(x)\,y = h(x), \tag{25}$$

  where $g(x)$ and $h(x)$ are given functions.

- A linear first-order differential equation is said to be **homogeneous** if $h(x) = 0$ for all x, and **inhomogeneous** or **non-homogeneous** otherwise.

This differential equation is of the general form

$$\frac{dy}{dx} = f(x, y)$$

used elsewhere in this unit, with

$$f(x, y) = -g(x)\,y + h(x).$$

Note that linearity refers to the dependent variable y. Terms like y^2 or $y\,(dy/dx)$ are excluded, but any function of the independent variable x is allowed. So, for example, the differential equation

$$\frac{dy}{dx} - x^2 y = x^3$$

is linear, with $g(x) = -x^2$ and $h(x) = x^3$, whereas the equation

$$\frac{dy}{dx} = xy^2$$

is not, due to the presence of the non-linear term y^2.

It can be shown that any initial-value problem based on equation (25) has a unique solution provided that $g(x)$ and $h(x)$ are continuous functions.

Exercise 11

Decide whether or not each of the following first-order differential equations is linear.

(a) $\dfrac{dy}{dx} + x^3 y = x^5$ (b) $\dfrac{dy}{dx} = x \sin x$ (c) $\dfrac{dz}{dt} = -3z^{1/2}$

(d) $\dot{y} + y^2 = t$ (e) $x\dfrac{dy}{dx} + y = y^2$ (f) $(1 + x^2)\dfrac{dy}{dx} + 2xy = 3x^2$

3.2 Linear constant-coefficient equations

In equation (25), $g(x)$ is the coefficient of y.

The simplest example of a linear equation occurs when the function $g(x)$ does not depend on x, that is, where the coefficient of y is constant. In the case of a homogeneous equation, this is just the simple example that we dealt with in the Introduction: if $g(x) = A$, then the homogeneous equation is

$$\frac{dy}{dx} + Ay = 0,$$

which has solution $y = y_0 \exp(-Ax)$, as you saw in Section 2.

Now consider the case of the *inhomogeneous* linear differential equation with constant coefficients, which is of the form

Equations of this type are met in the theory of electrical circuits.

$$\frac{dy}{dx} + Ay = h(x). \tag{26}$$

We will now use a trick to solve this equation, which at first sight is not obvious. We begin by multiplying both sides by e^{Ax}:

$$e^{Ax}\frac{dy}{dx} + Ae^{Ax}y = e^{Ax}\, h(x). \tag{27}$$

Now, using the product rule for differentiation, we notice that

$$\frac{d}{dx}\big(e^{Ax}y\big) = e^{Ax}\frac{dy}{dx} + Ae^{Ax}y.$$

This means that the left-hand side of equation (27) can be written as $\dfrac{d}{dx}\big(e^{Ax}y\big)$, so we have

$$\frac{d}{dx}\big(e^{Ax}y\big) = e^{Ax}\, h(x). \tag{28}$$

This differential equation can now be solved by integrating both sides with respect to x and rearranging the result.

It is easier to see how this works by considering particular examples, but for the record, the general method proceeds as follows. Integration gives

$$\int \frac{d}{dx}\left(e^{Ax}y\right)dx = \int e^{Ax}\,h(x)\,dx,$$

which becomes

$$e^{Ax}y = \int e^{Ax}\,h(x)\,dx,$$

so

$$y(x) = e^{-Ax}\left(\int e^{Ax}\,h(x)\,dx\right). \qquad (29)$$

We can omit the arbitrary constant of integration here because the remaining indefinite integral will still generate one.

There is no difficulty in dividing through by e^{Ax} because this is never equal to zero.

This shows that if we can perform the integral on the right-hand side, then we can solve our original differential equation (26). The integral will generate an arbitrary constant, and our solution will be the general solution of the differential equation.

Example 4

Solve the linear differential equation

$$\frac{dy}{dx} + 2y = x.$$

Solution

The differential equation has the same form as equation (26), with $A = 2$ and $h(x) = x$, so we must multiply by the factor e^{2x}. Multiplying both sides of the differential equation by e^{2x}, we get

$$e^{2x}\frac{dy}{dx} + e^{2x}2y = e^{2x}x.$$

Following equation (28), the differential equation can then be expressed in the form

$$\frac{d}{dx}\left(e^{2x}y\right) = e^{2x}x.$$

Integrating both sides gives

$$e^{2x}y = \int xe^{2x}\,dx.$$

The integral on the right-hand side can be evaluated by parts, using the formula

$$\int f(x)\,g'(x)\,dx = f(x)\,g(x) - \int g(x)\,f'(x)\,dx.$$

Choosing $f(x) = x$ and $g'(x) = e^{2x}$, we have $f'(x) = 1$ and $g(x) = \frac{1}{2}e^{2x}$, so

$$e^{2x}y = \tfrac{1}{2}xe^{2x} - \tfrac{1}{2}\int e^{2x}\,dx$$

$$= \tfrac{1}{2}xe^{2x} - \tfrac{1}{2}\left(\tfrac{1}{2}e^{2x} + C\right)$$

$$= \tfrac{1}{2}e^{2x}\left(x - \tfrac{1}{2}\right) - \tfrac{1}{2}C.$$

Thus

$$y(x) = \tfrac{1}{2}\left(x - \tfrac{1}{2} - Ce^{-2x}\right),$$

where C is an arbitrary constant.

We can check this answer by differentiation:

$$\frac{dy}{dx} + 2y = \tfrac{1}{2}\left(1 + 2Ce^{-2x}\right) + \left(x - \tfrac{1}{2} - Ce^{-2x}\right) = x,$$

as required.

Exercise 12

Solve the differential equation

$$\frac{dy}{dx} + y = e^{2x}$$

with the initial condition $y(0) = 0$. Check your solution by differentiation.

You have seen how to solve linear differential equations with constant coefficients. This method is easily generalised to the case where the coefficient is not constant. The general form of the technique is called the *integrating factor* method.

3.3   The integrating factor method

The secret to solving the linear constant-coefficient differential equation

$$\frac{dy}{dx} + Ay = h(x)$$

is to multiply both sides by e^{Ax} and to notice that

$$\frac{d}{dx}\left(e^{Ax}y\right) = e^{Ax}\frac{dy}{dx} + e^{Ax}Ay,$$

which is e^{Ax} times the left-hand side of the differential equation.

We will now try something very similar for the general linear differential equation

$$\frac{dy}{dx} + g(x)\,y = h(x). \tag{Eq. 25}$$

In this case, we multiply both sides by $e^{G(x)}$, where the function $G(x)$ remains to be decided. This gives

$$e^{G(x)}\frac{dy}{dx} + e^{G(x)}\,g(x)\,y = e^{G(x)}\,h(x). \tag{30}$$

We then notice that the chain rule of differentiation gives

$$\frac{d}{dx}\left(e^{G(x)}\,y\right) = e^{G(x)}\frac{dy}{dx} + e^{G(x)}\frac{dG}{dx}\,y.$$

This can be made equal to $e^{G(x)}$ times the left-hand side of the differential equation (25) *provided that* we take

$$\frac{dG}{dx} = g(x), \tag{31}$$

and this implies that

$$G(x) = \int g(x)\, dx.$$

We can omit the arbitary constant when evaluating this integral. This is because we need only one function $G(x)$ that satisfies equation (31). We do not need the general function to do so.

With this choice of $G(x)$, equation (30) can be written as

$$\frac{d}{dx}\left(e^{G(x)}\, y\right) = e^{G(x)}\, h(x),$$

and the solution of the differential equation is then obtained by integrating both sides and rearranging the result.

You will soon see how this works in explicit examples. For the moment, the key point is that we need to multiply both sides of the equation by the factor

$$p(x) = e^{G(x)} = \exp\left(\int g(x)\, dx\right). \tag{32}$$

This factor is called the **integrating factor** of the differential equation because it allows the left-hand side of the equation to be integrated exactly. This leads to the following procedure.

Procedure 3   The integrating factor method

This method applies to any first-order *linear* differential equation, that is, any equation of the form

$$\frac{dy}{dx} + g(x)\, y = h(x). \tag{Eq. 25}$$

1. Determine the integrating factor

$$p(x) = \exp\left(\int g(x)\, dx\right). \tag{Eq. 32}$$

The constant of integration is not needed here as it can be shown to cancel out in Step 3.

2. Multiply equation (25) by $p(x)$ to recast the differential equation as

$$p(x)\,\frac{dy}{dx} + p(x)\, g(x)\, y = p(x)\, h(x).$$

3. Rewrite the differential equation as

$$\frac{d}{dx}(p(x)\, y) = p(x)\, h(x). \tag{33}$$

It is a good idea to check that the derivative on the left-hand side reproduces the left-hand side of the preceding equation.

4. Integrate both sides of this equation, including an arbitrary constant, and rearrange the result to make $y(x)$ the subject of the equation. The result is the *general solution* of the differential equation.

Let us first apply this procedure to the constant coefficient equation (26), to check that it gives the correct solution (29).

Example 5

Use the integrating factor method in Procedure 3 to solve

$$\frac{dy}{dx} + Ay = h(x),$$

where A is a constant.

Solution

Comparing the equation in the question with equation (25), we see that $g(x) = A$. So the integrating factor, equation (32), is

$$p(x) = \exp\left(\int A\,dx\right) = \exp(Ax).$$

This is exactly the integrating factor that we used in Subsection 3.2.

Equation (33) then gives

$$\frac{d}{dx}\left(e^{Ax}y\right) = e^{Ax}\,h(x),$$

which is the same as equation (28). The remainder of the procedure follows the path that led to equation (29), so we get the solution

$$y(x) = e^{-Ax}\left(\int e^{Ax}\,h(x)\right).$$

As with the separation of variables method, it may not be possible to perform the necessary final integration. However, the remainder of this subsection gives examples and exercises for which the integrals can be done. It is important to note that the constant of integration must be included in the final integration, as this is what makes the solution a general one.

Example 6

Use the integrating factor method to find the general solution of the differential equation

$$\frac{dy}{dx} = x - \frac{2xy}{x^2 + 1}.$$

Solution

On rearranging the differential equation as

$$\frac{dy}{dx} + \frac{2xy}{x^2 + 1} = x,$$

we see that it has the form of a linear differential equation $dy/dx + g(x)\,y = h(x)$, with

$$g(x) = \frac{2x}{x^2 + 1} \quad \text{and} \quad h(x) = x.$$

The integrating factor (from equation (32)) is therefore

$$p(x) = \exp\left(\int \frac{2x}{x^2+1}\,dx\right).$$

Notice that $2x/(x^2+1)$ is of the form f'/f, so

$$\int \frac{2x}{x^2+1}\,dx = \ln|x^2+1|$$
$$= \ln(x^2+1) \quad \text{since } x^2+1 > 0.$$

The integrating factor is therefore

$$p(x) = \exp(\ln(x^2+1)) = x^2+1.$$

Remember that we do not need to include an arbitrary constant when finding an integrating factor.

Multiplying both sides of the differential equation by this factor yields

$$(x^2+1)\frac{dy}{dx} + 2xy = x(x^2+1),$$

and the differential equation becomes

$$\frac{d}{dx}\big((x^2+1)y\big) = x(x^2+1).$$

Integrating both sides gives

$$(x^2+1)y = \int x(x^2+1)\,dx$$
$$= \int (x^3+x)\,dx$$
$$= \tfrac{1}{4}x^4 + \tfrac{1}{2}x^2 + C,$$

where C is an arbitrary constant. Finally, to obtain an explicit solution, we divide by x^2+1 to get

$$y(x) = \frac{x^4 + 2x^2 + B}{4(x^2+1)},$$

where $B = 4C$ is an arbitrary constant.

The next example contains two differential equations that were solved in Exercise 7 using the method of separation of variables. Here, we solve them using the integrating factor method. You can compare the answers with those obtained earlier.

Example 7

Use the integrating factor method to find the general solution of each of the following differential equations.

(a) $\dfrac{dy}{dx} = \dfrac{y-1}{x}$ $\quad (x > 0)$

(b) $\dfrac{dy}{dx} = \dfrac{2y}{1+x^2}$

Solution

(a) On rearranging the differential equation as

$$\frac{dy}{dx} - \frac{1}{x}y = -\frac{1}{x}, \tag{34}$$

we see that it is of the linear form $dy/dx + g(x)\,y = h(x)$ with

$$g(x) = h(x) = -\frac{1}{x}.$$

The integrating factor (from equation (32)) is therefore

$$\begin{aligned} p(x) &= \exp\left(\int\left(-\frac{1}{x}\right)dx\right) \\ &= \exp(-\ln x) \quad \text{(since } x > 0\text{)} \\ &= \exp\left(\ln x^{-1}\right) \\ &= x^{-1} = \frac{1}{x}. \end{aligned}$$

Recall that $a \ln x = \ln(x^a)$.

Multiplying equation (34) by $p(x) = 1/x$ (and recalling that $x \neq 0$) gives

$$\frac{1}{x}\frac{dy}{dx} - \frac{1}{x^2}y = -\frac{1}{x^2}, \tag{35}$$

so the differential equation becomes

$$\frac{d}{dx}\left(\frac{1}{x}y\right) = -\frac{1}{x^2}. \tag{36}$$

It is always worth a quick check at this stage: is the left-hand side of equation (36) equal to the left-hand side of equation (35)?

Integration then gives

$$\frac{y}{x} = \int\left(-\frac{1}{x^2}\right)dx = \frac{1}{x} + C,$$

where C is an arbitrary constant. The general solution is therefore

$$y = 1 + Cx,$$

where C is an arbitrary constant.

(b) In order to put the given differential equation into the linear form $dy/dx + g(x)\,y = h(x)$, we need to bring the term in y to the left-hand side to obtain

$$\frac{dy}{dx} - \frac{2}{1 + x^2}y = 0. \tag{37}$$

The equation is homogeneous.

Hence in this case we have $g(x) = -2/(1 + x^2)$ and $h(x) = 0$.

To find the integrating factor, we must evaluate the integral

$$\int g(x)\,dx = \int\left(-\frac{2}{1 + x^2}\right)dx = -2\arctan x,$$

so the integrating factor is

$$\exp\left(\int g(x)\,dx\right) = \exp(-2\arctan x) = e^{-2\arctan x}.$$

Multiplying through by this factor gives

$$e^{-2\arctan x}\frac{dy}{dx} - e^{-2\arctan x}\frac{2y}{1+x^2} = 0.$$

Thus the differential equation can be rewritten as

$$\frac{d}{dx}\left(e^{-2\arctan x}y\right) = 0.$$

It follows, on integrating, that

$$e^{-2\arctan x}y = C, \quad \text{or equivalently,} \quad y(x) = Ce^{2\arctan x},$$

where C is an arbitrary constant. This is the general solution of the differential equation.

You can check that the derivative on the left gives the left-hand side of the previous equation (using the fact that $d(\arctan x)/dx = 1/(1+x^2)$).

Exercise 13

Find the general solution of each of the following differential equations.

(a) $\dfrac{dy}{dx} - y = e^x \sin x$ (b) $\dfrac{dy}{dx} = y + x$

Exercise 14

Use the integrating factor method to solve each of the following initial-value problems.

(a) $u' = xu, \quad u(0) = 2.$

(b) $t\dot{y} + 2y = t^2, \quad y(1) = 1$ and $t > 0.$

You saw the differential equation in part (a) in Exercise 9(a), where you solved it using separation of variables.

Exercise 15

Solve each of the following initial-value problems.

(a) $\dot{y} + y = t + 1, \quad y(1) = 0.$

(b) $e^{3t}\dot{y} = 1 - e^{3t}y, \quad y(0) = 3.$

Exercise 16

Find the general solution of each of the following differential equations.

(a) $x\dfrac{dy}{dx} - 3y = x \quad (x > 0)$

(b) $\dfrac{dv}{dt} + 4v = 3\cos 2t$

(*Hint*: If a and b are non-zero constants, then

$$\int e^{at}\cos bt \, dt = \frac{e^{at}}{a^2 + b^2}(a\cos bt + b\sin bt) + C,$$

where C is an arbitrary constant.)

You have now used a number of methods for solving first-order differential equations: direct integration, separation of variables and the integrating factor. Confronted with a fresh equation, the first issue is which method to try. The following exercise closes this discussion of analytic solutions by giving you practice at choosing an appropriate method.

Exercise 17

Which method(s) could you use to try to solve each of the following linear first-order differential equations? (You need not actually solve the equations.)

(a) $\dfrac{dy}{dx} + x^3 y = x^5$ (b) $\dfrac{dy}{dx} = x \sin x$ (c) $\dfrac{dv}{du} + 5v = 0$

(d) $(1 + x^2)\dfrac{dy}{dx} + 2xy = 1 + x^2$ (e) $\dfrac{dy}{dx} = y^2(1 + x^2)$

4   Direction fields

> The material in this section is non-assessable and will not be tested in continuous assessment or in the exam. However, you are advised to read this section and attempt the exercise, as this will provide valuable insights into the behaviour of solutions of differential equations.

Many of the differential equations that arise in physics and applied mathematics cannot be solved exactly. For this reason it is valuable to know about methods for obtaining approximate or qualitative information about solutions. It is also important to be aware of how computers may be used to give *numerical* solutions of differential equations, and this will be considered in Section 5.

In this section we show how qualitative information about the solutions of a first-order differential equation can be gleaned directly from the equation itself, without undertaking any form of integration process. The main concept here is the *direction field*, sketches of which usually give a good idea of how the graphs of solutions behave.

We start by considering what can be deduced about solutions of any differential equation of the form

$$\frac{dy}{dx} = f(x, y) \qquad\qquad \text{(Eq. 10)}$$

from direct observation of the equation.

In Subsection 1.1 we encountered the logistic equation

$$\frac{dP}{dt} = kP\left(1 - \frac{P}{M}\right),$$

(Eq. 9)

Here we have

$$f(t, P) = kP\left(1 - \frac{P}{M}\right).$$

where k and M are positive constants. In certain circumstances this is a useful mathematical model of population sizes, in which $P(t)$ denotes the size of the population at time t. The constant functions $P(t) = 0$ and $P(t) = M$ are particular solutions of the differential equation. This is because they both give $dP/dt = 0$ on the left-hand side and zero on the right-hand side, so the differential equation is satisfied in the form $0 = 0$. Within the population model, these solutions correspond to a complete absence of the population $(P = 0)$, and an equilibrium population level $(P = M)$ for which the birth rate exactly balances the death rate.

Spotting constant functions that are particular solutions of the differential equation is occasionally useful, but is of limited applicability. In general, more useful information can be deduced by noting that any particular solution $y(x)$ can be plotted as a graph of y against x in the xy-plane. At a given point (x_0, y_0), the gradient (or slope) of this graph is given by the value of dy/dx at (x_0, y_0), and according to the differential equation (10), this is given by $f(x_0, y_0)$. We therefore conclude that $f(x, y)$ represents the slope at (x, y) of a solution curve that passes through (x, y).

For example, if

$$\frac{dy}{dx} = f(x, y) = x + y,$$

(38)

then the slope of a solution curve that passes through the point $(1, 2)$ is $f(1, 2) = 1 + 2 = 3$. This slope is positive, so the graph is increasing from left to right through the point $(1, 2)$. The slope of a (different) solution curve that passes through $(2, -7)$ is $f(2, -7) = 2 - 7 = -5$. This slope is negative, so the corresponding graph is decreasing from left to right through the point $(2, -7)$. At the point $(3, -3)$, the slope is $f(3, -3) = 3 - 3 = 0$, so the solution curve that passes through this point is horizontal.

When looking at $f(x, y)$ in this way, it is referred to as a *direction field*, since it describes a *direction* (or slope) for each point (x, y) where $f(x, y)$ is defined.

Definition

A **direction field** associates a unique direction to each point within a specified region of the xy-plane. The direction associated with the point (x, y) can be indicated by drawing a short line segment through the point, with the appropriate slope. This can be regarded as a segment of the tangent line at (x, y) of the solution curve that passes through (x, y).

In particular, the direction field for the differential equation

$$\frac{dy}{dx} = f(x, y)$$

associates the direction $f(x, y)$ with the point (x, y). This is the slope at (x, y) of the graph of a particular solution $y(x)$ that passes through the point (x, y).

Direction fields can be visualised by constructing the short line segments at a finite set of points in an appropriate region of the plane, where typically the points are chosen to form a rectangular grid. An example is shown in Figure 10, which corresponds to the differential equation (38). In this case the chosen region is the set of points (x, y) such that $-2 \le x \le 2$ and $0 \le y \le 2$, and the rectangular grid consists of the points at intervals of 0.2 in both the x- and y-directions within this region.

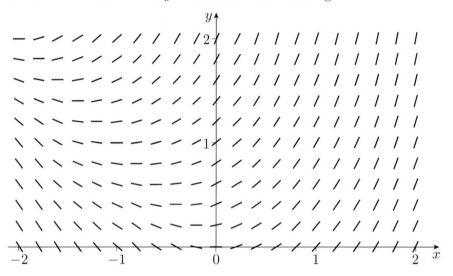

Figure 10   Part of the direction field for equation (38)

From this diagram, we can gain a good qualitative impression of how the graphs of particular solutions of equation (38) behave. The aim is to sketch curves on the diagram in such a way that the tangents to the curves are always parallel to the local slopes of the direction field. For example, starting from the point $(-1, 0.5)$ (that is, taking the initial condition to be $y(-1) = 0.5$), we expect the solution graph initially to fall as we move to the right. The magnitude of the negative slope decreases, however, and eventually reaches zero, after which the slope becomes positive and then increases. On this basis, we could sketch the graph of the corresponding particular solution and obtain something like the curve shown in Figure 11.

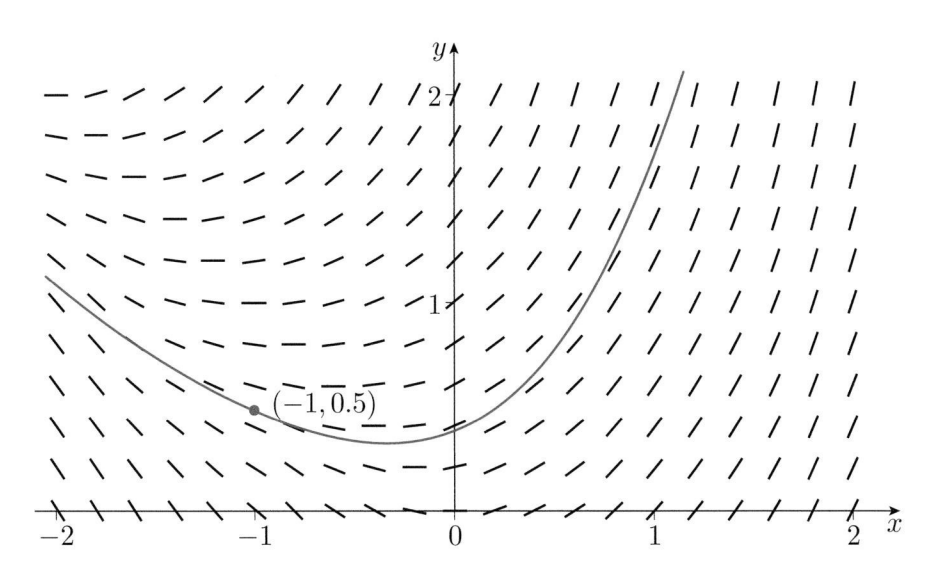

Figure 11   Part of the direction field for equation (38), and the particular solution satisfying $y(-1) = 0.5$ that passes through the point $(-1, 0.5)$

Exercise 18

(a) Part of the direction field for the logistic equation

$$\frac{dP}{dt} = P\left(1 - \frac{P}{1000}\right)$$

is sketched in the figure below.

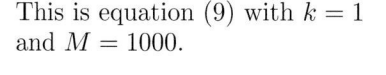

This is equation (9) with $k = 1$ and $M = 1000$.

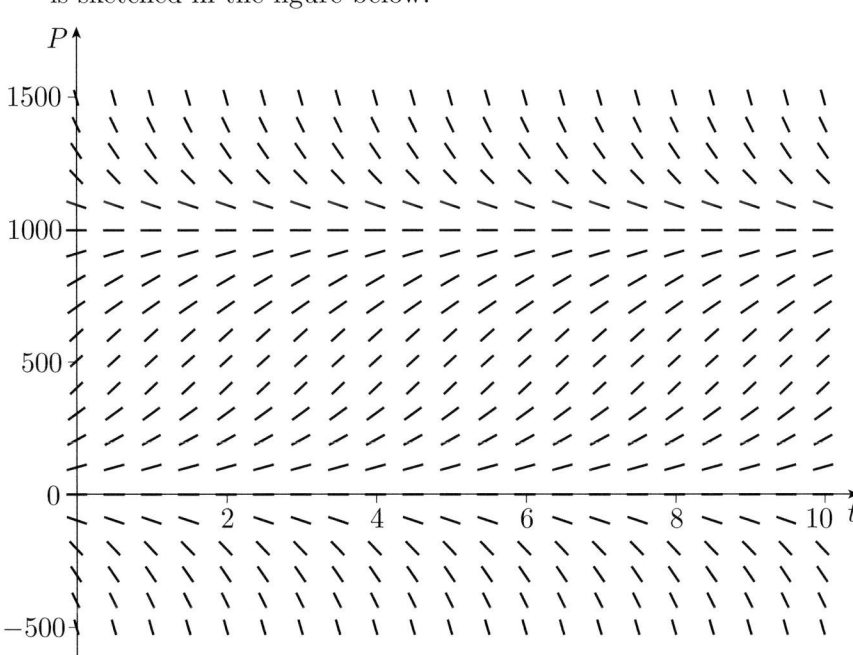

Using this diagram, sketch the solution curves that pass through the following points:

$$(0, 1500), \ (0, 1000), \ (0, 100), \ (0, 0), \ (0, -100).$$

From your results, describe the graphs of particular solutions of the differential equation.

(b) What does your answer to part (a) tell you about the predicted behaviour of a population whose size $P(t)$ at time t is modelled by this logistic equation?

When analysing problems involving differential equations it is sometimes qualitative information that is most important. For example, if we model the population size $P(t)$ of a species, it may be interesting to know whether the species dies out (does $P(t) \to 0$ as $t \to \infty$?) rather than having an accurate expression for P at a given value of t. Often the direction field approach gives direct access to insights that would be hard to extract from exact solutions. It can also be applied to differential equations for which no exact solutions can be found.

5 Numerical solutions and Euler's method

The material in this section is non-assessable and will not be tested in continuous assessment or in the exam. If you are running short of time, you can skip this section.

Numerical analysis

The method described here will give you a glimpse into a branch of mathematics called *numerical analysis*, which specialises in solving problems numerically on a computer. The problems extend beyond differential equations, and may involve the approximation of functions, matrix manipulation, or finding maxima and minima. This subject is part of mathematics, rather than computer programming, because there are significant theoretical issues to solve. For example, where possible, we need to choose methods that are not too sensitive to small changes in the input data. We also need to use methods that are efficient, and give high accuracy for a reasonable amount of computing time.

In many cases, an exact solution of a differential equation cannot be found, and the most useful approach is to use a computer to find a numerical solution. The study of *numerical methods* for the solution of differential equations is a large area of knowledge. This section describes *Euler's method*, which is a simple numerical method for first-order differential equations. Other methods are often used by experts, but most of these are just refinements of Euler's method.

Let us suppose that we wish to find a solution to the first-order differential equation

$$\frac{dy}{dx} = f(x, y)$$

with initial condition $y(x_0) = y_0$ (i.e. we seek a solution that passes through the point (x_0, y_0)). We will consider the solution for $x > x_0$.

We will approximate the solution of this initial-value problem by moving in a sequence of straight-line steps. Corresponding to the given initial condition $y(x_0) = y_0$, there is a point P_0 in the xy-plane with coordinates (x_0, y_0), and this is our starting point. At P_0, the function $y(x)$ has a particular slope, namely $f(x_0, y_0)$. We move off from P_0 along a straight line that has this slope, and continue until we have travelled a *small* horizontal distance h to the right of P_0. The point that has now been reached is labelled P_1, as in Figure 12 (where the distance h is exaggerated for clarity).

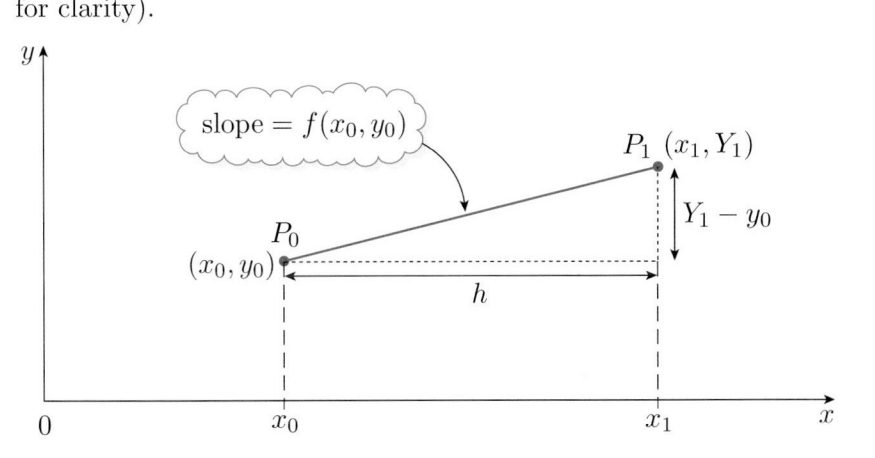

Figure 12   Graphical representation of the first step in Euler's method for numerically solving $y' = f(x, y)$

We denote the coordinates of P_1 by (x_1, Y_1). For comparison, the *exact* solution of the initial-value problem passes through a point (x_1, y_1), where $y_1 = y(x_1)$ is the value of the exact solution at $x = x_1$. Note that we cannot claim that $Y_1 = y_1$. This is unlikely to happen unless the exact solution function follows a straight line as x moves from x_0 to x_1. However, the hope is that because we headed off from x_0 along the correct slope, Y_1 will be reasonably close to the exact value, y_1. Furthermore, we expect that this approximation becomes better as the length h is decreased.

The next thing that we need to do is obtain formulas for x_1 and Y_1 in terms of the known quantities x_0, y_0, h and $f(x_0, y_0)$. Because the point P_1 is reached from P_0 by taking a step to the right of horizontal length h, we have

$$x_1 = x_0 + h. \tag{39}$$

We can also express Y_1 in terms of other quantities by equating two expressions for the slope of the line segment P_0P_1 (see Figure 12):

$$\frac{Y_1 - y_0}{h} = f(x_0, y_0),$$

which can be rearranged to give

$$Y_1 = y_0 + h\, f(x_0, y_0). \tag{40}$$

This completes the first stage of the method.

We now take a second step. This second step takes us from P_1 through a further horizontal distance h to the right, to the point labelled P_2 in Figure 13.

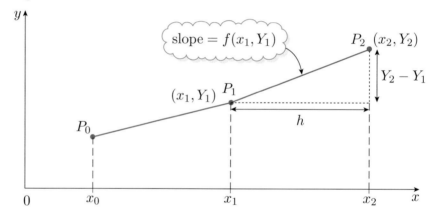

Figure 13   Graphical representation of the first two steps in Euler's method for numerically solving $y' = f(x, y)$

The coordinates of P_2 are denoted by (x_2, Y_2), and Y_2 gives an approximation to the exact solution value y_2 at the point $x = x_2$. Following the same logic as for the first step, we write

$$x_2 = x_1 + h$$

and

$$Y_2 = y_1 + h\, f(x_1, Y_1),$$

where $f(x_1, Y_1)$ is the slope dy/dx at the point $P_1 = (x_1, Y_1)$.

Having carried out two steps of the process, you can see that the same procedure can be applied to construct any number of further steps.

Suppose that after i steps we have reached the point P_i, with coordinates (x_i, Y_i). For the $(i + 1)$th step, we move away from P_i along the line with slope $f(x_i, Y_i)$ (as defined by the direction field at P_i). After moving through a horizontal distance h to the right, we reach the point P_{i+1} whose coordinates are denoted by (x_{i+1}, Y_{i+1}), as illustrated in Figure 14.

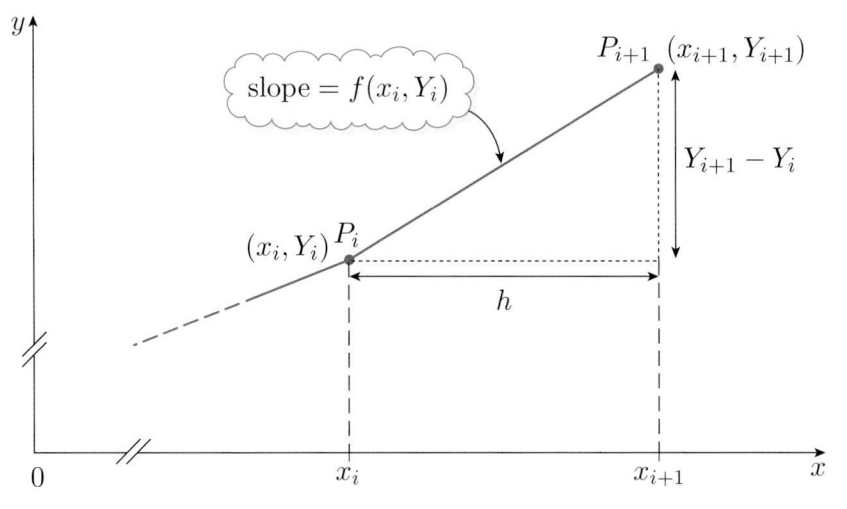

Figure 14   Graphical representation of the $(i + 1)$th step of Euler's method for numerically solving $y' = f(x, y)$

The point P_{i+1} provides an approximation Y_{i+1} to the exact solution value $y_{i+1} = y(x_{i+1})$ at $x = x_{i+1}$. Arguing as before, we have

$$x_{i+1} = x_i + h \tag{41}$$

and

$$Y_{i+1} = Y_i + h\, f(x_i, Y_i). \tag{42}$$

To sum up, we have a procedure for constructing a sequence of points

    P_i with coordinates (x_i, Y_i) for $i = 0, 1, 2, \ldots,$

where the values of x_i and Y_i for each value of i are determined by equations (41) and (42). The starting point for the sequence is the point P_0 with coordinates (x_0, Y_0), where $Y_0 = y_0$. The horizontal distance h by which we move to the right at each stage of the procedure is called the **step length** or **step size**.

The sequence of points $P_0 = (x_0, y_0)$, $P_1 = (x_1, Y_1)$, $P_2 = (x_2, Y_2)$, $\ldots$ provides an approximate solution to the initial-value problem based on the differential equation $dy/dx = f(x, y)$ and the initial condition $y(x_0) = y_0$. In other words, when the independent variable has value x_i, the exact solution $y(x_i)$ is approximated by Y_i. The method just used to generate this sequence is called *Euler's method.*

> ### Procedure 4   Euler's method
>
> To apply Euler's method to the initial-value problem
>
> $$\frac{dy}{dx} = f(x, y), \quad y(x_0) = y_0,$$
>
> proceed as follows.
>
> 1. Take x_0 and $Y_0 = y_0$ as starting values, choose a step length h, and set $i = 0$.
>
> 2. Calculate the x-coordinate x_{i+1} using the formula
>
> $$x_{i+1} = x_i + h. \qquad \text{(Eq. 41)}$$
>
> 3. Calculate a corresponding approximation Y_{i+1} to $y(x_{i+1})$, using the formula
>
> $$Y_{i+1} = Y_i + h\, f(x_i, Y_i). \qquad \text{(Eq. 42)}$$
>
> 4. If further approximate values are required, increase i by 1 and return to Step 2.

How well does Euler's method work? Figure 15 shows the constructed sequence of points and, for comparison, shows a graph representing the exact solution of the initial-value problem. This makes it clear that the successive points $P_1, P_2, P_3, \ldots$ are only *approximations* to points on the solution curve. In fact, the situation shown in Figure 15 is typical of the behaviour of the constructed approximations, in that they gradually move further and further from the exact solution curve. This is because at each step, the direction of movement is along the slope at $P_i = (x_i, Y_i)$ and not along the slope at the position reached by the exact solution (x_i, y_i), where $y_i = y(x_i)$.

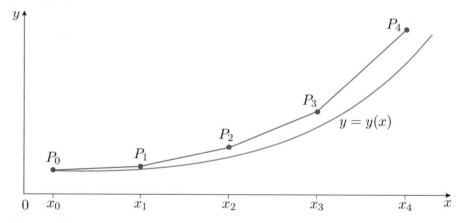

Figure 15   Graphical representation of the numerical and exact solutions of a differential equation

Improvements in accuracy can usually be achieved by *reducing the step length h*. This is illustrated in Figure 16. Of course, the improvement comes at the cost of having to use more steps, and therefore using more computer time.

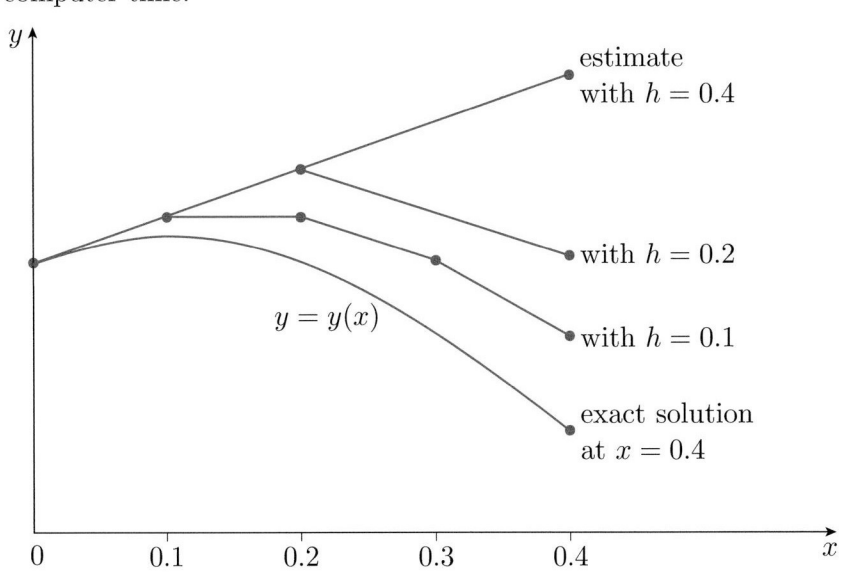

Figure 16   Comparison of the numerical and exact solutions of a differential equation for various step lengths h

The power of computers

Euler's method is not the method of choice for solving differential equations, but it has all of the essential features of more modern methods. For large values of $x - x_0$, an accurate solution requires a very small value of h, so many steps are needed.

This feature of repeating simple calculations many times over makes Euler's method (and similar techniques) very tedious for humans, but such calculations are ideally suited to computers. In fact, this type of work was one of the first applications of computers.

Once they had taken the step of programming a computer to solve equations, the ambitions of scientists to explore complex phenomena developed rapidly. Nowadays, it is not uncommon to program a computer to solve systems of differential equations with thousands of variables. Thirty years ago this might have been done using a supercomputer, such as the Cray-1 shown in Figure 17(a). This machine was state-of-the-art in 1978 when the first models were sold for approximately 8 million dollars. Nowadays its performance is easily surpassed by a typical home computer, and supercomputers have developed even further.

Figure 17(b) shows a rack from the Japanese K supercomputer (2009), which can complete in one second computations that would have taken the original Cray-1 four years.

(a)   (b)

Figure 17   (a) The Cray-1 supercomputer, introduced in 1978; (b) a rack from the Japanese K supercomputer, introduced in 2009

Learning outcomes

After studying this unit, you should be able to do the following.

- Understand and use the basic terminology relating to differential equations and their solutions.

- Check by substitution whether a given function is a solution of a given first-order differential equation or initial-value problem.

- Find from the general solution of a first-order differential equation the particular solution that satisfies a given initial condition.

- Recognise when a first-order differential equation is soluble by direct integration, and carry out that integration when appropriate.

- Recognise when a first-order differential equation is separable, and apply the method of separation of variables.

- Recognise when a first-order differential equation is linear, and solve such an equation by the integrating factor method.

Solutions to exercises

Solution to Exercise 1

We have $r(P) = k\left(1 - \dfrac{P}{M}\right)$, so we simply need to solve the following pair of simultaneous equations:

$$k\left(1 - \frac{10}{M}\right) = 1,$$

$$k\left(1 - \frac{10\,000}{M}\right) = 0.$$

From the second equation, since $k > 0$, we see immediately that $M = 10\,000$. Substituting in the first equation leads to

$$k\,\frac{999}{1000} = 1, \quad \text{so} \quad k = \frac{1000}{999}.$$

Solution to Exercise 2

(a) In each case, differences in notation notwithstanding, the differential equation has the form

$$\frac{dy}{dx} = f(x, y),$$

and we need to show that a given function $y = y(x)$ satisfies this equation. We can do this by substituting $y = y(x)$ into both sides of the equation and showing that the results are identical. Alternatively, if the right-hand side is simple, we can substitute $y = y(x)$ into the left-hand side and then rearrange the result to show that it is equal to the right-hand side.

In this case, to show that $y = 2e^x - (x^2 + 2x + 2)$ satisfies

$$\frac{dy}{dx} = f(x, y) = y + x^2,$$

we first differentiate y to get

$$\frac{dy}{dx} = 2e^x - 2x - 2.$$

Then, substituting the expression for y into $f(x, y)$, we get

$$f(x, y) = y + x^2 = 2e^x - (x^2 + 2x + 2) + x^2 = 2e^x - 2x - 2,$$

as required.

(b) To show that $y = \frac{1}{2}x^2 + \frac{3}{2}$ satisfies

$$\frac{dy}{dx} = x,$$

we simply differentiate y to get

$$\frac{dy}{dx} = x,$$

which establishes the required result.

(c) To show that $u = 2e^{x^2/2}$ satisfies

$$u' = f(x, u) = xu,$$

we differentiate u to get

$$u' = \frac{du}{dx} = 2xe^{x^2/2},$$

and then note that the right-hand side of the differential equation is

$$f(x, u) = xu = 2xe^{x^2/2},$$

as required.

(d) To show that

$$y = \sqrt{\frac{27 - x^2}{3}} = \left(\frac{27 - x^2}{3}\right)^{1/2},$$

with $(-3\sqrt{3} < x < 3\sqrt{3})$, satisfies

$$\frac{dy}{dx} = f(x, y) = -\frac{x}{3y} \quad (y \neq 0),$$

we first differentiate y to get

$$\frac{dy}{dx} = -\frac{x}{3}\left(\frac{27 - x^2}{3}\right)^{-1/2}.$$

Then, substituting the expression for y into $f(x, y)$, we get

$$f(x, y) = -\frac{x}{3y} = -\frac{x}{3}\left(\frac{27 - x^2}{3}\right)^{-1/2},$$

as required.

(e) To show that $y = t + e^{-t}$ satisfies

$$\dot{y} = f(t, y) = -y + t + 1,$$

we first differentiate y to get

$$\dot{y} = \frac{dy}{dt} = 1 - e^{-t}.$$

Then, substituting the expression for y into $f(t, y)$, we get

$$f(t, y) = -y + t + 1 = -(t + e^{-t}) + t + 1 = 1 - e^{-t},$$

as required.

(f) To show that $y = t + Ce^{-t}$ satisfies

$$\dot{y} = f(t, y) = -y + t + 1,$$

we first differentiate y to get

$$\dot{y} = \frac{dy}{dt} = 1 - Ce^{-t}.$$

Then, substituting the expression for y into $f(t, y)$, we get

$$f(t, y) = -y + t + 1 = -(t + Ce^{-t}) + t + 1 = 1 - Ce^{-t},$$

as required.

Solution to Exercise 3

(a) To verify that $y = C - \frac{1}{3}e^{-3x}$ satisfies

$$\frac{dy}{dx} = e^{-3x},$$

we differentiate y to get

$$\frac{dy}{dx} = -\frac{1}{3}(-3e^{-3x}) = e^{-3x},$$

as required.

(b) To verify that $u = Ce^t - t - 1$ satisfies

$$\dot{u} = f(t, u) = t + u,$$

we differentiate u to get

$$\dot{u} = \frac{du}{dt} = Ce^t - 1.$$

Then, substituting the expression for u into $f(t, u)$, we get

$$f(t, u) = t + u = Ce^t - 1,$$

as required.

(c) To verify that $P(t) = CMe^{kt}/(1 + Ce^{kt})$ satisfies

$$\frac{dP}{dt} = f(t, P) = kP\left(1 - \frac{P}{M}\right),$$

we differentiate $P(t)$ using the quotient rule. This gives

$$\frac{dP}{dt} = \frac{(CMke^{kt})(1 + Ce^{kt}) - (CMe^{kt})(Cke^{kt})}{(1 + Ce^{kt})^2} = \frac{CMke^{kt}}{(1 + Ce^{kt})^2}.$$

Then, substituting the expression for P into $f(t, P)$, we get

$$f(t, P) = k\frac{CMe^{kt}}{1 + Ce^{kt}}\left(1 - \frac{Ce^{kt}}{1 + Ce^{kt}}\right) = \frac{CMke^{kt}}{(1 + Ce^{kt})^2},$$

as required.

Solution to Exercise 4

(a) From Exercise 3(c) we know that

$$P(t) = \frac{CMe^{kt}}{1 + Ce^{kt}} = \frac{10Ce^{0.15t}}{1 + Ce^{0.15t}}$$

is a solution of the differential equation. Because $e^0 = 1$, the initial condition $P(0) = 1$ then implies that

$$1 = \frac{10C}{1 + C}, \quad \text{so} \quad C = \tfrac{1}{9}.$$

The particular solution consistent with the initial condition is therefore

$$P(t) = \frac{\frac{10}{9}e^{0.15t}}{1 + \frac{1}{9}e^{0.15t}} = \frac{10e^{0.15t}}{9 + e^{0.15t}}.$$

(b) Dividing top and bottom by $e^{0.15t}$, we see that

$$P(t) = \frac{10}{9e^{-0.15t} + 1}.$$

For large values of t, the exponential term in the denominator will be very small. The result is that P will approach the value 10 in the long term. As P is the population size measured in hundreds of thousands, the population is predicted to approach one million in the long term.

Solution to Exercise 5

(a) We apply direct integration to find the general solution. In each case, C is an arbitrary constant.

The differential equation $dy/dx = 6x$ has general solution

$$y = \int 6x \, dx = 3x^2 + C.$$

From the initial condition $y(1) = 5$, we have $5 = 3 + C$, so $C = 2$. The solution to the initial-value problem is therefore

$$y = 3x^2 + 2.$$

(b) The differential equation $dv/du = e^{4u}$ has general solution

$$v = \int e^{4u} \, du = \tfrac{1}{4}e^{4u} + C.$$

From the initial condition $v(0) = 2$, we have $2 = \tfrac{1}{4} + C$, so $C = \tfrac{7}{4}$. The solution to the initial-value problem is therefore

$$v = \tfrac{1}{4}(e^{4u} + 7).$$

(c) The differential equation $\dot{y} = 5 \sin 2t$ has general solution

$$y = \int 5 \sin 2t \, dt = -\tfrac{5}{2} \cos 2t + C.$$

From the initial condition $y(0) = 0$, we have $0 = -\tfrac{5}{2} + C$, so $C = \tfrac{5}{2}$. The solution to the initial-value problem is therefore

$$y = \tfrac{5}{2}(1 - \cos 2t).$$

Solution to Exercise 6

(a) The differential equation $dy/dx = xe^{-2x}$ has general solution

$$y = \int xe^{-2x}\, dx.$$

The integral can be found using integration by parts (see Unit 1).

Since differentiating x simplifies it, we take $f(x) = x$ and $g'(x) = e^{-2x}$. Then $f'(x) = 1$ and $g(x) = -\frac{1}{2}e^{-2x}$. So, using the formula

$$\int f(x)\, g'(x)\, dx = f(x)\, g(x) - \int f'(x)\, g(x)\, dx,$$

we get

$$\int xe^{-2x}\, dx = -\tfrac{1}{2}xe^{-2x} + \int \tfrac{1}{2}e^{-2x}\, dx$$
$$= -\tfrac{1}{2}xe^{-2x} - \tfrac{1}{4}e^{-2x} + C,$$

where C is an arbitrary constant. The general solution of the differential equation is therefore

$$y = -\tfrac{1}{4}(2x+1)e^{-2x} + C.$$

(b) The differential equation $\dot{p} = t/(1+t^2)$ has general solution

$$p = \int \frac{t}{1+t^2}\, dt.$$

Using the hint provided, we make the substitution $u = 1 + t^2$, for which $du/dt = 2t$. Writing the required integral as

$$\int \frac{t}{1+t^2}\, dt = \tfrac{1}{2} \int \frac{2t}{1+t^2}\, dt,$$

we then obtain

$$\int \frac{t}{1+t^2}\, dt = \int \frac{1}{u}\frac{du}{dt}\, dt = \tfrac{1}{2} \int \frac{1}{u}\, du$$
$$= \tfrac{1}{2}\ln u + C \quad (\text{since } u = 1 + t^2 > 0)$$
$$= \tfrac{1}{2}\ln(1+t^2) + C,$$

where C is an arbitrary constant. The general solution of the differential equation is therefore

$$p = \tfrac{1}{2}\ln(1+t^2) + C.$$

Solution to Exercise 7

(a) The differential equation is

$$\frac{dy}{dx} = \frac{y-1}{x}, \quad \text{where } x > 0,$$

which is of the form $dy/dx = g(x)\,h(y)$ with $g(x) = 1/x$ and $h(y) = y - 1$. For $h(y) = y - 1 \neq 0$, Procedure 2 gives

$$\int \frac{1}{y-1}\,dy = \int \frac{1}{x}\,dx.$$

Since $x > 0$ and $y - 1 \neq 0$, integration produces

$$\ln|y-1| = \ln x + C,$$

where C is an arbitrary constant. Taking the exponential of both sides of this equation, we get

$$|y-1| = e^{\ln x + C} = e^{C}e^{\ln x} = e^{C}x.$$

Hence

$$y = 1 \pm e^{C}x.$$

We therefore have a family of solutions given by

$$y(x) = 1 + Bx,$$

where $B = \pm e^{C}$ is an arbitrary non-zero constant.

The special case of the constant function $y(x) = 1$ is also a solution since if we substitute this into both sides of the differential equation, we get zero on both sides. This special case can be incorporated into the main family of solutions by setting $B = 0$.

So we conclude that any function of the form

$$y(x) = 1 + Bx$$

is a solution of the differential equation for $x > 0$. In fact, it is the general solution of the equation. (In Section 3, Example 7(a), you will see this established by a different method.)

(b) The differential equation is

$$\frac{dy}{dx} = \frac{2y}{1+x^2},$$

which is of the form $dy/dx = g(x)\,h(y)$ with $g(x) = 1/(1+x^2)$ and $h(y) = 2y$. For $h(y) = 2y \neq 0$, Procedure 2 gives

$$\int \frac{1}{y}\,dy = \int \frac{2}{1+x^2}\,dx.$$

For $y \neq 0$, integration produces

$$\ln|y| = 2(\arctan x + C),$$

where C is an arbitrary constant.

On solving this equation for y, we obtain

$$y = \pm e^{2\arctan x + 2C} = \pm e^{2C} e^{2\arctan x} = B e^{2\arctan x},$$

where $B = \pm e^{2C}$ is a non-zero but otherwise arbitrary constant.

The special case of the constant function $y(x) = 0$ is also a solution, since if we substitute this into both sides of the differential equation, we get zero on both sides. This special case can be incorporated into the main family of solutions by setting $B = 0$.

So we conclude that any function of the form

$$y(x) = B e^{2\arctan x},$$

where B is an arbitrary constant, is a solution of the differential equation. In fact, it is the general solution of the equation. (In Section 3, Example 7(b), you will see this established by a different method.)

Solution to Exercise 8

The differential equation is

$$\frac{dv}{du} = e^{u+v} = e^u e^v.$$

Dividing through by e^v and integrating with respect to u, we obtain

$$\int e^{-v}\, dv = \int e^u\, du.$$

Note that $e^v > 0$.

Integration produces

$$-e^{-v} = e^u + C,$$

where C is an arbitrary constant. So

$$e^{-v} = -e^u - C.$$

Taking the logarithm of both sides, we get

$$-v = \ln(-e^u - C),$$

so

$$v = -\ln(B - e^u),$$

where $B = -C$.

Since the argument of the ln function must be positive, we require that $B - e^u > 0$, so $B > e^u$. Hence B must be positive. Taking the logarithm of both sides gives $\ln B > \ln e^u$, so $\ln B > u$.

Therefore the general solution is

$$v = -\ln(B - e^u) \quad (u < \ln B),$$

where B is an arbitrary positive constant.

The initial condition $v(0) = 0$ gives $0 = -\ln(B - e^0)$, so $B - e^0 = 1$ and hence $B = 2$. The solution to the initial-value problem is therefore

$$v = -\ln(2 - e^u) \quad (u < \ln 2).$$

Solution to Exercise 9

(a) Each of these differential equations can be solved by separation of variables.

In this case the differential equation is

$$u' = \frac{du}{dx} = xu.$$

For the cases where $u \neq 0$, we divide through by u and integrate with respect to x. This gives

$$\int \frac{1}{u}\, du = \int x\, dx.$$

Integration produces

$$\ln|u| = \tfrac{1}{2}x^2 + C,$$

where C is an arbitrary constant. On solving this equation for u, we obtain

$$u = \pm e^{x^2/2 + C} = \pm e^C e^{x^2/2} = Be^{x^2/2},$$

where $B = \pm e^C$ is a non-zero but otherwise arbitrary constant.

The special case of the constant function $u(x) = 0$ is also a solution, since if we substitute this into both sides of the differential equation, we get zero on both sides. This special case can be incorporated into the main family of solutions by setting $B = 0$.

So we conclude that any function of the form

$$u(x) = Be^{x^2/2},$$

where B is an arbitrary constant, is a solution of the differential equation. This is the general solution.

(You verified that $u = 2e^{x^2/2}$ is a particular solution of this differential equation in Exercise 2(c).)

(b) The differential equation is

$$\dot{x} = \frac{dx}{dt} = 1 + x^2.$$

We divide through by $1 + x^2$ and integrate with respect to t. This gives

$$\int \frac{1}{1+x^2}\, dx = \int 1\, dt.$$

Integration then produces

$$\arctan x = t + C,$$

where C is an arbitrary constant. On solving for x, we get the general solution

$$x(t) = \tan(t + C).$$

We must restrict the domain of $x(t)$ to avoid values of t where tan is undefined. That is, we must ensure that $t + C \neq \left(n + \tfrac{1}{2}\right)\pi$, where n is an integer, but the precise choice of domain will depend on the initial conditions.

Solution to Exercise 10

(a) The given equation is

$$\frac{dP}{dt} = kP\left(1 - \frac{P}{M}\right).$$

First, note that the constant functions $P(t) = 0$ and $P(t) = M$ are both solutions of the differential equation, giving zero on both sides. The function $P(t) = 0$ is not allowed, however, since we are told that $P(t) > 0$. Ignoring for the moment the possibility that $P(t) = M$, we can use the method of separation of variables to obtain

$$\int \frac{1}{P(1 - P/M)}\, dP = \int k\, dt.$$

The integral on the left-hand side can be evaluated using the result given in the question with $a = 1/M$. We get

$$-\ln\left|\frac{1}{P} - \frac{1}{M}\right| = kt + C,$$

where C is an arbitrary constant. Hence

$$\left|\frac{1}{P} - \frac{1}{M}\right| = e^{-kt-C} = e^{-C}e^{-kt},$$

thus

$$\frac{1}{P} = \frac{1}{M} \pm e^{-C}e^{-kt} = \frac{1}{M} + Be^{-kt},$$

where B is a non-zero but otherwise arbitrary constant.

Now consider the constant solution $P(t) = M$. This can be incorporated into the above family of solutions by taking $B = 0$. So the restriction $B \neq 0$ can be dropped and the general solution of the differential equation is

$$P(t) = \left(\frac{1}{M} + Be^{-kt}\right)^{-1},$$

where B is an arbitrary constant.

From the initial condition $P(0) = 2M$, we get

$$\frac{1}{2M} = \frac{1}{M} + Be^0, \quad \text{so} \quad B = -\frac{1}{2M}.$$

The solution to the initial-value problem is therefore

$$P(t) = \left(\frac{1}{M} - \frac{1}{2M}e^{-kt}\right)^{-1}$$

$$= \frac{2M}{2 - e^{-kt}}.$$

(b) As $t \to \infty$ we have $e^{-kt} \to 0$, so the value of $P(t)$ approaches M.

Solution to Exercise 11

(a) The equation $dy/dx + x^3 y = x^5$ is linear, with $g(x) = x^3$ and $h(x) = x^5$.

(b) The equation $dy/dx = x \sin x$ is linear, with $g(x) = 0$ (for all x) and $h(x) = x \sin x$.

(c) The equation $dz/dt = -3z^{1/2}$ is not linear (because of the $z^{1/2}$ term).

(d) The equation $\dot{y} + y^2 = t$ is not linear (because of the y^2 term).

(e) The equation $x\,(dy/dx) + y = y^2$ is not linear (because of the y^2 term).

(f) The equation $(1 + x^2)\,(dy/dx) + 2xy = 3x^2$ is linear, since we can divide through by $1 + x^2$ to obtain

$$\frac{dy}{dx} + \frac{2xy}{1 + x^2} = \frac{3x^2}{1 + x^2},$$

which is of linear form with $g(x) = 2x/(1 + x^2)$ and $h(x) = 3x^2/(1 + x^2)$.

Solution to Exercise 12

The differential equation

$$\frac{dy}{dx} + y = e^{2x}$$

has the same form as equation (26), with $A = 1$ and $h(x) = e^{2x}$. Multiplying both sides of the differential equation by the factor $e^{Ax} = e^x$, we obtain

$$e^x \frac{dy}{dx} + e^x y = e^x e^{2x} = e^{3x},$$

and this can be written in the form

$$\frac{d}{dx}(e^x y) = \int e^{3x}\, dx.$$

Integrating both sides then gives

$$e^x y = \tfrac{1}{3} e^{3x} + C,$$

so

$$y(x) = \tfrac{1}{3} e^{2x} + C e^{-x}.$$

The initial condition $y(0) = 0$ gives $0 = \tfrac{1}{3} + C$, so $C = -\tfrac{1}{3}$. The particular solution consistent with the given initial condition is therefore

$$y(x) = \tfrac{1}{3}(e^{2x} - e^{-x}).$$

We check this by differentiating $y(x)$ to get

$$\frac{dy}{dx} = \tfrac{1}{3}(2e^{2x} + e^{-x}),$$

so

$$\frac{dy}{dx} + y = \tfrac{1}{3}(2e^{2x} + e^{-x}) + \tfrac{1}{3}(e^{2x} - e^{-x}) = e^{2x},$$

as required.

Solution to Exercise 13

(a) The given equation is

$$\frac{dy}{dx} - y = e^x \sin x.$$

Comparison with equations (25) and (32) shows that the integrating factor is

$$p(x) = \exp\left(\int (-1)\,dx\right) = \exp(-x) = e^{-x}.$$

Multiplying through by $p(x)$ then gives

$$e^{-x}\frac{dy}{dx} - e^{-x}y = \sin x.$$

Thus the differential equation can be rewritten as

$$\frac{d}{dx}(e^{-x}y) = \sin x.$$

(You should check that the derivative on the left-hand side is equal to the left-hand side of the preceding equation.)

On integrating, we find the general solution

$$e^{-x}y = -\cos x + C,$$

or equivalently,

$$y(x) = e^x(C - \cos x),$$

where C is an arbitrary constant.

(b) The given equation, when rearranged into the form of equation (25), is

$$\frac{dy}{dx} - y = x.$$

This has the same left-hand side as the differential equation in part (a), and hence the same integrating factor, $p(x) = e^{-x}$. Multiplying through by $p(x)$ gives

$$e^{-x}\frac{dy}{dx} - e^{-x}y = xe^{-x}.$$

Thus the differential equation can be rewritten as

$$\frac{d}{dx}(e^{-x}y) = xe^{-x}.$$

Integrating both sides, we get

$$e^{-x}y = \int xe^{-x}\,dx.$$

The integral on the right-hand side is integrated by parts, using the formula

$$\int f(x)\,g'(x)\,dx = f(x)\,g(x) - \int f'(x)\,g(x)\,dx$$

with $f(x) = x$ and $g'(x) = e^{-x}$.

We have $f'(x) = 1$ and $g(x) = -e^{-x}$, so

$$e^{-x}y = -xe^{-x} + \int e^{-x}\, dx$$

$$= -xe^{-x} - e^{-x} + C$$

$$= C - (x+1)e^{-x},$$

where C is an arbitrary constant. Multiplying through by e^x, the explicit form of the general solution is

$$y = Ce^x - (x+1).$$

Solution to Exercise 14

(a) The given equation, when rearranged into the form of equation (25), is

$$\frac{du}{dx} - xu = 0.$$

The integrating factor is

$$p(x) = \exp\left(\int (-x)\, dx\right) = \exp(-x^2/2) = e^{-x^2/2}.$$

Multiplying through by $p(x)$ gives

$$e^{-x^2/2}\frac{du}{dx} - xe^{-x^2/2}u = 0.$$

Thus the differential equation can be rewritten as

$$\frac{d}{dx}(e^{-x^2/2}u) = 0.$$

(You should check that the derivative on the left-hand side is equal to the left-hand side of the preceding equation.)

On integrating, we find the general solution

$$e^{-x^2/2}u = C,$$

or equivalently,

$$u(x) = Ce^{x^2/2},$$

where C is an arbitrary constant.

From the initial condition $u(0) = 2$, we have $2 = Ce^0$, so $C = 2$. Hence the solution of the initial-value problem is

$$u(x) = 2e^{x^2/2}.$$

(b) After division by t (which is allowed because we are told that $t > 0$), the given equation can be written as

$$\frac{dy}{dt} + \frac{2}{t}y = t.$$

The integrating factor is

$$p(x) = \exp\left(\int \frac{2}{t}\, dt\right) = \exp(2\ln t) = \exp(\ln(t^2)) = t^2.$$

Multiplying through by $p(t)$ gives

$$t^2 \frac{dy}{dt} + 2ty = t^3.$$

Thus the differential equation can be rewritten as

$$\frac{d}{dt}(t^2 y) = t^3.$$

(Again, it's worth checking that the derivative on the left-hand side gives the left-hand side of the preceding equation.)

On integrating, we find the general solution

$$t^2 y = \tfrac{1}{4} t^4 + C,$$

or equivalently,

$$y(t) = \tfrac{1}{4} t^2 + C t^{-2},$$

where C is an arbitrary constant.

From the initial condition $y(1) = 1$, we have $1 = \tfrac{1}{4} + C$, so $C = \tfrac{3}{4}$. Hence the solution of the initial-value problem is

$$y(t) = \tfrac{1}{4}(t^2 + 3t^{-2}).$$

Solution to Exercise 15

(a) The given equation is

$$\frac{dy}{dt} + y = t + 1.$$

So the integrating factor is

$$p(t) = \exp\left(\int 1 \, dt\right) = \exp(t) = e^t.$$

Multiplying through by $p(t)$ gives

$$e^t \frac{dy}{dt} + e^t y = (t + 1)e^t.$$

Thus the differential equation can be rewritten as

$$\frac{d}{dt}(e^t y) = (t + 1)e^t.$$

So

$$e^t y = \int (t + 1)e^t \, dt.$$

The integral on the right-hand side is evaluated by parts, using $f(t) = t + 1$ and $g'(t) = e^t$. We have $f'(t) = 1$ and $g(t) = e^t$, so

$$e^t y = (t + 1)e^t - \int e^t \, dt$$
$$= (t + 1)e^t - e^t + C$$
$$= te^t + C,$$

where C is an arbitrary constant.

Multiplying through by e^{-t}, the general solution in explicit form is

$$y(t) = Ce^{-t} + t.$$

From the initial condition $y(1) = 0$, we have $0 = Ce^{-1} + 1$, so $C = -e$. Hence the solution of the initial-value problem is

$$y(t) = t - e^{1-t}.$$

(b) After division by e^{3t} and rearrangement, the given equation becomes $dy/dt + y = e^{-3t}$. This has the same left-hand side as the differential equation in part (a), and hence the same integrating factor, $p(t) = e^t$. Multiplying through by $p(t)$ gives

$$e^t \frac{dy}{dt} + e^t y = e^{-2t}.$$

Thus the differential equation can be rewritten as

$$\frac{d}{dt}(e^t y) = e^{-2t}.$$

On integrating, we find the general solution

$$e^t y = -\tfrac{1}{2}e^{-2t} + C,$$

or equivalently,

$$y(t) = Ce^{-t} - \tfrac{1}{2}e^{-3t},$$

where C is an arbitrary constant.

From the initial condition $y(0) = 3$, we have $3 = Ce^0 - \tfrac{1}{2}e^0$, so $C = \tfrac{7}{2}$. Hence the solution of the initial-value problem is

$$y(t) = \tfrac{1}{2}(7e^{-t} - e^{-3t}).$$

Solution to Exercise 16

(a) After division by x (where $x > 0$), the given equation becomes $dy/dx - (3/x)y = 1$. The integrating factor is therefore

$$
\begin{aligned}
p(x) &= \exp\left(\int \left(-\frac{3}{x}\right) dx\right) \\
&= \exp(-3\ln x) \quad (\text{since } x > 0) \\
&= \exp(\ln(x^{-3})) \\
&= x^{-3}.
\end{aligned}
$$

Multiplying through by $p(x)$ gives

$$x^{-3}\frac{dy}{dx} - 3x^{-4}y = x^{-3}.$$

Thus the differential equation can be rewritten as

$$\frac{d}{dx}(x^{-3}y) = x^{-3}.$$

On integrating, we find the general solution

$$x^{-3}y = -\tfrac{1}{2}x^{-2} + C,$$

or equivalently,

$$y(x) = Cx^3 - \tfrac{1}{2}x,$$

where C is an arbitrary constant.

(b) The given equation is $dv/dt + 4v = 3\cos 2t$. The integrating factor is

$$p(t) = \exp\left(\int 4\,dt\right) = \exp(4t) = e^{4t}.$$

Multiplying through by $p(t)$ gives

$$e^{4t}\frac{dv}{dt} + 4e^{4t}v = 3e^{4t}\cos 2t.$$

Thus the differential equation can be rewritten as

$$\frac{d}{dt}(e^{4t}v) = 3e^{4t}\cos 2t.$$

On integrating (using the hint for the right-hand side, with $a = 4$ and $b = 2$), we find

$$e^{4t}v = \tfrac{3}{20}e^{4t}(4\cos 2t + 2\sin 2t) + C,$$

where C is an arbitrary constant. Multiplying through by e^{-4t}, the general solution in explicit form is

$$v(t) = \tfrac{3}{10}(2\cos 2t + \sin 2t) + Ce^{-4t}.$$

Solution to Exercise 17

(a) and (d) require the integrating factor method.

(b) is best solved by direct integration.

(c) can be solved by separation of variables or the integrating factor method.

(e) requires separation of variables.

Solution to Exercise 18

(a) The diagram shows that the slope is zero at all points on the horizontal lines $P = 0$ and $P = 1000$, so these correspond to constant solutions of the differential equation. (As pointed out earlier in the text, these two solutions can also be spotted directly from the form of the differential equation.)

The graphs of solutions through a starting point above the line $P = 1000$ appear to decrease, but at a slower and slower rate, tending from above towards the asymptote $P = 1000$ as t increases.

The graphs of solutions through starting points in the region $0 < P < 1000$ are increasing, with slope growing before the level $P = 500$ is reached and declining thereafter. For large values of t, these graphs tend from below towards the asymptote $P = 1000$.

For a starting point in the region $P < 0$, the graphs decrease without limit and with steeper and steeper slope.

These various cases are illustrated in the figure below.

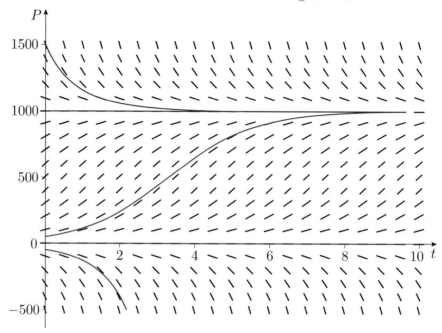

(b) If the differential equation is considered as a model of population behaviour, then the region $P < 0$ must be excluded. The above analysis leads to the following predictions for the population.

- If the population size is zero at the start, then it remains zero.

- If the population size is 1000 at the start, then it remains fixed at this level.

- If the population starts at a level higher than 1000, then it declines (more and more gradually) towards 1000.

- If the population starts at a level below 1000 (but above 0), then it increases (more and more gradually) towards 1000.

- Solutions with $P < 0$ are unphysical in the context of population models.

Acknowledgements

Grateful acknowledgement is made to the following sources:

Figure 3: Andrew Butko.

Figure 4: Wallace 63 / http://commons.wikimedia.org/wiki/File:Smilodon_head.jpg. This file is licensed under the Creative Commons Attribution-Share Alike 3.0.

Figure 7: NASA.

Figure 8: NASA.

Figure 17(a): Taken from http://en.wikipedia.org/wiki/File:Cray_1_IMG_9126.jpg. This file is licensed under the Creative Commons Attribution-Share Alike 2.0 France licence.

Figure 17(b): Taken from http://en.wikipedia.org/wiki/File:Keisoku-Fujitsu.jpg. This file is licensed under the Creative Commons Attribution-Share Alike 3.0 Unported licence.

Every effort has been made to contact copyright holders. If any have been inadvertently overlooked, the publishers will be pleased to make the necessary arrangements at the first opportunity.

Second-order differential equations

Introduction

In this unit we move from first-order differential equations to second-order differential equations, that is, differential equations involving a second (but no higher) derivative. Examples of such equations are

$$\frac{d^2y}{dx^2} - 3\frac{dy}{dx} + 2y = 4e^x \quad \text{and} \quad 3\frac{d^2y}{dx^2} + y = x\sin x.$$

Second-order differential equations play a central role in the physical sciences. They are found, for example, in laws describing mechanical systems, wave motion, electric currents and quantum phenomena.

To take a simple case, consider a particle of mass m that moves in one dimension along the x-axis. At any given time t, the particle's position is $x(t)$, and its velocity and acceleration are given by the derivatives dx/dt and d^2x/dt^2. There are no general laws for the position or velocity of the particle, but there is a very important law for its acceleration: *Newton's second law* tells us that

$$\text{mass} \times \text{acceleration} = \text{force},$$

which implies that

$$m\frac{d^2x}{dt^2} = F, \tag{1}$$

where F is the force acting on the particle. The force need not be constant, and may vary with the position x or the velocity dx/dt of the particle. So, depending on the precise details, we get a second-order differential equation for x as a function of t, and the solution of this equation tells us how the particle can move.

The system known as a *simple harmonic oscillator* provides a good example. Here, a particle of mass m is suspended at the lower end of a spring that is attached to a fixed support (Figure 1). The particle moves up and down along a vertical x-axis, subject to a force F provided by the spring and gravity. If the system is left to settle, the particle comes to rest at a point of equilibrium, which we label $x = 0$. Because the particle does not spontaneously move away from this position, we can infer that $F = 0$ when $x = 0$.

When the particle is displaced from $x = 0$, the force F tends to draw the particle back towards $x = 0$. We consider the case where the force is proportional to the displacement from equilibrium, and take

$$F = -kx, \tag{2}$$

where k is a positive constant. The negative sign in this equation ensures that the force always acts in a direction that tends to restore the particle to its equilibrium position.

Putting equations (1) and (2) together, we get the differential equation

$$m\frac{d^2x}{dt^2} = -kx.$$

The *order* of a differential equation is defined in Unit 2. A second-order differential equation may or may not include a first derivative.

Don't worry if you have not met Newton's second law before: the essential aims of this unit do not rely on it.

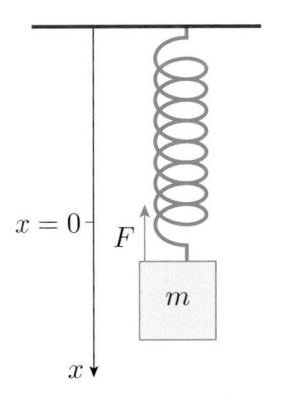

Figure 1 A particle of mass m moves along the x-axis subject to a force F provided by a spring and gravity

Recalling that $k > 0$ and $m > 0$, we can also express this as

$$\frac{d^2x}{dt^2} = -\omega^2 x, \tag{3}$$

where $\omega = \sqrt{k/m}$ is a positive constant. Equation (3) is called the *equation of motion* of a simple harmonic oscillator. It is a second-order differential equation whose solution tells us how the particle can move.

This unit develops systematic techniques to solve equations like this. For the moment, we will simply guess the solution and check that it works. You know that

$$\frac{d}{dt}(\sin t) = \cos t \quad \text{and} \quad \frac{d}{dt}(\cos t) = -\sin t,$$

so

$$\frac{d^2}{dt^2}(\sin t) = -\sin t \quad \text{and} \quad \frac{d^2}{dt^2}(\cos t) = -\cos t.$$

In other words, taking the second derivative of a sine or cosine function gives the same function back again, but with a minus sign. This is very close to the behaviour needed to solve equation (3). We therefore try a function of the form

$$x(t) = C\sin(\omega t) + D\cos(\omega t), \tag{4}$$

where C and D are any constants, and ω is the constant in equation (3). Differentiating this function once, and then again, we get

$$\frac{dx}{dt} = C\omega\cos(\omega t) - D\omega\sin(\omega t),$$

$$\frac{d^2x}{dt^2} = -C\omega^2\sin(\omega t) - D\omega^2\cos(\omega t) = -\omega^2 x.$$

So the function in equation (4) does indeed satisfy equation (3). In fact, it is the general solution of this differential equation.

Notice that our solution involves two constants, C and D, whose values are not specified. These constants have arbitrary values, and they are called *arbitrary constants*. It is typical for the general solutions of a second-order differential equation to have *two* arbitrary constants. The values of these constants depend on how the system is released, and you will see how they are determined later in this unit. To take a definite case, suppose that $C = 2$, $D = 3$ and $\omega = 4$, when measured in suitable units. Then we have the particular solution

$$x(t) = 2\sin(4t) + 3\cos(4t), \tag{5}$$

and this is plotted in Figure 2. The wiggles in this graph correspond to the oscillations performed by a system like the particle on the end of the spring in Figure 1.

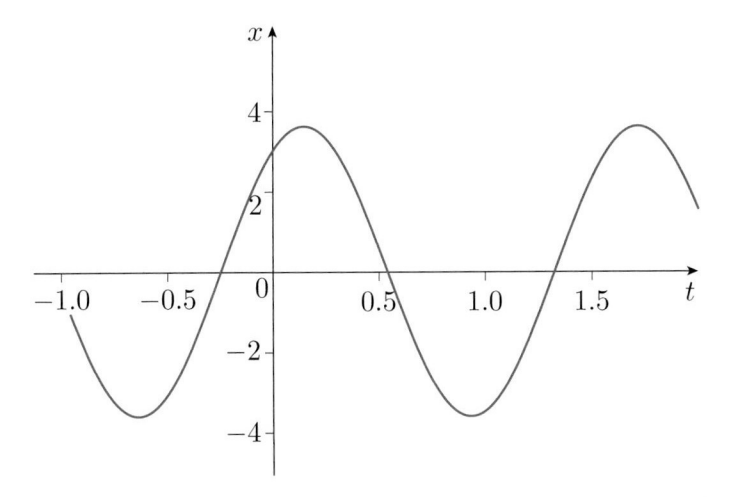

Figure 2 A graph of equation (5), which is a particular solution of equation (3)

The simple harmonic motion described by equation (4) continues forever, but we know from everyday experience that oscillations generally die away after a while. We can get a more realistic description by including an additional force in our model – one that will dampen the oscillations down. We take the additional force to be $-\gamma\, dx/dt$, where γ is a positive constant, leading to the differential equation

$$m\frac{d^2x}{dt^2} = -kx - \gamma\frac{dx}{dt}. \tag{6}$$

This is the equation of motion of a *damped harmonic oscillator*. Later in this unit you will see that (in appropriate circumstances) it has solutions that oscillate but diminish and eventually die away.

We can also add in another force, $f(t)$, which is applied to the particle by some external agency. We assume that this force is known directly as a function of time (and does not depend on the position or velocity of the particle.) Under these circumstances, Newton's second law leads to the differential equation

$$m\frac{d^2x}{dt^2} = -kx - \gamma\frac{dx}{dt} + f(t), \tag{7}$$

and this is the equation of motion of a *forced damped harmonic oscillator*. If the external force is oscillatory, the response of the system may depend very sensitively on the frequency of the external force. This phenomenon is called *resonance*; it will be explored at the end of this unit.

Harmonic oscillators are everywhere

Harmonic oscillators play a central role in physics and its applications. If a system performs small oscillations about an equilibrium point, then it is generally a good approximation to model it as a harmonic oscillator, including the additional terms in equations (6) and (7) when necessary.

It should come as no surprise that the to-and-fro motion of a pendulum clock can be modelled by a harmonic oscillator. On a smaller scale, vibrating molecules and vibrating crystals are also modelled as harmonic oscillators.

Equations similar to (7) are also used to describe the oscillations of currents in electrical circuits that allow radios to be tuned to selected stations. Moreover, each frequency in an electromagnetic field can be regarded as a harmonic oscillator, and this is a key insight used in advanced physics when electromagnetic fields are treated quantum mechanically.

A more everyday example is provided by the suspension system of a mountain bike (or any other vehicle). The rider is protected from the vibrations caused by a rough track by a rugged suspension system, such as that shown in Figure 3, and this can also be modelled by equation (7).

Figure 3   The suspension system of a mountain bike is designed to absorb shocks. The rear part of the frame can rotate about a pivot point, compressing or extending the spring.

Study guide

This unit requires no previous knowledge beyond that needed for Unit 2, apart from some familiarity with complex numbers. The relevant material on complex numbers was reviewed in Unit 1.

The differential equations discussed in this unit all belong to one broad class: they are all *linear constant-coefficient second-order differential equations*. These equations play such an important role in physics and areas of applied mathematics that they easily deserve a unit to themselves.

Section 1 introduces some basic principles and terminology. Sections 2 and 3 give methods for finding the general solutions for our class of second-order differential equations: Section 2 covers so-called *homogeneous equations*, while Section 3 covers *inhomogeneous equations*. Section 4 then explains how extra information can be used to help us to select particular solutions that are appropriate in given situations.

For the most part, the unit presents the topic of second-order differential equations in purely mathematical terms, and its learning aims can be fully met without reference to physical laws. However, it is illuminating to see physical interpretations of the mathematical equations, so Subsection 2.4 and Section 5 revisit the oscillators considered in the Introduction.

Although the differential equations discussed in this unit and the last may seem to belong to a limited range of classes, in practice they encompass most of what a mathematical scientist needs to know about differential equations. The results obtained in this unit will be used again in Units 6 and 12.

1 Some preliminary remarks

As for first-order differential equations, second-order differential equations can be written using a variety of notations for functions and derivatives.

If t is the independent variable and y is the dependent variable, we can regard y as a function of t and write $y = f(t)$. More usually, however, we write $y = y(t)$, using the same symbol y for both the variable and the function. (The merits of this notation were discussed in Unit 1.) The first derivative of y with respect to t may be written as dy/dt, $\dot{y}$ or y', and the second derivative as d^2y/dt^2, $\ddot{y}$ or y''.

Of course, the independent variable is not always t, and the dependent variable is not always y!

This section makes some general comments that will be important for understanding the methods introduced in Sections 2 and 3.

1.1 Requirement for two arbitrary constants

In Unit 1 you saw that when we solve a first-order differential equation, we get a general solution containing one *arbitrary constant*. The value of the arbitrary constant is undetermined in general, but it can be found by using additional information provided by an initial condition. Here we consider the corresponding result for second-order equations. You saw in the Introduction that the differential equation for a simple harmonic oscillator (equation (3)) has a general solution (equation (4)) that contains two arbitrary constants. This turns out to be the general rule.

> You can assume that the general solution of any second-order differential equation contains two arbitrary constants.

To further illustrate this point, consider the differential equation

$$\frac{d^2y}{dt^2} = a, \tag{8}$$

where t is the independent variable, and a is a given constant. This equation describes the motion of a particle with constant acceleration a. To take a definite case, we will measure distance in metres and time in seconds, and suppose that $a = 3$ in these units. Our differential equation then becomes

$$\frac{d^2y}{dt^2} = 3. \tag{9}$$

An equation like this can be solved by integrating both sides twice. The first integration gives

$$\frac{dy}{dt} = \int 3 \, dt = 3t + C,$$

where C is an arbitrary constant. A second integration then gives

$$y(t) = \int (3t + C) \, dt = \tfrac{3}{2}t^2 + Ct + D, \tag{10}$$

where D is another arbitrary constant. Equation (10) is the *general solution* of the differential equation. It gives a formula that describes the collection of all possible solutions of the equation. As promised, this formula contains two arbitrary constants, C and D.

If we take definite values for C and D, we get a *particular solution* of the differential equation. For example, if we take $C = 2$ and $D = 3$, then the particular solution is

$$y(t) = \tfrac{3}{2}t^2 + 2t + 3.$$

In the context of straight-line motion, this solution tells us where the particle is located at each instant t. Moreover, differentiating both sides gives

$$\frac{dy}{dt} = 3t + 2,$$

so it also gives the velocity dy/dt of the particle at each instant t.

How do we determine the arbitrary constants? You have seen that a second-order differential equation has *two* arbitrary constants, so we need *two* pieces of information to determine them. A whole section of this unit (Section 4) is devoted to ways of finding the arbitrary constants, but we will make a brief comment now.

One way of finding the arbitrary constants is to use initial conditions. However, it is not enough to specify the value of the function $y(t)$ at a fixed time $t = t_0$. We also need extra information, and this can be provided by giving the value of the derivative dy/dt at the *same* fixed time, $t = t_0$.

Example 1

The following description of motion is based on units of metres and seconds. At $t = 0$, a car has initial position $y = 100$ and initial velocity $u = 4$. Between $t = 0$ and $t = 10$, the car travels with constant acceleration $a = 3$ along a straight road.

Find the particular solution of equation (9) in this case, and use it to predict the car's position and velocity at $t = 10$.

Solution

Following the above calculation, the general solution of equation (9) is

$$y(t) = \tfrac{3}{2}t^2 + Ct + D, \tag{Eq. 10}$$

where C and D are arbitrary constants. The initial conditions are $y(0) = 100$ and $y'(0) = 4$. The first condition gives

$$100 = \tfrac{3}{2} \times 0^2 + C \times 0 + D = D.$$

Differentiating equation (10) gives $y'(t) = 3t + C$, so the second condition gives

$$4 = 3 \times 0 + C = C.$$

The condition $y'(0) = 4$ could also be written as $\dot{y}(0) = 4$ or as $\left.\dfrac{dy}{dt}\right|_{t=0} = 4$.

We conclude that the arbitrary constants have values $C = 4$ and $D = 100$. The required particular solution is therefore

$$y(t) = \tfrac{3}{2}t^2 + 4t + 100.$$

Differentiating this function gives the car's velocity as a function of time:

$$y'(t) = 3t + 4.$$

We obtain $y(10) = 290$ and $y'(10) = 34$. So at time 10 seconds, the car's position is 290 metres and its velocity is 34 metres per second.

The solution of second-order differential equations is rarely as easy as the solution of equation (9). In fact, the approach of repeated direct integration works only for equations of the form

$$\frac{d^2y}{dx^2} = f(x),$$

and requires that both integrations can be carried out.

Initial conditions and Newton's second law

You have seen that Newton's second law leads to second-order differential equations, and that the general solution of a second-order differential equation contains *two* arbitrary constants.

The need for two arbitrary constants connects to everyday experience. If you throw a stone upwards, and want to predict its future motion, it is not enough to know where the stone was released. You need to know both its initial position *and* its initial velocity. These two bits of information are sufficient to determine the two arbitrary constants in the general solution, and hence select a unique particular solution.

A single differential equation has a multitude of particular solutions, distinguished by different arbitrary constants. In the context of mechanics, this is a great unifying feature. We do not need different rules to explain the various motions of falling apples, cricket balls, asteroids or orbiting satellites. All these motions can be modelled by the same differential equation (obtained from Newton's second law and the law of gravitation). If the motions are different, it is because the initial conditions are different. In a nutshell: a differential equation provides unity, and initial conditions provide variety.

1.2 Linearity and superposition

This unit considers second-order differential equations that are *linear* and have *constant coefficients*. You met linear constant-coefficient equations in Unit 2 in the context of first-order differential equations. But what do the terms 'linear' and 'constant-coefficient' mean in the context of second-order equations? The answer lies in the following definitions.

Compare the definitions for first-order equations in Unit 2. The important feature is the *linear* combination of y and its derivatives on the left-hand side.

Definitions

- A second-order differential equation for $y = y(x)$ is **linear** if it can be expressed in the form

$$a(x) \frac{d^2 y}{dx^2} + b(x) \frac{dy}{dx} + c(x)\, y = f(x),$$

where $a(x)$, $b(x)$, $c(x)$ and $f(x)$ are given continuous functions, and $a(x)$ is not equal to the zero function.

- A linear second-order differential equation is said to be **constant-coefficient** if the functions $a(x)$, $b(x)$ and $c(x)$ are all constants, so that the equation is of the form

$$a \frac{d^2 y}{dx^2} + b \frac{dy}{dx} + cy = f(x), \tag{11}$$

where $a \neq 0$.

If $a = 0$, then the equation is first-order.

- A linear constant-coefficient second-order differential equation is said to be **homogeneous** if $f(x) = 0$ for all x, and **inhomogeneous** otherwise.

The term **non-homogeneous** is sometimes used instead of inhomogeneous.

Linear constant-coefficient second-order differential equations can be written in other ways. For example, we can divide equation (11) through by a to obtain an equation of the form

$$\frac{d^2y}{dx^2} + \beta\frac{dy}{dx} + \gamma y = \phi(x),$$

where β and γ are constants, and this more closely resembles the definition of linear first-order differential equations from Unit 2.

Exercise 1

Consider the following second-order differential equations.

(i) $\dfrac{d^2y}{dx^2} = x^2$ (ii) $3\dfrac{d^2y}{dx^2} + 4\dfrac{dy}{dx} + y = x^2$ (iii) $3\dfrac{d^2y}{dx^2} + 4\dfrac{dy}{dx} + y = 0$

(iv) $xy'' + x^2y = 0$ (v) $2y\dfrac{d^2y}{dx^2} + xy = 3\dfrac{dy}{dx}$ (vi) $2y\dfrac{d^2y}{dx^2} + 4y = 3\dfrac{dy}{dx}$

(vii) $2\dfrac{d^2t}{d\theta^2} + 3\dfrac{dt}{d\theta} + 4t = \sin\theta$ (viii) $\ddot{x} = -4t$ (ix) $\ddot{x} = -4x$

(a) For each equation, identify the dependent and independent variables.

(b) Which of the equations are linear?

(c) Which of the equations are linear and constant-coefficient?

(d) Which of the linear constant-coefficient equations are homogeneous?

The principle of superposition

We now introduce a key principle that will turn out to be extremely useful throughout this unit. The principle is a fundamental property of all linear differential equations, but we discuss it here in the context of linear constant-coefficient second-order equations.

Suppose that we have a solution $y_1(x)$ of the differential equation

$$a\frac{d^2y}{dx^2} + b\frac{dy}{dx} + cy = f_1(x),$$

and a solution $y_2(x)$ of the differential equation

$$a\frac{d^2y}{dx^2} + b\frac{dy}{dx} + cy = f_2(x).$$

In principle, the coefficients a, b and c could be functions of x, but our interest in this unit is confined to the case where they are constants.

Then the *principle of superposition* states that any linear combination $k_1\, y_1(x) + k_2\, y_2(x)$, where k_1 and k_2 are constants, is a solution of the differential equation

$$a\frac{d^2y}{dx^2} + b\frac{dy}{dx} + cy = k_1\, f_1(x) + k_2\, f_2(x). \tag{12}$$

It is not difficult to see why this is true. If we substitute $k_1 y_1 + k_2 y_2$ into the left-hand side of equation (12), we get

$$a\frac{d^2}{dx^2}(k_1 y_1 + k_2 y_2) + b\frac{d}{dx}(k_1 y_1 + k_2 y_2) + c(k_1 y_1 + k_2 y_2)$$

$$= a\left(k_1\frac{d^2 y_1}{dx^2} + k_2\frac{d^2 y_2}{dx^2}\right) + b\left(k_1\frac{dy_1}{dx} + k_2\frac{dy_2}{dx}\right) + c(k_1 y_1 + k_2 y_2)$$

$$= k_1\left(a\frac{d^2 y_1}{dx^2} + b\frac{dy_1}{dx} + cy_1\right) + k_2\left(a\frac{d^2 y_2}{dx^2} + b\frac{dy_2}{dx} + cy_2\right)$$

$$= k_1 f_1(x) + k_2 f_2(x),$$

as required.

This important result is summarised as follows.

The principle of superposition

If $y_1(x)$ is a solution of the linear second-order differential equation

$$a\frac{d^2 y}{dx^2} + b\frac{dy}{dx} + cy = f_1(x),$$

and $y_2(x)$ is a solution of the linear second-order differential equation

$$a\frac{d^2 y}{dx^2} + b\frac{dy}{dx} + cy = f_2(x)$$

(with the same left-hand side), then the function

$$y(x) = k_1\, y_1(x) + k_2\, y_2(x),$$

where k_1 and k_2 are any constants, is a solution of the differential equation

$$a\frac{d^2 y}{dx^2} + b\frac{dy}{dx} + cy = k_1\, f_1(x) + k_2\, f_2(x).$$

The power of this principle is obvious: it enables us to find new solutions by adding together existing ones.

An important special case arises when $f_1(x) = f_2(x) = 0$. In this case we see that if $y_1(x)$ and $y_2(x)$ are both solutions of the homogeneous equation

$$a\frac{d^2 y}{dx^2} + b\frac{dy}{dx} + cy = 0, \tag{13}$$

then any linear combination

$$y(x) = k_1\, y_1(x) + k_2\, y_2(x),$$

where k_1 and k_2 are constants, is also a solution of the *same* homogeneous equation (13).

A note on terminology

Like all human languages, the language of science and mathematics tends to evolve and fragment into dialects.

In physics, the *principle of superposition* is sometimes given a meaning that is slightly more restricted than that used here. It is said to apply when 'any linear combination of solutions of a given equation is also a solution of the *same* equation'. This restricted form of the principle applies to any homogeneous equation like (13), but not to inhomogeneous ones. You may meet this alternative usage in other Open University texts, but the more general form of the principle, as given in the box above, is what is needed in this unit.

2 Homogeneous differential equations

This section develops a method for finding the *general solutions* of *homogeneous* linear constant-coefficient second-order differential equations. Section 3 will consider the general solutions of inhomogeneous equations, and Section 4 will discuss how particular solutions are selected in given situations.

Before the method for homogeneous equations is described in detail, it is helpful to look at two simple cases.

2.1 Two simple cases

In this section, we return to the equation of motion of a simple harmonic oscillator. Before tackling this, however, we will solve the closely-related equation

$$\frac{d^2y}{dt^2} - \omega^2 y = 0, \tag{14}$$

where ω is a given positive constant. This differs from the equation for a simple harmonic oscillator only in the sign of the coefficient of y, which is negative in this case.

Our method of solution is very simple. We notice that a function $y = e^{\lambda t}$, where λ is any constant, can be differentiated, and then differentiated again, to give

$$\frac{dy}{dt} = \lambda e^{\lambda t} \quad \text{and} \quad \frac{d^2y}{dt^2} = \lambda^2 e^{\lambda t}.$$

If we substitute this function into the differential equation (14), we get

$$\lambda^2 e^{\lambda t} - \omega^2 e^{\lambda t} = 0.$$

The exponential factors can be cancelled (because they are never equal to zero) and we are left with a simple algebraic equation for λ:

$$\lambda^2 - \omega^2 = 0.$$

This equation has two solutions: $\lambda = \omega$ and $\lambda = -\omega$. So we have found two distinct solutions of equation (14), namely

$$y = e^{\omega t} \quad \text{and} \quad y = e^{-\omega t}.$$

The argument then goes as follows:

- The differential equation is homogeneous, so the principle of superposition guarantees that any linear combination of the solutions $y = e^{\omega t}$ and $y = e^{-\omega t}$ is also a solution of the differential equation. Hence the function

$$y(t) = Ce^{\omega t} + De^{-\omega t}, \tag{15}$$

  where C and D are arbitrary constants, satisfies equation (14).

- Then remember that the general solution of a second-order differential equation contains two arbitrary constants. The function $y(t) = Ce^{\omega t} + De^{-\omega t}$ satisfies the differential equation and contains two arbitrary constants. This means that it is the *general solution* of equation (14). The arbitrary constants could take any values, but if we want our solution to be real-valued, they must be real.

Now we consider the equation of motion of a simple harmonic oscillator, which can be written in the form (from equation (3))

$$\frac{d^2y}{dt^2} + \omega^2 y = 0, \tag{16}$$

where ω is a given positive constant.

The tactics for solving this equation are just the same. We try a solution of the form $e^{\lambda t}$, where λ is an undetermined constant. Substituting this into the differential equation, we obtain

$$\lambda^2 e^{\lambda t} + \omega^2 e^{\lambda t} = 0.$$

Then, cancelling the (non-zero) exponential factors, we get the algebraic equation

$$\lambda^2 + \omega^2 = 0.$$

The solutions of this equation are the complex numbers $\lambda = i\omega$ and $\lambda = -i\omega$, and corresponding to these we have two distinct solutions of equation (16):

$$y = e^{i\omega t} \quad \text{and} \quad y = e^{-i\omega t}.$$

Using the principle of superposition, and the fact that the general solution of a second-order differential equation contains two arbitrary constants, we can follow an argument like that given above to conclude that the general solution of equation (16) is

$$y(t) = Ae^{i\omega t} + Be^{-i\omega t}, \tag{17}$$

where A and B are arbitrary constants (which may be complex numbers in this case).

There is nothing wrong with this solution, but we can put it in a more familiar form by using Euler's formula

$$e^{ix} = \cos x + i \sin x.$$

Substituting $x = \omega t$ gives

$$e^{i\omega t} = \cos(\omega t) + i \sin(\omega t),$$

while substituting $x = -\omega t$ gives

$$e^{-i\omega t} = \cos(-\omega t) + i \sin(-\omega t) = \cos(\omega t) - i \sin(\omega t).$$

We therefore see that the general solution is

$$\begin{aligned} y(t) &= A e^{i\omega t} + B e^{-i\omega t} \\ &= A[\cos(\omega t) + i \sin(\omega t)] + B[\cos(\omega t) - i \sin(\omega t)] \\ &= (A + B)\cos(\omega t) + i(A - B)\sin(\omega t), \end{aligned}$$

and this can be expressed as

$$y(t) = C \cos(\omega t) + D \sin(\omega t), \tag{18}$$

where $C = A + B$ and $D = i(A - B)$ are arbitrary constants. If $y(t)$ is real, then the constants C and D are real-valued. In this case, the constants A and B are not real-valued, but that does not matter. The important thing is that we have obtained the general solution of equation (16) in the form of equation (18) and this, of course, agrees with the solution given in the Introduction.

2.2   Solution in the general case

The method just described works far more generally. Suppose that we wish to solve the differential equation

$$a \frac{d^2 y}{dx^2} + b \frac{dy}{dx} + cy = 0, \tag{19}$$

For variety, we use the symbol x for the independent variable.

where a, b and c are constants, with $a \neq 0$. This is the general form of a homogeneous linear second-order equation with constant coefficients.

Then we start by substituting the **trial solution**

$$y = e^{\lambda x},$$

where λ is an undetermined constant, into the differential equation. We have $dy/dx = \lambda e^{\lambda x}$ and $d^2y/dx^2 = \lambda^2 e^{\lambda x}$, so substituting $y = e^{\lambda t}$ into the left-hand side of equation (19) gives

$$\begin{aligned} a \frac{d^2 y}{dx^2} + b \frac{dy}{dx} + cy &= a\lambda^2 e^{\lambda x} + b\lambda e^{\lambda x} + c e^{\lambda x} \\ &= (a\lambda^2 + b\lambda + c)e^{\lambda x}. \end{aligned}$$

Hence $y = e^{\lambda x}$ is a solution of equation (19) provided that λ satisfies the quadratic equation

$$a\lambda^2 + b\lambda + c = 0. \tag{20}$$

This equation plays such an important role in solving linear constant-coefficient second-order differential equations that it is given a special name.

> **Definition**
>
> The **auxiliary equation** of the homogeneous linear constant-coefficient second-order differential equation
>
> $$a\frac{d^2y}{dx^2} + b\frac{dy}{dx} + cy = 0$$
>
> is the quadratic equation
>
> $$a\lambda^2 + b\lambda + c = 0.$$

There is no need to write down all the steps that led to the auxiliary equation. You can just use the rules that emerge from the calculation leading to equation (20): the auxiliary equation is obtained from the differential equation by

replacing $\dfrac{d^2y}{dx^2}$ by λ^2, $\dfrac{dy}{dx}$ by λ, and y by 1.

Example 2

Write down the auxiliary equation of the differential equation

$$3\frac{d^2y}{dx^2} - 2\frac{dy}{dx} + 4y = 0.$$

Solution

The auxiliary equation is

$$3\lambda^2 - 2\lambda + 4 = 0.$$

Exercise 2

Write down the auxiliary equation of each of the following differential equations.

(a) $\dfrac{d^2y}{dx^2} - 5\dfrac{dy}{dx} + 6y = 0$ (b) $y'' - 9y = 0$ (c) $\ddot{x} + 2\dot{x} = 0$

We know that $y = e^{\lambda x}$ is a solution of equation (19) provided that λ satisfies the corresponding auxiliary equation. But the auxiliary equation is a quadratic equation, so it has two roots, λ_1 and λ_2 say. For the moment, we assume that these are distinct: $\lambda_1 \neq \lambda_2$. Corresponding to these roots, there are two distinct solutions of differential equation (19):

$$y_1(x) = e^{\lambda_1 x} \quad \text{and} \quad y_2(x) = e^{\lambda_2 x}.$$

We now follow the logic of the preceding subsection. The principle of superposition implies that any linear combination of $y_1(x)$ and $y_2(x)$ satisfies the differential equation. It therefore follows that the function

$$y(x) = C\,y_1(x) + D\,y_2(x), \tag{21}$$

where C and D are arbitrary constants, satisfies the differential equation. This solution contains two arbitrary constants, as expected for the general solution of a second-order differential equation. We therefore conclude that equation (21) is the general solution of equation (19). This important result is summarised as a theorem.

Theorem 1 General solution of homogeneous equations

Given a homogeneous linear second-order differential equation

$$a\frac{d^2y}{dx^2} + b\frac{dy}{dx} + cy = 0,$$

with constant coefficients $a \neq 0$, b and c, the auxiliary equation is

$$a\lambda^2 + b\lambda + c = 0.$$

This usually has two distinct roots, λ_1 and λ_2, associated with two distinct solutions $y_1(x) = e^{\lambda_1 x}$ and $y_2(x) = e^{\lambda_2 x}$. Provided that the roots are distinct, the general solution of the differential equation is

$$y(x) = Ce^{\lambda_1 x} + De^{\lambda_2 x}, \tag{22}$$

where C and D are arbitrary constants.

The roots of the auxiliary equation are

$$\lambda_1 = \frac{-b + \sqrt{b^2 - 4ac}}{2a} \quad \text{and} \quad \lambda_2 = \frac{-b - \sqrt{b^2 - 4ac}}{2a}. \tag{23}$$

It does not matter which of the roots is called λ_1 and which is called λ_2.

Assuming that the coefficients a, b and c are real, there are three cases to consider, depending on the sign of the discriminant $b^2 - 4ac$:

- For $b^2 - 4ac > 0$, the roots are distinct and real.

- For $b^2 - 4ac < 0$, the roots are distinct and complex.

- For $b^2 - 4ac = 0$, the roots are equal and real.

We consider each of these cases in turn.

Distinct real roots

Example 3

(a) Write down the auxiliary equation of the differential equation

$$\frac{d^2y}{dx^2} - 3\frac{dy}{dx} + 2y = 0,$$

and find its roots λ_1 and λ_2.

(b) Use Theorem 1 to write down the general solution of the differential equation, and verify that your answer does satisfy the differential equation.

Solution

(a) The auxiliary equation is

$$\lambda^2 - 3\lambda + 2 = 0.$$

This equation may be solved, for example, by factorising it in the form

$$(\lambda - 1)(\lambda - 2) = 0,$$

to give the two roots $\lambda_1 = 1$ and $\lambda_2 = 2$.

Using the formula
$$\lambda_1, \lambda_2 = \frac{-b \pm \sqrt{b^2 - 4ac}}{2a}$$
produces the same answer.

(b) Since $\lambda_1 = 1$ and $\lambda_2 = 2$ are the roots of the auxiliary equation, the functions $y_1 = e^x$ and $y_2 = e^{2x}$ are solutions of the differential equation. Theorem 1 then shows that the general solution of the differential equation is

$$y(x) = C\,y_1(x) + D\,y_2(x)$$
$$= Ce^x + De^{2x},$$

where C and D are arbitrary constants.

To check that this function satisfies the differential equation, we differentiate it and then differentiate again, to get

$$\frac{dy}{dx} = Ce^x + 2De^{2x} \quad \text{and} \quad \frac{d^2y}{dx^2} = Ce^x + 4De^{2x}.$$

Substituting into the left-hand side of the differential equation then gives

$$\frac{d^2y}{dx^2} - 3\frac{dy}{dx} + 2y$$
$$= \left(Ce^x + 4De^{2x}\right) - 3\left(Ce^x + 2De^{2x}\right) + 2\left(Ce^x + De^{2x}\right)$$
$$= C(1 - 3 + 2)e^x + D(4 - 6 + 2)e^{2x}$$
$$= 0,$$

as required. Hence $y = Ce^x + De^{2x}$ is a solution of the differential equation, for all values of C and D.

Exercise 3

Use the auxiliary equation and Theorem 1 to find the general solution of each of the following differential equations.

(a) $\dfrac{d^2y}{dx^2} + 5\dfrac{dy}{dx} + 6y = 0$ (b) $2\dfrac{d^2y}{dx^2} + 3\dfrac{dy}{dx} = 0$ (c) $\dfrac{d^2z}{du^2} - 4z = 0$

Distinct complex conjugate roots

When the discriminant $b^2 - 4ac$ is negative, equations (23) produce two complex roots that are complex conjugates of one another:

$$\lambda_1 = \alpha + \beta i \quad \text{and} \quad \lambda_2 = \alpha - \beta i,$$

where α and β are real. The corresponding functions $y_1(x) = Ae^{\lambda_1 x}$ and $y_2(x) = Be^{\lambda_2 x}$ satisfy the differential equation, and the general solution takes the form

$$y(x) = Ae^{\lambda_1 x} + Be^{\lambda_2 x} = Ae^{(\alpha + \beta i)x} + Be^{(\alpha - \beta i)x}, \tag{24}$$

Recall that the complex conjugate of $\alpha + \beta i$ is $\alpha - \beta i$.

where A and B are arbitrary constants (which may be complex in this case). We usually need a real-valued solution, so it is best to express our result without using complex numbers. This can be achieved by first writing equation (24) as

$$\begin{aligned} y(x) &= Ae^{(\alpha + \beta i)x} + Be^{(\alpha - \beta i)x} \\ &= Ae^{\alpha x}e^{i\beta x} + Be^{\alpha x}e^{-i\beta x} \\ &= e^{\alpha x}\left(Ae^{i\beta x} + Be^{-i\beta x}\right). \end{aligned}$$

We can simplify this by using Euler's formula. Following the same argument as that which led to equation (18), but with βx in place of ωt, we conclude that

$$y(x) = e^{\alpha x}\left(C\cos(\beta x) + D\sin(\beta x)\right), \tag{25}$$

where $C = A + B$ and $D = i(A - B)$ are arbitrary constants. If the required solution is real-valued, then C and D are real-valued, and equation (25) is the most convenient form of the general solution.

Example 4

(a) Write down the auxiliary equation of the differential equation

$$\dfrac{d^2y}{dx^2} - 6\dfrac{dy}{dx} + 13y = 0,$$

and show that its roots are $\lambda_1 = 3 + 2i$ and $\lambda_2 = 3 - 2i$.

(b) Hence write down the general solution of the differential equation in terms of sines and cosines.

Solution

(a) The auxiliary equation is

$$\lambda^2 - 6\lambda + 13 = 0.$$

The standard formula for the roots of a quadratic gives

$$\lambda = \frac{6 \pm \sqrt{36 - 4 \times 1 \times 13}}{2} = \frac{6 \pm \sqrt{-16}}{2} = 3 \pm 2i,$$

so the two complex conjugate roots are $\lambda_1 = 3 + 2i$ and $\lambda_2 = 3 - 2i$.

(b) The roots are $\alpha \pm i\beta$, where $\alpha = 3$ and $\beta = 2$, so using equation (25), the general solution of the differential equation is

$$y(x) = e^{3x}(C \cos 2x + D \sin 2x),$$

where C and D are arbitrary constants.

Exercise 4

Use the auxiliary equation and Theorem 1 to find the general solution of each of the following differential equations.

(a) $\dfrac{d^2y}{dx^2} + 4\dfrac{dy}{dx} + 8y = 0$ (b) $\dfrac{d^2\theta}{dt^2} + 9\theta = 0$

Equal roots

There is a special case where the method based on Theorem 1 does not work. This is when the two roots of the auxiliary equation are *equal*.

To see what the problem is, suppose that we have two solutions $y_1(x)$ and $y_2(x)$ of a homogeneous linear second-order differential equation. Then the principle of superposition tells us that any linear combination

$$y(x) = C\,y_1(x) + D\,y_2(x) \tag{26}$$

is also a solution, and we have argued that this must be the general solution because it contains two arbitrary constants. But suppose that the functions $y_1(x)$ and $y_2(x)$ are constant multiples of one another, so that $y_2(x) = k\,y_1(x)$ for all x, where k is a constant. In this case, we can rewrite equation (26) as

$$y(x) = C\,y_1(x) + Dk\,y_1(x) = (C + kD)\,y_1(x),$$

which shows that there is really only one arbitrary constant, $A = C + kD$, in this case.

If two functions are constant multiples of one another, then they are said to be **linearly dependent**. In order for equation (26) to be the general solution of the homogeneous linear second-order differential equation, the functions y_1 and y_2 must *not* be constant multiples of one another; we say that they must be **linearly independent** solutions.

If both the roots of the auxiliary equation are equal to λ, then the function $y_1(x) = e^{\lambda x}$ provides one solution of the differential equation, but we still need another *linearly independent* solution in order to construct the general solution. Fortunately, there is a simple way of finding this extra solution, illustrated by the following example.

Example 5

(a) Write down the auxiliary equation of the differential equation

$$\frac{d^2y}{dx^2} + 6\frac{dy}{dx} + 9y = 0,$$

and find its roots.

(b) Deduce that $y_1 = e^{-3x}$ is a solution of the differential equation.

(c) By substituting into the differential equation, show that $y_2 = xe^{-3x}$ is also a solution.

(d) Deduce that $y = (C + Dx)e^{-3x}$ is a solution of the differential equation for any values of the constants C and D. Is this the general solution of the differential equation?

Solution

(a) The auxiliary equation is

$$\lambda^2 + 6\lambda + 9 = 0.$$

The left-hand side is the perfect square $(\lambda + 3)^2$, so the auxiliary equation has equal roots $\lambda_1 = \lambda_2 = -3$.

(b) Since $\lambda_1 = -3$ is a root of the auxiliary equation, $y_1 = e^{-3x}$ is a solution of the differential equation.

(c) To show that $y_2 = xe^{-3x}$ is a solution of the differential equation, we differentiate it twice and substitute into the differential equation. Differentiation gives

$$\frac{dy_2}{dx} = e^{-3x} + x(-3e^{-3x}) = (1 - 3x)e^{-3x},$$

Here we are using the product rule for differentiation.

$$\frac{d^2y_2}{dx^2} = -3e^{-3x} + (1 - 3x)(-3e^{-3x}) = (-6 + 9x)e^{-3x}.$$

Substituting these into the left-hand side of the differential equation then gives

$$\begin{aligned} \frac{d^2y_2}{dx^2} + 6\frac{dy_2}{dx} + 9y_2 &= (-6 + 9x)e^{-3x} + 6(1 - 3x)e^{-3x} + 9xe^{-3x} \\ &= (-6 + 6)e^{-3x} + (9 - 18 + 9)xe^{-3x} \\ &= 0. \end{aligned}$$

Hence $y_2 = xe^{-3x}$ is a solution of the differential equation.

(d) Since $y_1 = e^{-3x}$ and $y_2 = xe^{-3x}$ are both solutions of the same homogeneous differential equation, the principle of superposition tells us that

$$y = Ce^{-3x} + Dxe^{-3x} = (C + Dx)e^{-3x}$$

is also a solution of this equation for any values of C and D.

This solution contains two arbitrary constants C and D that cannot be combined because the functions e^{-3x} and xe^{-3x} are linearly independent (i.e. they are not constant multiples of one another). It is therefore the *general solution* of the differential equation.

If you want to prove this, you can substitute $y = xe^{\lambda x}$ into the left-hand side of equation (19), and use the fact that λ satisfies the auxiliary equation, with $\lambda = -b/2a$ for equal roots.

The method used in the above example always works when the auxiliary equation has equal roots. (The proof follows the same method as the example, but using symbols instead of numbers.) Thus whenever the auxiliary equation has equal roots $\lambda_1 = \lambda_2$, the *general solution* of the homogeneous equation is

$$y(x) = (C + Dx)e^{\lambda_1 x}, \tag{27}$$

where C and D are arbitrary constants.

Exercise 5

Use the auxiliary equation method to find the general solution of the following differential equations.

(a) $\dfrac{d^2 y}{dx^2} + 2\dfrac{dy}{dx} + y = 0$ (b) $\ddot{s} - 4\dot{s} + 4s = 0$

2.3 General procedure and further practice

We have now considered all the cases that can arise when solving a homogeneous linear second-order differential equation with constant coefficients. This subsection summarises the method of solution as a procedure, and gives exercises for further practice.

Procedure 1   General solution of a homogeneous linear constant-coefficient second-order differential equation

The general solution of the homogeneous linear constant-coefficient second-order differential equation

$$a\frac{d^2 y}{dx^2} + b\frac{dy}{dx} + cy = 0, \tag{Eq. 19}$$

where a, b, c are real constants with $a \neq 0$, may be found as follows.

1.   Write down the auxiliary equation

$$a\lambda^2 + b\lambda + c = 0, \tag{Eq. 20}$$

and find its roots λ_1 and λ_2.

---

2. (a) If the auxiliary equation has two distinct real roots λ_1 and λ_2, then the general solution is

$$y = Ce^{\lambda_1 x} + De^{\lambda_2 x}. \tag{Eq. 22}$$

(b) If the auxiliary equation has a pair of complex conjugate roots $\lambda_1 = \alpha + \beta i$ and $\lambda_2 = \alpha - \beta i$, then the general solution is

$$y = e^{\alpha x}(C \cos \beta x + D \sin \beta x). \tag{Eq. 25}$$

(c) If the auxiliary equation has two equal real roots $\lambda_1 = \lambda_2$, then the general solution is

$$y = (C + Dx)e^{\lambda_1 x}. \tag{Eq. 27}$$

In each of these cases, C and D are arbitrary constants.

Exercise 6

Use Procedure 1 to find the general solution of each of the following differential equations.

(a) $\dfrac{d^2 y}{dx^2} + 4y = 0$ (b) $\dfrac{d^2 y}{dx^2} - 9y = 0$

(c) $\dfrac{d^2 y}{dx^2} + 2\dfrac{dy}{dx} = 0$ (d) $\dfrac{d^2 y}{dx^2} - 2\dfrac{dy}{dx} + y = 0$

(e) $\dfrac{d^2 y}{dx^2} + 4\dfrac{dy}{dx} + 29y = 0$ (f) $u''(x) - 6u'(x) + 8u(x) = 0$

Exercise 7

(a) Write down the auxiliary equation of the differential equation

$$3\frac{dy}{dx} - y - 2\frac{d^2 y}{dx^2} = 0.$$

(b) Solve this auxiliary equation, and write down the general solution of the differential equation.

Exercise 8

Find the general solution of each of the following differential equations.

(a) $\dfrac{d^2 y}{dx^2} + 2\dfrac{dy}{dx} + 2y = 0$ (b) $\dfrac{d^2 y}{dx^2} - 16y = 0$

(c) $\dfrac{d^2 y}{dx^2} + 4y = 4\dfrac{dy}{dx}$ (d) $\dfrac{d^2 \theta}{dt^2} + 3\dfrac{d\theta}{dt} = 0$

Exercise 9

For which values of the constant k does the differential equation

$$\frac{d^2y}{dx^2} + 4k\frac{dy}{dx} + 4y = 0$$

have a general solution with oscillating behaviour, that is, a general solution which involves sines and cosines?

2.4 Damped harmonic oscillators

> Apart from equations (31) and (32), and the definitions of *amplitude, phase constant, angular frequency* and *period*, this subsection contains no new mathematical ideas, so if you are short of time, you may choose to read it quickly. However, many students find it invaluable to think about the solutions of differential equations in the context of real oscillating systems.

We consider again the *damped harmonic oscillator* that was discussed in the Introduction. This system was illustrated in Figure 1. It consists of an object of mass m that moves along the x-axis, with position $x(t)$ at time t. A spring exerts a force $-kx$ on the object, pulling it towards the equilibrium position $x = 0$. The object also experiences a damping (or frictional) force that is taken to be proportional to the object's velocity dx/dt. Under these circumstances, the object obeys the equation of motion given in equation (6). This is the homogeneous linear constant-coefficient differential equation

$$m\frac{d^2x}{dt^2} + \gamma\frac{dx}{dt} + kx = 0, \tag{28}$$

where m, k and γ are positive constants. The damped harmonic oscillator is a good model for vehicle suspension systems, but equations like (28) appear in many other contexts where oscillations occur.

Let us begin with the special case of no damping ($\gamma = 0$). Equation (28) then reduces to the equation of motion of a simple harmonic oscillator

$$\frac{d^2x}{dt^2} + \omega^2 x = 0,$$

where $\omega = \sqrt{k/m}$. You saw earlier that the general solution of this equation is

$$x(t) = C\cos(\omega t) + D\sin(\omega t), \tag{Eq. 18}$$

where C and D are arbitrary constants.

To interpret this solution, it is helpful to note that it can also be written as

$$x(t) = A\sin(\omega t + \phi), \tag{29}$$

where A and ϕ are arbitrary constants. To see why this works, expand the right-hand side of equation (29), to get

$$x(t) = A\sin(\omega t)\cos\phi + A\cos(\omega t)\sin\phi.$$

Then comparing with equation (18), we see that equation (29) is valid provided that

$$C = A\sin\phi \quad \text{and} \quad D = A\cos\phi. \tag{30}$$

Recall the trigonometric identity
$$\sin(A + B)$$
$$= \sin A\cos B + \cos A\sin B.$$

Squaring and adding these equations gives

$$C^2 + D^2 = A^2(\sin^2\phi + \cos^2\phi) = A^2,$$

so

$$A = \sqrt{C^2 + D^2}. \tag{31}$$

Dividing the first equation in (30) by the second, we also have

$$\frac{C}{D} = \frac{A\sin\phi}{A\cos\phi} = \tan\phi,$$

so

$$\phi = \arctan(C/D). \tag{32}$$

In equation (31) we have chosen the positive square root for A; this involves no loss of generality because $\sin(\omega t + \pi) = -\sin(\omega t)$, so increasing the value of ϕ by π is equivalent to reversing the sign of A. Values of ϕ that differ by an integer multiple of 2π correspond to the same motion, so we can restrict ϕ to a range such as $0 \leq \phi < 2\pi$.

Figure 4 shows a graph of the solution.

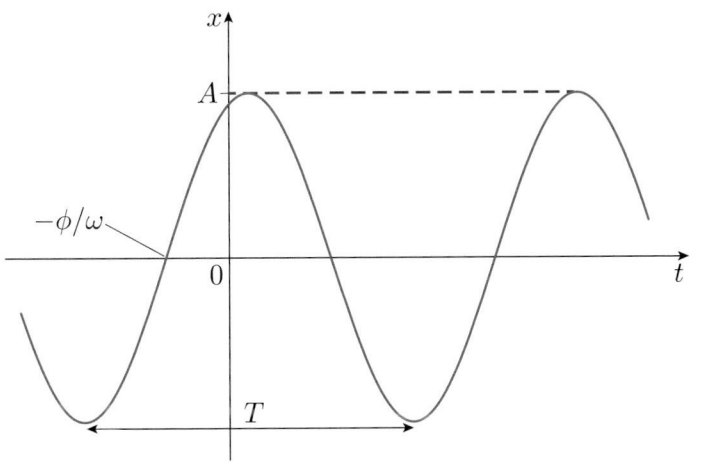

Figure 4   Simple harmonic motion with amplitude A, phase constant ϕ and period T

The constant $A \geq 0$ is the **amplitude** of the oscillation, which is the magnitude of the maximum displacement from the equilibrium position $x = 0$. The constant ϕ is called the **phase constant**. This is related to the time when the oscillator passes through the equilibrium position: according to equation (29), $x = 0$ at time $t = -\phi/\omega$. The oscillation consists of identical cycles, endlessly repeated. The time taken to complete one of these cycles is the **period** of the oscillation, and is given the symbol T. Because the sine function has period 2π, we have

$$\omega T = 2\pi$$

and so

$$T = \frac{2\pi}{\omega} = 2\pi\sqrt{\frac{m}{k}}.$$

As you might expect, the period is reduced if m is reduced (a lighter particle) or if k is increased (a stiffer spring). The quantity $1/T$ is called the **frequency** of the oscillation, and represents the number of cycles completed per unit time. The constant $\omega = 2\pi/T$ is called the **angular frequency**.

ω is sometimes called the **natural angular frequency**.

Now let us return to the case where damping is present ($\gamma > 0$). In this case, the relevant homogeneous differential equation is (28), which can be written more simply as

$$\frac{d^2x}{dt^2} + 2\Gamma\frac{dx}{dt} + \omega^2 x = 0, \tag{33}$$

where the **damping parameter** $\Gamma = \gamma/(2m)$ is a measure of the damping, and $\omega = \sqrt{k/m}$ is the angular frequency of the corresponding *undamped* oscillator. The corresponding auxiliary equation is

$$\lambda^2 + 2\Gamma\lambda + \omega^2 = 0, \tag{34}$$

and this has solutions

$$\lambda = -\Gamma \pm \sqrt{\Gamma^2 - \omega^2}. \tag{35}$$

Depending on the value of the discriminant $\Gamma^2 - \omega^2$, there are three different types of solution, which correspond to three different types of motion. These exemplify the three cases described in Subsection 2.2: distinct complex roots, distinct real roots and equal roots.

Underdamped motion: $\Gamma < \omega$

When $\Gamma < \omega$, the discriminant $\Gamma^2 - \omega^2$ is negative, and the roots of the auxiliary equation are complex numbers:

$$\lambda = -\Gamma \pm i\Omega, \quad \text{where } \Omega = \sqrt{\omega^2 - \Gamma^2}. \tag{36}$$

The general solution is therefore

$$x(t) = e^{-\Gamma t}\left[C\cos(\Omega t) + D\sin(\Omega t)\right], \tag{37}$$

where C and D are arbitrary constants. Transforming the term in square brackets, just as in equation (29), we can also write this as

$$x(t) = Ae^{-\Gamma t}\sin(\Omega t + \phi). \tag{38}$$

Figure 5 shows graphs of this function for different values of the arbitrary constants A and ϕ. (Section 4 will explain how these arbitrary constants can be determined from given initial conditions.)

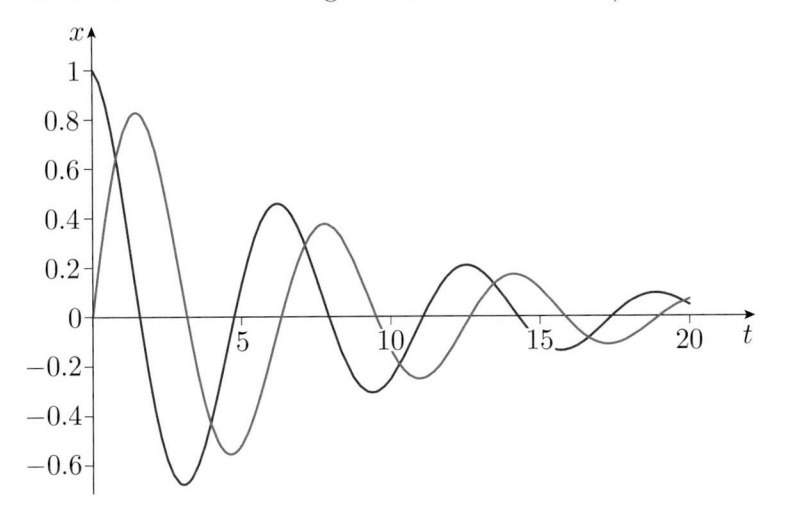

Figure 5   Two solutions for an underdamped harmonic oscillator with $\omega = 1$ and $\Gamma = 1/8$, corresponding to $A = 1$, $\phi = 0$ (orange curve) and $A = 1$, $\phi = \pi/2$ (purple curve)

This motion is called **underdamped** because the damping force is weak enough for the motion of the particle to oscillate to and fro. The angular frequency Ω of the damped oscillator is smaller than the angular frequency ω of the corresponding undamped oscillator (see equation (36)). Each cycle of the damped oscillator takes a period $T = 2\pi/\Omega$, which is longer than the period $2\pi/\omega$ of the corresponding simple harmonic oscillation, although this effect is slight if $\Gamma \ll \omega$. The amplitude of the damped oscillations is $Ae^{-\Gamma t}$, which decreases exponentially with time. In this context, Γ may be called the **decay constant**. If Γ approaches zero, the decay constant approaches zero and the angular frequency Ω approaches ω, so in this limit the system behaves like a simple harmonic oscillator.

Overdamped motion: $\Gamma > \omega$

When $\Gamma > \omega$, the discriminant $\Gamma^2 - \omega^2$ is positive, and the roots of the auxiliary equation are real negative numbers:

$$\lambda_1 = -\Gamma - \sqrt{\Gamma^2 - \omega^2} \quad \text{and} \quad \lambda_2 = -\Gamma + \sqrt{\Gamma^2 - \omega^2}.$$

In this case, the general solution of the homogeneous differential equation is

$$x(t) = Ce^{\lambda_1 t} + De^{-\lambda_2 t}, \tag{39}$$

where C and D are arbitrary constants. Figure 6 shows graphs of this function for different values of the arbitrary constants C and D.

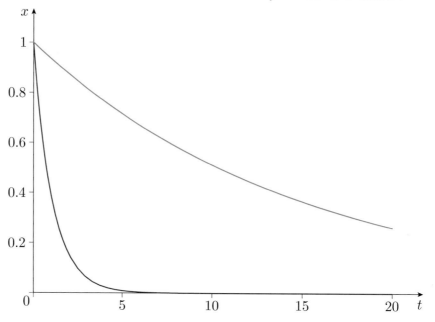

Figure 6   Two solutions for an overdamped harmonic oscillator with $\omega = 1/4$ and $\Gamma = 1/2$, corresponding to $C = 1$, $D = 0$ (orange curve) and $C = 0$, $D = 1$ (purple curve)

Because λ_1 and λ_2 are both negative, the solution dies away exponentially, and there are no oscillations. This motion is called **overdamped** because the damping force is strong enough to prevent oscillations. When Γ approaches ω from above, both roots approach the value Γ, and the solution is proportional to $e^{-\Gamma t}$.

Critically damped motion: $\Gamma = \omega$

When $\Gamma = \omega$, the discriminant $\Gamma^2 - \omega^2$ is equal to zero. In this case the general solution is

$$x(t) = (C + Dt)e^{-\Gamma t}, \tag{40}$$

where C and D are arbitrary constants. Figure 7 shows graphs of this function for different values of the arbitrary constants C and D.

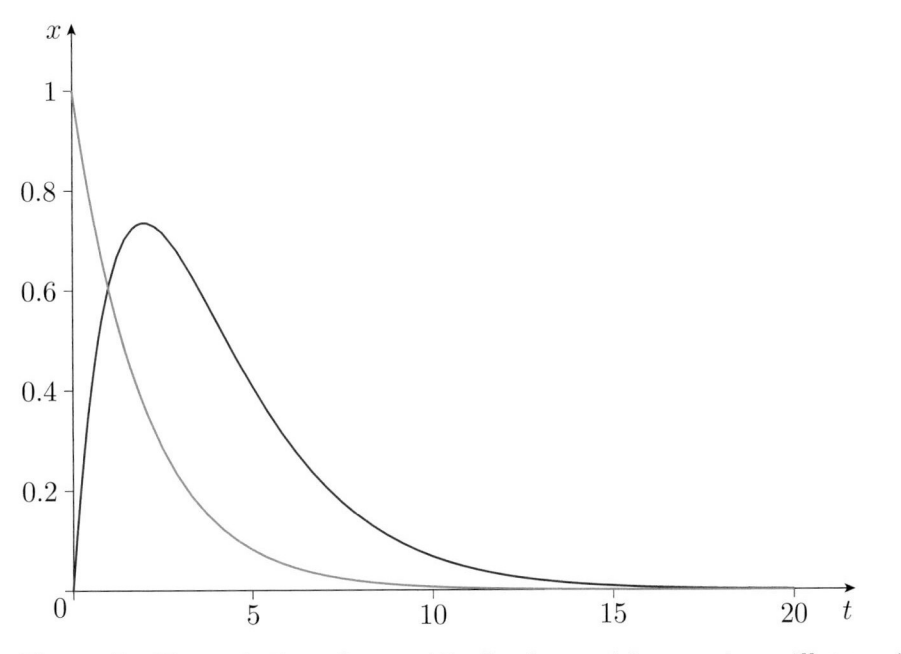

Figure 7   Two solutions for a critically damped harmonic oscillator with $\omega = \Gamma = 1/2$, corresponding to $C = 1$, $D = 0$ (orange curve) and $C = 0$, $D = 1$ (purple curve)

The motion is described as **critically damped**. A vehicle suspension system is usually set up to be close to critical damping, so that it is soft enough to move in response to a bumpy road, without allowing oscillations.

Exercise 10

Small oscillations of the pendulum shown in Figure 8 can be described by the homogeneous differential equation

$$m\frac{d^2\theta}{dt^2} + \gamma\frac{d\theta}{dt} + \frac{mg}{l}\theta = 0,$$

where m is the mass of the bob, l is the length of the string, g is the magnitude of the acceleration due to gravity, and γ is a damping constant. With mass measured in kilograms, length in metres and time in seconds, the values of these constants are $m = 0.80$, $l = 2.0$, $g = 9.8$ and $\gamma = 0.016$.

(a) Is this oscillation underdamped, overdamped or critically damped?

(b) What is the period of the oscillation?

(c) If the initial amplitude of the oscillation is $\theta = 0.20$ (in radians), what is the amplitude at $t = 100$?

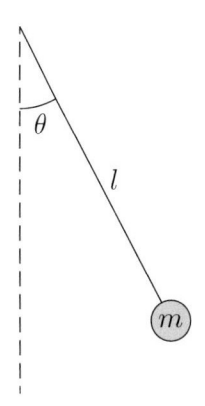

Figure 8   A pendulum

Exercise 11

A critically damped harmonic oscillator is described by the differential equation (28), with $m = 1$ and $k = 4$ (in suitable units). Determine the value of Γ in these units, and write down an expression for the general solution $x(t)$.

---

3 Inhomogeneous differential equations

3.1 General method of solution

Section 2 focused on finding the general solution of *homogeneous* linear constant-coefficient second-order differential equations. This section explains how to find the general solution of *inhomogeneous* linear constant-coefficient second-order differential equations – that is, equations of the form

$$a\frac{d^2y}{dx^2} + b\frac{dy}{dx} + cy = f(x),$$

where a, b, c are constants, with $a \neq 0$, and $f(x)$ is a given continuous function of x. The basic method for finding the general solution of such an equation depends on the principle of superposition, and is illustrated in the following example.

Example 6

Exercise 3(a) showed that the homogeneous equation

$$\frac{d^2y}{dx^2} + 5\frac{dy}{dx} + 6y = 0 \tag{41}$$

The notation $y_c(x)$ and $y_p(x)$ (see below) will be explained shortly.

has the general solution $y_c(x) = Ce^{-2x} + De^{-3x}$, where C and D are arbitrary constants.

Use this fact, together with the principle of superposition, to show that the inhomogeneous equation

$$\frac{d^2y}{dx^2} + 5\frac{dy}{dx} + 6y = 12 \tag{42}$$

has a solution $y(x) = Ce^{-2x} + De^{-3x} + 2$ for any C and D.

Solution

We can show that the constant function $y_p(x) = 2$ is a particular solution of the inhomogeneous equation by substituting it into the left-hand side. This gives

$$\frac{d^2y_p}{dx^2} + 5\frac{dy_p}{dx} + 6y_p = 0 + 5 \times 0 + 6 \times 2 = 12,$$

which is the same as the right-hand side, as required.

We know that $y_c(x) = Ce^{-2x} + De^{-3x}$ is a solution of equation (41) for any C and D, and $y_p(x) = 2$ is a solution of equation (42). The principle of superposition then tells us that $y_c(x) + y_p(x)$ is a solution of

$$\frac{d^2y}{dx^2} + 5\frac{dy}{dx} + 6y = 12 + 0 = 12,$$

which is identical to equation (42). Hence $y(x) = Ce^{-2x} + De^{-3x} + 2$ is a solution of equation (42) for any C and D.

The solution found in the example above contains two arbitrary constants, C and D (which appear as coefficients of two linearly independent functions, e^{-2x} and e^{-3x}). We expect the general solution of any second-order differential equation to contain two independent arbitrary constants, so $y(x) = Ce^{-2x} + De^{-3x} + 2$ is the general solution of equation (42). We will now generalise this idea, but first it is helpful to introduce some terminology.

Corresponding to the inhomogeneous equation (42), we have the homogeneous equation (41), obtained by replacing the function on the right-hand side by zero. This is called the *associated homogeneous equation*. The solutions y_c and y_p also have special names in this context: $y_c(x)$, the general solution of the associated homogeneous equation (41), is called the *complementary function*, and $y_p(x)$, a particular solution of the inhomogeneous equation (42), is called a *particular integral*.

Definitions

Let

$$a\frac{d^2y}{dx^2} + b\frac{dy}{dx} + cy = f(x) \tag{43}$$

be an inhomogeneous linear constant-coefficient second-order differential equation.

- Its **associated homogeneous equation** is

$$a\frac{d^2y}{dx^2} + b\frac{dy}{dx} + cy = 0. \tag{44}$$

- The general solution $y_c(x)$ of the associated homogeneous equation is known as the **complementary function** for the original inhomogeneous equation (43).

- Any particular solution $y_p(x)$ of the original inhomogeneous equation (43) is referred to as a **particular integral** for that equation.

The particular integral is not unique – many different choices can be made, but that does not matter. Suppose that y_{p_1} and y_{p_2} are two different particular integrals for equation (43). Then the principle of superposition tells us that $y_{p_2} - y_{p_1}$ is a solution of the equation

$$a\frac{d^2y}{dx^2} + b\frac{dy}{dx} + cy = f(x) - f(x) = 0,$$

which is the associated homogeneous equation (44). But we know that the general solution of this equation is given by the complementary function y_c, so it follows that $y_{p_2} - y_{p_1} = y_c$, or equivalently,

$$y_{p_2} = y_c + y_{p_1}.$$

The term *particular integral* is used here, rather than the term particular solution, which we reserve for a solution that contains definite numbers rather than arbitrary constants (see Section 4).

Since any solution can be written in this form, it follows that $y_c + y_{p_1}$ is the *general solution* of the inhomogeneous equation (43). We have therefore proved the following important result.

Theorem 2   General solution of an inhomogeneous equation

The **general solution** of a linear constant-coefficient second-order differential equation is given by

$$y(x) = y_c(x) + y_p(x),$$

where $y_c(x)$ is the complementary function (the general solution of the associated homogeneous equation) and $y_p(x)$ is a particular integral of the inhomogeneous equation.

Note that $y_c(x)$, being the general solution of the associated homogeneous equation, will contain *two* arbitrary constants, whereas $y_p(x)$, being a particular solution of equation (43), will contain none. You have already seen how to find the complementary function $y_c(x)$ in Subsection 2.2. There is no general recipe for finding a particular integral $y_p(x)$, but there are methods for 'guessing' a suitable solution, which work in most cases. The following example illustrates the general technique.

Example 7

Find the general solution of the differential equation

$$\frac{d^2y}{dx^2} + 9y = 9x + 9. \tag{45}$$

Solution

The associated homogeneous equation is

$$\frac{d^2y}{dx^2} + 9y = 0,$$

which has the general solution

$$y_c = C \cos 3x + D \sin 3x,$$

where C and D are arbitrary constants. This is the complementary function for equation (45).

A particular integral for equation (45) is

$$y_p = x + 1.$$

This may be verified by differentiation and substitution: $y_p'' = 0$, so substituting into the left-hand side of equation (45) gives

$$y_p'' + 9y_p = 0 + 9(x+1) = 9x + 9,$$

which is the same as the right-hand side of equation (45), as required.

See Exercise 4(b), although there different symbols are used for the variables.

You will see in the next subsection how to find such a particular integral.

The general solution of equation (45) is therefore, by Theorem 2,

$$y = y_c + y_p = C \cos 3x + D \sin 3x + x + 1,$$

where C and D are arbitrary constants.

The method of Example 7 may be summarised as follows.

Procedure 2   General solution of an inhomogeneous linear constant-coefficient second-order differential equation

The **general solution** of the inhomogeneous linear constant-coefficient second-order differential equation

$$a\frac{d^2y}{dx^2} + b\frac{dy}{dx} + cy = f(x)$$

is found as follows.

1. First find the complementary function $y_c(x)$, i.e. the general solution of the associated homogeneous equation

    $$a\frac{d^2y}{dx^2} + b\frac{dy}{dx} + cy = 0,$$

    using Procedure 1.

2. Then find a particular integral $y_p(x)$.

3. The general solution is then $y(x) = y_c(x) + y_p(x)$.

The reason why y_c is found first will become clear in Subsection 3.3.

It is worth noting that, by Theorem 2, *any* choice of particular integral in Procedure 2 gives the *same* general solution. Formulas obtained for the general solution may look different for different choices of particular integral, but they are in fact always equivalent. For example, in Example 7 the particular integral $y_p = x + 1$ was chosen, and the general solution was obtained as $y = C \cos 3x + D \sin 3x + x + 1$. It would have been equally valid to have chosen $y_p = x + 1 + \sin 3x$ as the particular integral. In that case, the general solution would have been obtained as $y = C \cos 3x + D \sin 3x + x + 1 + \sin 3x$. This form looks a little different, but it may be written as $y = C \cos 3x + (D + 1) \sin 3x + x + 1$; and since C and D are arbitrary constants, this form of the general solution represents exactly the same family of solutions.

Exercise 12

For each of the following differential equations:

*   Write down its associated homogeneous equation and its complementary function y_c.

*   Find a particular integral of the form $y_p = p$, where p is a constant.

*   Write down the general solution of the differential equation.

The complementary functions can be found from Exercise 6(a) and Example 3.

(a) $\dfrac{d^2y}{dx^2} + 4y = 8$ (b) $\dfrac{d^2y}{dx^2} - 3\dfrac{dy}{dx} + 2y = 6$

In Exercise 12, where the right-hand sides of the equations are constants, it is possible to find a particular integral almost 'by inspection'; but this method is generally inadequate. Fortunately, there exist procedures for finding a particular integral for equations involving wide classes of right-hand-side functions $f(x)$. The remainder of this section considers some of the simpler cases, where it is possible to determine the *general form* of a particular integral by inspection, although some manipulation is needed to determine the values of certain coefficients.

3.2   The method of undetermined coefficients

You have seen that the linear constant-coefficient second-order differential equation

$$a\frac{d^2y}{dx^2} + b\frac{dy}{dx} + cy = f(x) \qquad \text{(Eq. 43)}$$

has the general solution $y(x) = y_c(x) + y_p(x)$, where the complementary function $y_c(x)$ is found by solving the associated homogeneous equation, using Procedure 1. However, the methods for finding a particular integral $y_p(x)$ are another matter.

We can proceed by guessing that $y_p(x)$ takes some general form, called a **trial solution**, which involves one or more constants (or coefficients) whose values are initially undetermined. Then, by substituting the trial solution into the differential equation, we can hope to find the values of these coefficients, and hence find a particular integral. This is called the **method of undetermined coefficients**.

You saw an example of this method in Exercise 12. There the function $f(x)$ on the right-hand side of the differential equation is a *constant*, and the trial solution is taken to be of the form $y_p = p$, where p is an unknown constant, whose value is determined by substituting into the differential equation.

The choice of trial solution depends on the function $f(x)$ on the right-hand side of equation (43). We will look at three cases:

- polynomial functions
- functions with exponential behaviour
- sinusoidal functions.

When we have considered examples for each case, we will gather everything together as a general procedure. Bear in mind, though, that the method finds only a particular integral for the differential equation; to find the *general solution* you also need to find the complementary function and add this to the particular integral, according to Procedure 2.

Polynomial functions

If $f(x)$ is a given polynomial, we have

$$f(x) = m_n x^n + m_{n-1} x^{n-1} + \cdots + m_1 x + m_0,$$

where $m_0, m_1, \ldots, m_n$ are given constants. This class of functions includes constant functions ($n = 0$), linear functions ($n = 1$), quadratic functions ($n = 2$) and higher-order polynomials ($n \geq 3$).

Let us start by considering the case where $f(x)$ is a linear function (a polynomial of degree 1).

Example 8

Find a particular integral for

$$3\frac{d^2y}{dx^2} - 2\frac{dy}{dx} + y = 4x + 2.$$

Solution

We try a solution of the form

$$y = p_1 x + p_0,$$

where p_1 and p_0 are coefficients to be determined so that the differential equation is satisfied. To try this solution, we need the first and second derivatives of y:

$$\frac{dy}{dx} = p_1, \quad \frac{d^2y}{dx^2} = 0.$$

Substituting these into the left-hand side of the differential equation gives

$$3\frac{d^2y}{dx^2} - 2\frac{dy}{dx} + y = 3 \times 0 - 2p_1 + (p_1 x + p_0)$$
$$= p_1 x + (p_0 - 2p_1).$$

For $y = p_1 x + p_0$ to be a solution of the differential equation, we require that

$$p_1 x + (p_0 - 2p_1) = 4x + 2 \quad \text{for all } x. \tag{46}$$

To find the two unknown coefficients p_1 and p_0, we compare the coefficients on both sides of equation (46). Comparing the terms in x gives $p_1 = 4$. Comparing the constant terms gives $p_0 - 2p_1 = 2$, so $p_0 = 2 + 2p_1 = 2 + 2 \times 4 = 10$. Therefore we have the particular integral

$$y_p = 4x + 10.$$

Check: If $y_p = 4x + 10$, then $dy_p/dx = 4$, $d^2y_p/dx^2 = 0$, and substituting into the left-hand side of the differential equation gives

$$3\frac{d^2y_p}{dx^2} - 2\frac{dy_p}{dx} + y_p = 3 \times 0 - 2 \times 4 + (4x + 10) = 4x + 2,$$

as required.

For simplicity, we denote the trial solution by y, with no subscript p.

Notice that we can get two separate bits of information from the same equation because it applies for all x.

In the example above, the target function $f(x) = 4x + 2$ was a linear function, and the trial solution $p_1 x + p_0$ was also a linear function. When this trial solution was substituted into the left-hand side of the differential equation, it produced another linear function, $p_1 x + (p_0 - 2p_1)$, whose coefficients could be compared with those of the target function.

This is really the key to the method. The idea is to choose a trial solution that includes undetermined constants which, when substituted into the left-hand side of the differential equation, generates a function that can be compared directly with the target function $f(x)$, allowing the constants to be found.

This generally means that the trial solution should be chosen to belong to the same class of functions as $f(x)$ on the right-hand side of the equation. However, we must choose a trial solution that is general enough, so that its first and second derivatives also belong to the same class as the trial solution itself. This is illustrated in the following exercise.

Exercise 13

Use trial solutions of the form $y = p_1 x + p_0$ to find particular integrals for each of the following differential equations.

(a) $\dfrac{d^2 y}{dx^2} - 2\dfrac{dy}{dx} + 2y = 2x + 3$ (b) $\dfrac{d^2 y}{dx^2} + 2\dfrac{dy}{dx} + y = 2x$

Note that the trial solution $y = p_1 x + p_0$ was suggested in Exercise 13(b), even though $f(x)$ is just a multiple of x and contains no constant term. In fact, a trial solution of the form $p_1 x$ would not work in this case. The reason is that we need to take the first and second derivatives of the trial solution and substitute them into the differential equation. These derivatives must belong to the class encompassed by the trial solution. In this case, the first derivative of $p_1 x$ is the constant function p_1, so the trial solution must contain a constant term.

In general, the following advice can be given:

You saw examples of this in Exercise 12.

- If $f(x) = m_0$ is a constant function, then you should use a constant trial solution of the form $y = p_0$.

- If $f(x) = m_1 x + m_0$ is a linear function, then you should use a linear trial solution of the form $y = p_1 x + p_0$. Even if $m_0 = 0$, you should not initially assume that $p_0 = 0$.

- More generally, if $f(x) = m_n x^n + m_{n-1} x^{n-1} + \cdots + m_1 x + m_0$, where $m_n \neq 0$, then you should use a trial solution of the form $y = p_n x^n + p_{n-1} x^{n-1} + \cdots + p_1 x + p_0$. Even if some of the coefficients $m_0, m_1, \ldots, m_{n-1}$ are equal to zero, you should not initially assume that any of the coefficients $p_0, p_1, \ldots, p_n$ are equal to zero.

Exercise 14

Find a particular integral for

$$y'' - y = t^2.$$

Functions with exponential behaviour

Now let us suppose that the target function $f(x)$ on the right-hand side of the inhomogeneous equation takes the form $f(x) = me^{kx}$, where m and k are constants. In general, such functions are not *the* exponential function, but we can say that they exhibit **exponential behaviour**. The following example shows how to find a particular integral in such a case.

Example 9

Find a particular integral for

$$\frac{d^2y}{dx^2} + 9y = 2e^{3x}.$$

Solution

We try a solution of the form

$$y = pe^{3x},$$

where p is an undetermined coefficient that can be found by requiring that the differential equation is satisfied. Differentiating $y = pe^{3x}$ gives

$$\frac{dy}{dx} = 3pe^{3x}, \quad \frac{d^2y}{dx^2} = 9pe^{3x}.$$

Since the derivative of e^{3x} is $3e^{3x}$, the exponent $(3x)$ appearing in $y(x)$ should be the same as that appearing in $f(x)$, then only the coefficient p is to be determined.

Substituting these into the left-hand side of the differential equation gives

$$\frac{d^2y}{dx^2} + 9y = 9pe^{3x} + 9pe^{3x} = 18pe^{3x}.$$

Therefore, for $y = pe^{3x}$ to be a solution of the differential equation, we require that $18pe^{3x} = 2e^{3x}$ for all x. Hence $p = \frac{1}{9}$, and

$$y_{\mathrm{p}} = \tfrac{1}{9}e^{3x}$$

is a particular integral for the given differential equation.

The general rule is as follows: when $f(x) = me^{kx}$, we use a trial solution of the form $y(x) = pe^{kx}$, where p is an undetermined constant. The value of k in $y(x)$ is the same as in $f(x)$.

Exercise 15

Find a particular integral for

$$2\frac{d^2y}{dx^2} - 2\frac{dy}{dx} + y = 2e^{-x}.$$

Sinusoidal functions

Finally, let us suppose that the target function $f(x)$ on the right-hand side of the inhomogeneous equation takes the form

$$f(x) = m \cos kx + n \sin kx,$$

where m, n and k are constants. Any such function is said to be **sinusoidal**. In this case, the appropriate trial solution is

$$y(x) = p \cos kx + q \sin kx,$$

where p and q are undetermined constants. Following earlier ideas, the trial solution must be general enough to be in the same class as its first and second derivatives. So even if $f(x)$ contains only a sine or only a cosine, the trial solution $y(x)$ must contain both a sine and a cosine. However, the value of the constant k in $y(x)$ should always be the same as that in $f(x)$.

Example 10

Find a particular integral for

$$\frac{d^2y}{dx^2} + 2\frac{dy}{dx} + 2y = 10 \sin 2x.$$

Solution

We try a solution of the form

$$y = p \cos 2x + q \sin 2x,$$

where p and q are coefficients whose values are to be found by substituting into the differential equation. Differentiating y gives

$$\frac{dy}{dx} = -2p \sin 2x + 2q \cos 2x, \quad \frac{d^2y}{dx^2} = -4p \cos 2x - 4q \sin 2x.$$

Substituting these into the left-hand side of the differential equation gives

$$\frac{d^2y}{dx^2} + 2\frac{dy}{dx} + 2y = (-4p \cos 2x - 4q \sin 2x) + 2(-2p \sin 2x + 2q \cos 2x)$$
$$+ 2(p \cos 2x + q \sin 2x)$$
$$= (-2p + 4q) \cos 2x + (-4p - 2q) \sin 2x.$$

This can be equated to the right-hand side of the differential equation, so

$$(-2p + 4q) \cos 2x + (-4p - 2q) \sin 2x = 10 \sin 2x \quad \text{for all } x. \tag{47}$$

Comparing coefficients works because the cos and sin functions are linearly independent. To find p and q, we compare the coefficients of cos and sin on both sides of equation (47). For this equation to be true for all x, we must have

$$-2p + 4q = 0 \quad \text{and} \quad -4p - 2q = 10.$$

Solving these simultaneous equations, we conclude that $p = -2$, $q = -1$, so

$$y_\text{p}(x) = -2 \cos 2x - \sin 2x$$

is a particular integral for the given differential equation.

Exercise 16

Find a particular integral for

$$\frac{d^2y}{dt^2} - \frac{dy}{dt} = \cos 3t + \sin 3t.$$

The following procedure summarises the results of this subsection.

Procedure 3   Method of undetermined coefficients

To find a **particular integral** for the inhomogeneous linear constant-coefficient second-order differential equation

$$a\frac{d^2y}{dx^2} + b\frac{dy}{dx} + cy = f(x),$$

use a trial solution $y(x)$ with a form similar to that of $f(x)$. The following table gives appropriate trial solutions for simple cases.

Target function $f(x)$	Trial solution $y(x)$
$m_n x^n + m_{n-1}x^{n-1} + \cdots$ $+ m_1 x + m_0$	$p_n x^n + p_{n-1}x^{n-1} + \cdots$ $+ p_1 x + p_0$
me^{kx}	pe^{kx}
$m\cos kx + n\sin kx$	$p\cos kx + q\sin kx$

There are exceptional cases where these trial solutions do not work; see Subsection 3.3.

The full trial solutions in the right-hand column should be used even when some of the coefficients in $f(x)$ are missing (as in $m_2 x^2$ or $m\cos kx$, for example).

To determine the coefficients in $y(x)$, differentiate it twice, substitute into the left-hand side of the differential equation, and equate coefficients of corresponding terms.

Exercise 17

What form of trial solution y should you use in order to find a particular integral for each of the following differential equations?

(a) $\dfrac{d^2y}{dx^2} - y = e^{3x}$ (b) $\dfrac{d^2y}{dx^2} + 2\dfrac{dy}{dx} - 4y = \sin 3x$

In this question, you need not *find* the particular integrals.

To round off this discussion of inhomogeneous differential equations, the following exercise gives a variety of equations for further practice.

See Exercise 6(a) and
Exercise 3(c).

Exercise 18

Find the general solutions of the following differential equations.

The complementary functions of the differential equations in parts (a) and (c) are $C \cos 2t + D \sin 2t$ and $Ce^{-2x} + De^{2x}$, respectively.

(a) $\dfrac{d^2\theta}{dt^2} + 4\theta = 2t$

(b) $\dfrac{d^2y}{dx^2} + 4y = 10 \sin 3x$

(c) $\dfrac{d^2y}{dx^2} - 4y = 15e^{-x}$

3.3 Exceptional cases

There are some exceptional cases for which Procedure 3 fails. You will not encounter these exceptions in assignments or in the exam, but it is useful to have some idea of what can go wrong, and how a particular integral can be found under such circumstances.

To take a definite case, consider the differential equation

$$\frac{d^2y}{dx^2} - 4y = 2e^{2x}. \tag{48}$$

The associated homogeneous equation is

$$\frac{d^2y}{dx^2} - 4y = 0,$$

See Exercise 3(c).

and this has general solution $y = Ce^{-2x} + De^{2x}$. The difficulty is now apparent. Procedure 3 suggests that we use the trial solution $y = pe^{2x}$, but this happens to be a solution of the associated homogeneous equation (with $C = 0$, $D = p$), so substituting $y = pe^{2x}$ into the left-hand side of equation (48) gives zero for any value of p, and this cannot be equal to the non-zero right-hand side.

Difficulties like this are generally overcome by multiplying whichever trial solution is suggested in Procedure 3 by the independent variable, x. So the trial solution to use for equation (48) would be

$$y = pxe^{2x}.$$

Calculating the derivatives of this function, we get

$$\frac{dy}{dx} = pe^{2x} + 2pxe^{2x} = p(1 + 2x)e^{2x},$$

$$\frac{d^2y}{dx^2} = 2pe^{2x} + 2p(1 + 2x)e^{2x} = 4p(1 + x)e^{2x}.$$

Substituting these into the left-hand side of the differential equation gives

$$\frac{d^2y}{dx^2} - 4y = 4p(1 + x)e^{2x} - 4pxe^{2x} = 4pe^{2x}.$$

Therefore $y = pxe^{2x}$ is a solution of the differential equation provided that $4pe^{2x} = 2e^{2x}$ for all x. Hence $p = \frac{1}{2}$, and

$$y_p = \tfrac{1}{2}xe^{2x}$$

is a particular integral for differential equation (48).

A similar technique works when the inhomogeneous term is a constant, as illustrated in the following example.

Example 11

The motion of a small ball bearing dropped into viscous oil can be modelled by the differential equation

$$m\ddot{x} + r\dot{x} - mg = 0,$$

where m is the mass of the ball, r is a constant related to the viscosity of the oil, g is the magnitude of the acceleration due to gravity, and x is the vertical distance from the point of release.

(a) Find the general solution $x(t)$ of this differential equation.

(b) Use your answer to part (a) to show that the velocity of the ball approaches the limiting value mg/r as t becomes very large.

Solution

(a) The inhomogeneous equation is

$$m\ddot{x} + r\dot{x} = mg,$$

and the auxiliary equation for the associated homogeneous equation is

$$m\lambda^2 + r\lambda = 0.$$

This has solutions $\lambda = 0$ and $\lambda = -r/m$, so the complementary function is

$$x_c = C + De^{-rt/m}.$$

The inhomogeneous term is the constant function mg, so Procedure 3 suggests a trial solution $x = p_0$. However, this is a solution of the associated homogeneous equation (with $C = p_0$, $D = 0$). Hence we try $x = p_0 t$ instead. Differentiating and substituting gives

$$rp_0 = mg,$$

so

$$p_0 = \frac{mg}{r}.$$

Hence a particular integral is

$$x_p = \frac{mgt}{r},$$

and the general solution is

$$x(t) = C + De^{-rt/m} + \frac{mgt}{r},$$

where C and D are arbitrary constants.

(b) The velocity is

$$\dot{x} = -\frac{Dr}{m} e^{-rt/m} + \frac{mg}{r}.$$

This approaches the limiting value mg/r as $t \to \infty$.

This answer can also be obtained directly from the differential equation. If the velocity tends towards a constant value, the acceleration $\ddot{x}$ approaches zero, and the differential equation itself tells us that $\dot{x}$ tends to mg/r.

3.4 Combined cases

Another situation that crops up occasionally is when the inhomogeneous term is a linear combination of polynomial, sinusoidal and exponential functions. You know what to do when the inhomogeneous term is $x + 1$, and you also know what to do if it is e^{2x}, but what if the inhomogeneous term is $2e^{2x} + 18(x + 1)$? The secret is to use the principle of superposition to split the problem into smaller tasks. Again, we include this topic for interest and completeness: assignments and the exam will not contain questions on such combined cases.

Example 12

Find a particular integral for

$$\frac{d^2y}{dx^2} + 9y = 2e^{3x} + 18x + 18. \tag{49}$$

Solution

In Example 9 (Subsection 3.2), you saw that $y_\text{p} = \frac{1}{9}e^{3x}$ is a particular integral for

$$\frac{d^2y}{dx^2} + 9y = 2e^{3x}.$$

In Example 7 (Subsection 3.1), you saw that $y_\text{p} = x + 1$ is a particular integral for

$$\frac{d^2y}{dx^2} + 9y = 9x + 9.$$

Therefore, by the principle of superposition, a particular integral for equation (49) is

$$y_\text{p} = \tfrac{1}{9}e^{3x} + 2(x + 1) = \tfrac{1}{9}e^{3x} + 2x + 2.$$

This approach can be used more generally. To find a particular integral for

$$a\frac{d^2y}{dx^2} + b\frac{dy}{dx} + cy = k_1\, f_1(x) + k_2\, f_2(x), \tag{50}$$

where k_1 and k_2 are constants, we can split the task up – finding the particular integral $g_1(x)$ that applies when just $f_1(x)$ is on the right-hand side, and the particular integral $g_2(x)$ that applies when just $f_2(x)$ is on the right-hand side. The principle of superposition then tells us that $k_1\, g_1(x) + k_2\, g_2(x)$ is a particular integral for equation (50).

Exercise 19

Find a particular integral for the differential equation

$$2\frac{d^2x}{dt^2} + 3\frac{dx}{dt} + 2x = 12\cos 2t + 10.$$

(Neither of the terms on the right-hand side satisfies the associated homogeneous equation, so this is not an exceptional case.)

Exercise 20

Find the general solutions of the following differential equations (starting from scratch with no complementary functions given).

(a) $u''(t) + 4u'(t) + 5u(t) = 5$ (b) $3\frac{d^2y}{dx^2} - 2\frac{dy}{dx} - y = e^{2x}$

4 Initial conditions and boundary conditions

In Sections 2 and 3 you saw how to find the general solution of a homogeneous or inhomogeneous linear constant-coefficient second-order differential equation. In practice, however, we usually need to select a *particular solution* that satisfies certain additional conditions. This section explains how this is done.

In Unit 2 you saw that the general solution of a first-order differential equation contains *one* arbitrary constant, and that a single additional condition (called an initial condition) is enough to fix the value of this constant and hence determine the particular solution. In the case of a second-order differential equation, the general solution contains *two* arbitrary constants, and *two* additional conditions are required.

There are two types of additional conditions for second-order differential equations: *initial conditions* and *boundary conditions*. Problems involving such conditions are called *initial-value problems* and *boundary-value problems*, respectively, and are discussed in Subsections 4.1 and 4.2.

4.1 Initial-value problems

For a first-order differential equation, an initial condition is one that specifies the value of the dependent variable ($y = a$, say) at a given value of the independent variable ($t = t_0$); this is often written in the form $y(t_0) = a$.

For a second-order differential equation, the initial conditions specify the value of the dependent variable ($y = a$) *and* the value of its derivative ($dy/dy = b$), for the *same* given value of the independent variable ($t = t_0$), and they are often written in the form $y(t_0) = a$, $y'(t_0) = b$.

Very often, t_0 represents the initial time when a system is released and we are interested in the subsequent motion. But this is not essential; we could equally well be interested in the prior motion that leads up to given values of x and dx/dt at some final time t_0. Indeed, initial values may have nothing to do with time at all if the independent variable represents some other quantity such as position. The only essential point is that values of the dependent variable and its derivative must both be given at the *same* value of the independent variable.

Initial conditions arise naturally in many mechanical problems, where the initial values of the position x and velocity dx/dt are often specified. For example, we may know that a ball is thrown vertically upwards, at $t = 0$, from an initial position with an initial velocity.

The pendulum in Figure 9 gives another example. When the string of the pendulum makes its greatest angle θ_0 with the vertical, the pendulum changes its direction of swing and comes momentarily to rest. So if the pendulum changes direction at $t = t_0$, we have the initial conditions $\theta = \theta_0$ and $d\theta/dt = 0$ when $t = t_0$.

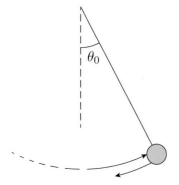

Figure 9 Possible initial conditions for a pendulum

Definitions

- **Initial conditions** associated with a second-order differential equation with dependent variable y and independent variable x specify that y and dy/dx take values a and b, respectively, when x takes the value x_0. These conditions can be written as

$$y = a \text{ and } \frac{dy}{dx} = b \text{ when } x = x_0$$

  or as

$$y(x_0) = a, \quad y'(x_0) = b.$$

  The numbers x_0, a and b are often referred to as **initial values**.

- The combination of a second-order differential equation and initial conditions is called an **initial-value problem**.

The following example shows how initial conditions can be used to find the two arbitrary constants in the general solution, and hence determine a particular solution of a second-order differential equation.

Example 13

The general solution of the differential equation

$$\frac{d^2y}{dx^2} - 3\frac{dy}{dx} + 2y = 0$$

is

$$y = Ce^x + De^{2x}, \tag{51}$$

where C and D are arbitrary constants (see Example 3). Find the particular solution that satisfies the initial conditions $y = 0$ and $dy/dx = 1$ when $x = 0$.

Solution

One of the initial conditions involves dy/dx, so we take the derivative of the general solution (51), getting

$$\frac{dy}{dx} = Ce^x + 2De^{2x}. \tag{52}$$

The initial conditions state that $y(0) = 0$, $y'(0) = 1$. Substituting $x = 0$, $y = 0$ into equation (51) gives

$$0 = Ce^0 + De^0 = C + D,$$

while substituting $x = 0$, $dy/dx = 1$ into equation (52) gives

$$1 = Ce^0 + 2De^0 = C + 2D.$$

Solving these equations gives $C = -1$, $D = 1$, so the required particular solution is

$$y = -e^x + e^{2x}.$$

Note that when you are checking a particular solution, you should check that it satisfies the initial or boundary conditions as well as the differential equation.

All the initial-value problems that you will meet in this module have *unique* solutions, so if you can find a solution that satisfies the initial conditions, then this is *the* solution.

Exercise 21

Solve the following initial-value problems.

(a) The general solution of $u''(t) + 9u(t) = 0$ is $u = C\cos 3t + D\sin 3t$, where C and D are arbitrary constants (see Exercise 4(b)). Find the particular solution that satisfies the initial conditions $u\left(\frac{\pi}{2}\right) = 0$, $u'\left(\frac{\pi}{2}\right) = 1$.

(b) The general solution of $u''(t) + 4u'(t) + 5u(t) = 5$ is $u = e^{-2t}(C\cos t + D\sin t) + 1$, where C and D are arbitrary constants (see Exercise 20(a)). Find the particular solution that satisfies the initial conditions $u(0) = 3$, $u'(0) = 1$.

4.2   Boundary-value problems

In initial-value problems, the two conditions used to select a particular solution both refer to the *same* value of the independent variable. But this need not be the case. If the independent variable is x, then we could have one condition for $x = x_1$ and another for $x = x_2$, say. Such conditions are called *boundary conditions*. Later in the module (Unit 12) you will meet equations called *partial differential equations* which explain a vast range of phenomena; in many cases, these equations lead to second-order differential equations supplemented by boundary conditions.

Boundary conditions arise, for example, in considering the shape of a chain of length L that is suspended between two points, with heights h_1 and h_2 (see Figure 10). If $y(x)$ is the height of the chain at a horizontal distance x from an origin, then the equation for $y(x)$ has to satisfy two boundary conditions: $y(x_1) = h_1$ and $y(x_2) = h_2$. This pair of boundary conditions gives the value of y at two different points. In other contexts, each boundary condition could specify the value of either y or dy/dx (or even a relationship between them).

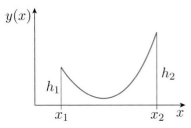

Figure 10   Finding the shape of a hanging chain with fixed ends

The conditions are called 'boundary' conditions because (as in the chain example) they often refer to conditions at the endpoints x_1 and x_2 of an interval in which we want to explore the solutions of a differential equation. (This is not essential, however.)

> **Definitions**
>
> Consider a second-order differential equation with dependent variable y and independent variable x.
>
> - **Boundary conditions** associated with such an equation specify the values of y (or dy/dx, or some combination of y and dy/dx) at two *different* values of x. For example, they could specify that $y(x_1) = y_1$ and $y(x_2) = y_2$. The numbers x_1, x_2, y_1 and y_2 are often referred to as **boundary values**.
>
> - The combination of a second-order differential equation and boundary conditions is called a **boundary-value problem**.

The following example shows how boundary conditions can be used to find values for the two arbitrary constants that appear in the general solution of a second-order differential equation, and hence find a particular solution.

Example 14

The differential equation

$$\frac{d^2y}{dx^2} + 9y = 0$$

has general solution

$$y = C\cos 3x + D\sin 3x, \tag{53}$$

where C and D are arbitrary constants (see Exercise 4(b)). Find the particular solution that satisfies the boundary conditions $y = 0$ when $x = 0$ and $dy/dx = 1$ when $x = \frac{\pi}{3}$.

Solution

One of the boundary conditions involves dy/dx, so we need the derivative of the general solution (53):

$$\frac{dy}{dx} = -3C \sin 3x + 3D \cos 3x. \tag{54}$$

The boundary conditions state that $y(0) = 0$, $y'\left(\frac{\pi}{3}\right) = 1$. Substituting $x = 0$, $y = 0$ into equation (53) gives

$$0 = C \cos 0 + D \sin 0 = C,$$

so $C = 0$. Substituting $x = \frac{\pi}{3}$, $y' = 1$ and $C = 0$ into equation (54) gives

$$1 = 3D \cos \pi = -3D.$$

Therefore $C = 0$ and $D = -\frac{1}{3}$, so the required particular solution is

$$y = -\frac{1}{3} \sin(3x).$$

Unlike initial-value problems, some boundary-value problems may have *no solutions* even when the differential equation is linear and constant-coefficient, and has a continuous function on the right-hand side. The following example illustrates this point.

Example 15

The differential equation

$$\frac{d^2y}{dx^2} + 4y = 0$$

has general solution $y = C \cos 2x + D \sin 2x$, where C and D are arbitrary constants (see Exercise 6(a)). Try to find a solution to the boundary-value problem based on this differential equation and the boundary conditions $y(0) = 0$, $y\left(\frac{\pi}{2}\right) = 1$.

Solution

Substituting each of the boundary conditions into the general solution in turn gives

$$0 = C \cos 0 + D \sin 0 = C,$$
$$1 = C \cos \pi + D \sin \pi = -C.$$

There is no solution for which $C = 0$ and $C = -1$, so there is no solution of the differential equation that satisfies the given boundary conditions.

An outcome of 'no solution' need not be unreasonable. If a physical system obeys a differential equation, and there is no solution consistent with a given set of boundary conditions, then those boundary conditions must be unrealistic. For example, the chain in Figure 10 cannot hang from points that are further apart than its fixed length.

It is also possible for boundary-value problems to have solutions that are *not unique*, as the following important example illustrates.

Example 16

At a given moment in time, the displacement y of an oscillating guitar string at a distance x from one of its ends satisfies the differential equation

$$\frac{d^2y}{dx^2} + k^2y = 0$$

for a fixed constant k, which is proportional to the frequency of the oscillation (i.e. the pitch of sound produced). The string is held fixed at its ends, $x = 0$ and $x = L$, so that $y(x)$ satisfies the boundary conditions $y(0) = 0$ and $y(L) = 0$. Find the possible solutions to this boundary-value problem, and show that solutions can be found only if $k = \pi n/L$, where n is an integer.

Solution

The general solution of the differential equation is

$$y(x) = A\sin(kx) + B\cos(kx),$$

where A and B are arbitrary constants.

The boundary condition $y(0) = 0$ implies that $B = 0$, so $y(x) = A\sin(kx)$. In order to satisfy the boundary condition $y(L) = 0$, we must have $A\sin(kL) = 0$. This equation has the trivial solution $A = 0$, which corresponds to $y(x) = 0$. For $A \neq 0$, it gives the condition $\sin(kL) = 0$, which implies that $kL = n\pi$, where n is an integer. Hence $k = n\pi/L$ and we conclude that the displacement of the guitar string must be of the form

$$y(x) = A\sin\left(\frac{n\pi x}{L}\right). \tag{55}$$

When considering the possible sinusoidal shapes adopted by an oscillating guitar string, we can restrict n to the positive integers $n = 1, 2, 3, \ldots$. This is because $A\sin(-n\pi x/L) = -A\sin(n\pi x/L)$, so changing the sign of n is equivalent to changing the sign of A. The value $n = 0$ can also be omitted, because it is equivalent to taking $A = 0$.

Motions with different values of n are said to be different **modes of oscillation** of the string. The first three modes of oscillation are shown schematically in Figure 11; in each case, the largest excursions of the string from the equilibrium $y = 0$ position are indicated.

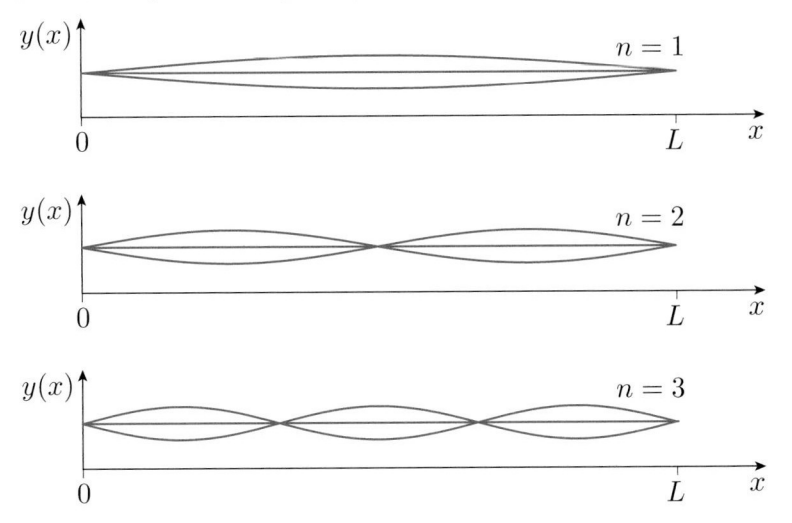

Figure 11 The first three modes of oscillation of a guitar string. These modes produce sounds of different pitches.

The fact that there are many different solutions satisfying the boundary conditions should not alarm you. This just means that the boundary conditions restrict the possible solutions, but extra information (in the form of initial conditions telling us how the guitar string is released) is needed to determine the precise motion that arises in a given situation.

Partial differential equations

The boundary conditions allow us to identify the possible modes, but further information is needed to predict the actual motion of the string. You will see how this works in Unit 12, when we discuss a more general type of differential equation, called a *partial differential equation*. The process of solving a partial differential equation often leads to a boundary-value problem for a second-order differential equation, and this is the main reason why boundary-value problems are important in physics and engineering.

An example arises in quantum mechanics, which can give rise to a differential equation very like that for a vibrating string. In this context, the fact that the constant k takes discrete values corresponds to the fact that the system has discrete energy levels, a phenomenon called the *quantisation of energy*.

This question refers to the differential equation

$$u''(x) + 4u(x) = 0,$$

which has the general solution $u = C\cos 2x + D\sin 2x$, where C and D are arbitrary constants (see Exercise 6(a)).

Each part gives a set of additional conditions. State whether these are initial conditions or boundary conditions, and find the solution (or solutions) that satisfy both the differential equation and the additional conditions.

(a) $u(0) = 1$, $u'(0) = 0$ (b) $u(0) = 0$, $u\left(\frac{\pi}{2}\right) = 0$

(c) $u\left(\frac{\pi}{2}\right) = 0$, $u'\left(\frac{\pi}{2}\right) = 0$ (d) $u(-\pi) = 1$, $u\left(\frac{\pi}{4}\right) = 2$

5 Resonance

The material in this section is non-assessable and will not be tested in continuous assessment or in the exam. However, we strongly advise students of physical science to study it, as these ideas will be used in higher-level modules.

In Subsection 2.4, we used the physical example of a damped harmonic oscillator to gain insights into the solutions of homogeneous linear constant-coefficient second-order differential equations. This final section does something similar for inhomogeneous equations.

Suppose that an object of mass m moves to and fro along the x-axis around an equilibrium position $x = 0$. The object has position $x(t)$ at time t. It experiences a force $-kx$ due to a spring, and a damping force $-\gamma\,dx/dt$ that opposes the motion of the object, where the constants m, k and γ are all positive. Up to this point, the system is just the damped harmonic oscillator considered earlier.

Now suppose that an additional time-dependent force $f(t)$ is applied to the object. This force is due to some external agency, and does not depend on the object's position or velocity. Then Newton's second law tells us that

$$-kx - \gamma\frac{dx}{dt} + f(t) = m\frac{d^2x}{dt^2},$$

which is equivalent to the inhomogeneous linear constant-coefficient second-order differential equation

$$m\frac{d^2x}{dt^2} + \gamma\frac{dx}{dt} + kx = f(t). \tag{56}$$

This system is known as a **forced damped harmonic oscillator**, and the external force is called the **driving force**.

A very important case occurs when the externally-applied driving force is a sinusoidal function of time. We therefore take

$$f(t) = F_0 \sin \omega t,$$

where F_0 and ω are positive constants. Under these circumstances, equation (56) can be written in the form

$$\frac{d^2x}{dt^2} + 2\Gamma\frac{dx}{dt} + \omega_0^2 x = a_0 \sin \omega t, \tag{57}$$

where $\Gamma = \gamma/2m$, $\omega_0 = \sqrt{k/m}$ and $a_0 = F_0/m$ are all positive constants. Here, ω_0 is the angular frequency of the simple harmonic oscillator (in the absence of damping or external forces). We include the subscript zero to distinguish ω_0 from the angular frequency ω of the driving force.

According to Procedure 2, the general solution of equation (57) is the sum of a complementary function $x_c(t)$ and a particular integral $x_p(t)$. The complementary function is the general solution of the associated homogeneous equation

$$\frac{d^2x}{dt^2} + 2\Gamma\frac{dx}{dt} + \omega_0^2 x = 0,$$

and you saw in Subsection 2.4 that this general solution contains an exponentially decaying factor $e^{-\Gamma t}$. Because of this factor, the complementary function represents a short-lived or transient contribution to the motion, which eventually dies away. Once this transient contribution has become negligible, the system settles down to a steady-state motion, given by the particular integral, which we focus on here.

This decay is a direct consequence of the damping force.

The required particular integral can be found using the methods of Subsection 3.2. We can substitute a trial solution

$$x(t) = p\cos(\omega t) + q\sin(\omega t)$$

into differential equation (57), and find p and q by matching the coefficients of $\cos(\omega t)$ and of $\sin(\omega t)$ on both sides of the equation. The method is identical to that used in Example 10.

The algebra gets a little messy, so we now introduce an alternative approach, which is more efficient in this case. The key ingredient is Euler's formula, which tells us that

$$a_0 e^{i\omega t} = a_0 \cos(\omega t) + i a_0 \sin(\omega t),$$

the imaginary part of which is equal to the right-hand side of equation (57). We therefore consider a differential equation that is closely related to equation (57), namely

$$\frac{d^2z}{dt^2} + 2\Gamma\frac{dz}{dt} + \omega_0^2 z = a_0 e^{i\omega t}. \tag{58}$$

Because the right-hand side of this equation is complex, the function $z(t)$ in this equation must also be complex.

Substituting $z(t) = u(t) + i\,v(t)$ into equation (58), and equating real parts and imaginary parts on both sides, we get

$$\frac{d^2u}{dt^2} + 2\Gamma\frac{du}{dt} + \omega_0^2 u = a_0\cos(\omega t),$$

$$\frac{d^2v}{dt^2} + 2\Gamma\frac{dv}{dt} + \omega_0^2 v = a_0\sin(\omega t).$$

It follows that $v(t)$, which is the imaginary part of $z(t)$, satisfies the main equation of interest, equation (57). Our tactic will therefore be to solve equation (58) for $z(t)$ and then take its imaginary part; this is an effective shortcut because equation (58) is easier to solve than equation (57).

Substituting the trial solution $z = pe^{i\omega t}$ into equation (58), we get

$$\left[(i\omega)^2 + 2\Gamma(i\omega) + \omega_0^2\right] pe^{i\omega t} = a_0 e^{i\omega t},$$

from which we obtain the particular integral

$$z(t) = a_0\frac{e^{i\omega t}}{\omega_0^2 - \omega^2 + 2i\Gamma\omega}.$$

Multiplying top and bottom by $\omega_0^2 - \omega^2 - 2i\Gamma\omega$ and using Euler's formula, this can be written as

$$z(t) = a_0\frac{\left[\cos(\omega t) + i\sin(\omega t)\right]\left[(\omega_0^2 - \omega^2) - 2i\Gamma\omega\right]}{(\omega_0^2 - \omega^2)^2 + 4\Gamma^2\omega^2}. \tag{59}$$

The solution that we need is the imaginary part of this expression. Multiplying out the brackets and picking out the coefficient of i, we conclude that equation (57) has the particular integral

$$x(t) = a_0\frac{(\omega_0^2 - \omega^2)\sin(\omega t) - 2\Gamma\omega\cos(\omega t)}{(\omega_0^2 - \omega^2)^2 + 4\Gamma^2\omega^2},$$

which is of the expected form

$$x(t) = p\cos(\omega t) + q\sin(\omega t),$$

where

$$p = \frac{-2\Gamma\omega}{(\omega_0^2 - \omega^2)^2 + 4\Gamma^2\omega^2} \quad\text{and}\quad q = \frac{(\omega_0^2 - \omega^2)a_0}{(\omega_0^2 - \omega^2)^2 + 4\Gamma^2\omega^2}.$$

The interpretation of this expression is clarified by writing it in the form

$$x(t) = A\sin(\omega t + \phi), \tag{60}$$

where A is the amplitude and ϕ is the phase constant. These can be found by using the argument that led to equations (31) and (32) in Subsection 2.4. We have $A = \sqrt{p^2 + q^2}$ and $\tan\phi = p/q$, so

$$A = \frac{a_0}{\sqrt{(\omega_0^2 - \omega^2)^2 + 4\Gamma^2\omega^2}} \tag{61}$$

and

$$\tan\phi = -\frac{2\Gamma\omega}{\omega_0^2 - \omega^2}. \tag{62}$$

Equation (60) gives the response of the system to the driving force once the transient motion associated with the complementary function has died away. Not surprisingly, the system performs a sinusoidal oscillation with the same angular frequency ω as the driving force. However, the amplitude A and phase constant ϕ behave in interesting ways. We focus on cases where the oscillator is underdamped ($\Gamma < \omega_0$).

Figure 12(a) shows the amplitude A as a function of the driving angular frequency ω for four different values of the damping parameter Γ. In each case, the amplitude is greatest when ω is equal to the natural angular frequency ω_0 of the corresponding undriven undamped oscillator. This effect appears as a peak in the graph, which becomes higher and narrower as the damping parameter Γ is reduced. This phenomenon is called **resonance**, and the angular frequency $\omega = \omega_0$ at which the response is greatest is called the **resonant angular frequency**.

The resonance behaviour illustrated in Figure 12 appears only if the oscillator is underdamped. A forced *overdamped* oscillator still performs sinusoidal oscillations, but its amplitude always decreases as ω increases.

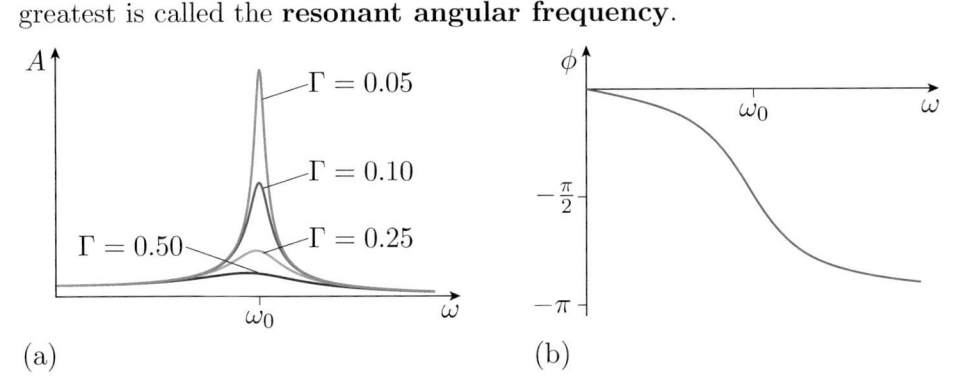

(a)   (b)

Figure 12   The response of a forced underdamped harmonic oscillator with $\omega_0 = 1$ as a function of the driving angular frequency ω:
(a) the amplitude A for $\Gamma = 0.50$, $\Gamma = 0.25$, $\Gamma = 0.10$ and $\Gamma = 0.05$;
(b) the corresponding phase constant ϕ

The phase constant ϕ is plotted in Figure 12(b). In general, the oscillation of the responding system lags behind the driving force, so ϕ is negative. The phase constant does not depend on the amplitude of the driving force, but it does depend on its angular frequency. At low angular frequencies, the lag is small. At the resonant angular frequency, the lag is a quarter of a cycle, and this grows to half a cycle at frequencies that are much larger than ω_0.

In plotting the graph in Figure 12(b), it was assumed that ϕ is a continuous function of ω. The arctan function was therefore allowed to extend beyond the range from $-\pi/2$ to $\pi/2$.

Exercise 23

Suppose that the displacement $x(t)$ of a forced damped harmonic oscillator obeys the inhomogeneous equation

$$\frac{d^2x}{dt^2} + 2\Gamma\frac{dx}{dt} + \omega_0^2 x = a_0 \cos(\omega t),$$

where Γ, ω_0 and a_0 are positive constants. Use the method based on equation (58) to find a particular integral for this equation, and hence obtain an expression for the amplitude as a function of ω.

Exercise 24

Use equation (61) to obtain simple formulas for the amplitude of oscillation of a forced underdamped oscillator in the following cases.

Express all your answers as simple fractions (involving a_0, ω_0, Γ and ω as necessary). You will need to make suitable approximations in the first two cases.

(a) $\omega \ll \omega_0$ (b) $\omega \gg \omega_0$ (c) $\omega = \omega_0$

Examples of resonance effects

Resonance occurs when an oscillation is sustained by an external influence, and the amplitude of the oscillation peaks strongly at a particular angular frequency of the external influence.

A familiar example occurs when you push a swing. Swings are designed to have little friction, so Γ is small and there is a pronounced resonance effect. You can get a motion of large amplitude if you push at the same angular frequency as the natural angular frequency of the swing.

Simple radio receivers (Figure 13) use the phenomenon of resonance to select which radio station to receive. Every radio station works at a different 'carrier' frequency. A circuit inside the receiver obeys the same equation as the damped harmonic oscillator, with electrical current playing the role of displacement $x(t)$. Tuning the radio receiver changes the natural frequency of this circuit, bringing it into resonance with the frequencies of various radio stations. In a radio receiver, Γ is very small, so the receiver responds to only a very narrow band of frequencies, allowing a single station to be selected.

The image shown in Figure 14 is from a magnetic resonance imaging (MRI) machine. In this case, the oscillating quantity is provided by magnetic properties of atomic nuclei, and the resonant frequency depends on the strength of an applied magnetic field. Images are obtained by placing the patient in a strong *non-uniform* magnetic field, so that different parts of the body are characterised by different resonant frequencies.

Finally, when a light wave (or other electromagnetic wave) is shone on a material, it causes the electrons in the material to oscillate to and fro. In a classical model, the electrons behave like forced damped harmonic oscillators, with the driving force supplied by the light wave. Energy is transferred from the light wave to the oscillating electrons, so some of the light is absorbed. We can therefore use the equations of forced damped harmonic motion to model the absorption of light in materials.

Figure 13   A simple radio receiver, which uses the phenomenon of resonance to select which transmission to receive

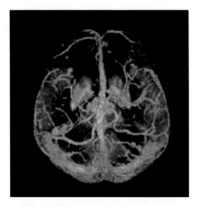

Figure 14   A false-colour MRI image of a brain of a healthy volunteer, emphasising the veins on top and the basal ganglia beneath

The absorption of light by single atoms is best described by quantum mechanics. Rather remarkably, however, resonance peaks in absorption are still predicted. Figure 15 is an image of the spectrum of sunlight. Among the dark lines there are lines due to absorption of light by helium in the solar atmosphere. These lines are found where the frequency of vibration of the sunlight is in resonance with frequencies of helium atoms. This approach demonstrated the existence of helium many years before it was isolated on the Earth.

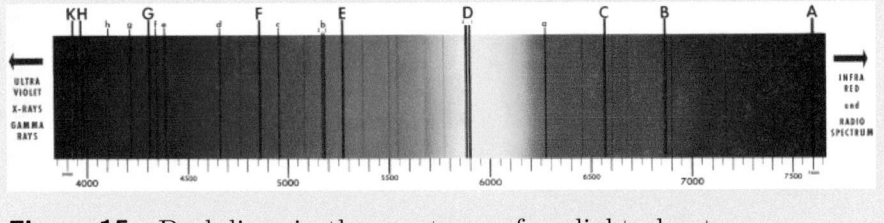

Figure 15 Dark lines in the spectrum of sunlight, due to a resonance with atoms in the atmosphere of the Sun, which demonstrates the existence of helium

Learning outcomes

After studying this unit, you should be able to do the following.

- Understand and use the terminology relating to linear constant-coefficient second-order differential equations.

- Understand the key role of the principle of superposition in the solution of linear constant-coefficient second-order differential equations.

- Obtain the general solution of a homogeneous linear constant-coefficient second-order differential equation using the solutions of its auxiliary equation.

- Use the method of undetermined coefficients to find a particular integral for an inhomogeneous linear constant-coefficient second-order differential equation with certain simple forms of right-hand-side function.

- Obtain the general solution of an inhomogeneous linear constant-coefficient second-order differential equation by combining its complementary function with a particular integral.

- Use the general solution together with a pair of initial or boundary conditions to obtain, when possible, a particular solution of a linear constant-coefficient second-order differential equation.

Solutions to exercises

Solution to Exercise 1

(a) In equations (i)–(vi), the (dependent, independent) variable pairs are all (y, x). In equations (vii), (viii) and (ix) they are (t, θ), (x, t) and (x, t), respectively.

(b) Equations (i), (ii), (iii), (iv), (vii), (viii) and (ix) are linear. (Equations (v) and (vi) are non-linear.)

(c) All of the linear equations are constant-coefficient except for (iv). So the linear constant-coefficient equations are (i), (ii), (iii), (vii), (viii) and (ix).

(d) Of the linear constant-coefficient equations, only (iii) and (ix) are homogeneous.

Solution to Exercise 2

(a) $\lambda^2 - 5\lambda + 6 = 0$

(b) $\lambda^2 - 9 = 0$

(c) $\lambda^2 + 2\lambda = 0$

Solution to Exercise 3

(a) The auxiliary equation is $\lambda^2 + 5\lambda + 6 = 0$. This can be factorised as $(\lambda + 2)(\lambda + 3) = 0$, giving the roots $\lambda_1 = -2$ and $\lambda_2 = -3$. The general solution is therefore

$$y = Ce^{-2x} + De^{-3x},$$

where C and D are arbitrary constants.

(b) The auxiliary equation is $2\lambda^2 + 3\lambda = 0$. This can be factorised as $\lambda(2\lambda + 3) = 0$, so its roots are $\lambda_1 = 0$ and $\lambda_2 = -\frac{3}{2}$. The general solution is therefore

Recall that $e^0 = \exp(0) = 1$.

$$y = Ce^0 + De^{-3x/2} = C + De^{-3x/2},$$

where C and D are arbitrary constants.

(c) The auxiliary equation is $\lambda^2 - 4 = 0$, i.e. $\lambda^2 = 4$, so its roots are $\lambda_1 = -2$ and $\lambda_2 = 2$. The general solution is therefore

$$z = Ce^{-2u} + De^{2u},$$

where C and D are arbitrary constants. (This differential equation is a special case of equation (14) discussed in Subsection 2.1.)

Solution to Exercise 4

(a) The auxiliary equation is $\lambda^2 + 4\lambda + 8 = 0$, which has solutions

$$\lambda = \frac{-4 \pm \sqrt{16 - 32}}{2} = -2 \pm 2i.$$

The general solution is therefore

$$y = e^{-2x}(C \cos 2x + D \sin 2x).$$

(b) The auxiliary equation is $\lambda^2 + 9 = 0$, which has solutions

$$\lambda = \pm 3i.$$

These are of the form $\alpha \pm \beta i$, where $\alpha = 0$ and $\beta = 3$.

The general solution is therefore

$$\theta = e^0(C \cos 3t + D \sin 3t) = C \cos 3t + D \sin 3t.$$

Of course, this is one of the simple cases discussed at the beginning of this section: it corresponds to simple harmonic motion.

Solution to Exercise 5

(a) The auxiliary equation is $\lambda^2 + 2\lambda + 1 = 0$, which can be factorised as $(\lambda + 1)^2 = 0$, giving equal roots $\lambda_1 = \lambda_2 = -1$. The general solution is therefore

$$y = (C + Dx)e^{-x},$$

where C and D are arbitrary constants.

(b) The auxiliary equation is $\lambda^2 - 4\lambda + 4 = 0$, which can be factorised as $(\lambda - 2)^2 = 0$, giving equal roots $\lambda_1 = \lambda_2 = 2$. The general solution is therefore

$$s = (C + Dt)e^{2t},$$

where C and D are arbitrary constants.

Solution to Exercise 6

(a) The auxiliary equation is $\lambda^2 + 4 = 0$, which has solutions $\lambda = \pm 2i$. The general solution is therefore

$$y = C \cos 2x + D \sin 2x.$$

In all cases, C and D are arbitrary constants.

(You could also have written down this general solution directly from equation (18).)

(b) The auxiliary equation is $\lambda^2 - 9 = 0$, which has solutions $\lambda = \pm 3$. The general solution is therefore

$$y = Ce^{3x} + De^{-3x}.$$

(You could also have written down this general solution directly from equation (15).)

(c) The auxiliary equation is $\lambda^2 + 2\lambda = 0$, which has solutions $\lambda_1 = 0$ and $\lambda_2 = -2$. The general solution is therefore

$$y = C + De^{-2x}.$$

(d) The auxiliary equation is $\lambda^2 - 2\lambda + 1 = 0$, which has solutions $\lambda_1 = \lambda_2 = 1$. The general solution is therefore
$$y = (C + Dx)e^x.$$

(e) The auxiliary equation is $\lambda^2 + 4\lambda + 29 = 0$, which has solutions
$$\lambda = \frac{-4 \pm \sqrt{16 - 116}}{2} = -2 \pm 5i.$$
The general solution is therefore
$$y = e^{-2x}(C \cos 5x + D \sin 5x).$$

(f) The auxiliary equation is $\lambda^2 - 6\lambda + 8 = 0$, which factorises as $(\lambda - 4)(\lambda - 2) = 0$ and has solutions $\lambda_1 = 4$ and $\lambda_2 = 2$. The general solution is therefore
$$u = Ce^{4x} + De^{2x}.$$

Solution to Exercise 7

(a) The auxiliary equation is
$$3\lambda - 1 - 2\lambda^2 = 0,$$
or equivalently,
$$2\lambda^2 - 3\lambda + 1 = 0,$$
which factorises as
$$(2\lambda - 1)(\lambda - 1) = 0.$$

(b) The two solutions of the auxiliary equation are $\lambda_1 = \frac{1}{2}$ and $\lambda_2 = 1$, so the general solution of the differential equation is
$$y = Ce^{x/2} + De^x,$$
where C and D are arbitrary constants.

Solution to Exercise 8

(a) The auxiliary equation is
$$\lambda^2 + 2\lambda + 2 = 0.$$
This has solutions $\lambda_1 = -1 + i$ and $\lambda_2 = -1 - i$, so the general solution is
$$y = e^{-x}(C \cos x + D \sin x).$$

(b) The auxiliary equation is
$$\lambda^2 - 16 = 0.$$
This has solutions $\lambda_1 = 4$ and $\lambda_2 = -4$, so the general solution is
$$y = Ce^{4x} + De^{-4x}.$$

(c) The auxiliary equation is
$$\lambda^2 - 4\lambda + 4 = 0.$$

This has solutions $\lambda_1 = \lambda_2 = 2$, so the general solution is

$$y = (C + Dx)e^{2x}.$$

(d) The auxiliary equation is

$$\lambda^2 + 3\lambda = 0.$$

This has solutions $\lambda_1 = 0$ and $\lambda_2 = -3$, so the general solution is

$$\theta = C + De^{-3t}.$$

Solution to Exercise 9

The auxiliary equation $\lambda^2 + 4k\lambda + 4 = 0$ can be solved using the formula method to give $\lambda = -2k \pm 2\sqrt{k^2 - 1}$. So there are complex conjugate solutions, leading to a general solution involving sines and cosines, when $k^2 < 1$, i.e. when $-1 < k < 1$.

Solution to Exercise 10

(a) The differential equation can be written in the form

$$\frac{d^2\theta}{dt^2} + 2\Gamma\frac{d\theta}{dt} + \omega^2\theta = 0,$$

where

$$\Gamma = \frac{\gamma}{2m} = \frac{0.016}{2 \times 0.80} = 0.01,$$

and the angular frequency of the corresponding undamped oscillator is

$$\omega = \sqrt{\frac{mg}{ml}} = \sqrt{\frac{9.8}{2.0}} = 2.21.$$

We therefore have $\Gamma < \omega$, and the oscillation is underdamped.

(b) The angular frequency of the damped pendulum is

$$\Omega = \sqrt{\omega^2 - \Gamma^2} = \sqrt{2.21^2 - 0.01^2} = 2.21.$$

This is typical: the angular frequency is not very sensitive to damping when $\Gamma \ll \omega$.

We therefore have

$$T = \frac{2\pi}{\Omega} = 2.84,$$

so the period of oscillation is 2.8 seconds.

(c) The amplitude is given by $Ae^{-\Gamma t}$, where A is a constant. If the amplitude is 0.2 radians at time zero, the amplitude at time $t = 100$ is

$$Ae^{-\Gamma t} = 0.20e^{-0.01\times 100} = 0.2e^{-1} = 0.074 \quad \text{(in radians).}$$

Solution to Exercise 11

The condition for critical damping is $\Gamma = \omega = \sqrt{k/m}$, so in this case $\Gamma = \sqrt{4} = 2$. The general solution is therefore

$$x(t) = (C + Dt)e^{-2t}.$$

Solution to Exercise 12

(a) The associated homogeneous equation is

$$\frac{d^2y}{dx^2} + 4y = 0.$$

The complementary function (see Exercise 6(a)) is

$$y_c = C\cos 2x + D\sin 2x.$$

Trying a solution of the form $y_p = p$, where p is a constant, in the original equation $d^2y/dx^2 + 4y = 8$ gives $0 + 4p = 8$, so $p = 2$. Thus a particular integral is

$$y_p = 2.$$

By Procedure 2, the general solution is

$$y = C\cos 2x + D\sin 2x + 2.$$

(b) The associated homogeneous equation is

$$\frac{d^2y}{dx^2} - 3\frac{dy}{dx} + 2y = 0.$$

The complementary function (see Example 3) is

$$y_c = Ce^x + De^{2x}.$$

Trying a solution of the form $y_p = p$ in the original equation $d^2y/dx^2 - 3dy/dx + 2y = 6$ gives $0 - 0 + 2p = 6$, so $p = 3$. Thus a particular integral is

$$y_p = 3.$$

By Procedure 2, the general solution is

$$y = Ce^x + De^{2x} + 3.$$

Solution to Exercise 13

(a) Substituting $y = p_1 x + p_0$ and its derivatives into the differential equation gives

$$0 - 2p_1 + 2(p_1 x + p_0) = 2p_1 x + (2p_0 - 2p_1) = 2x + 3.$$

Equating the coefficients of x gives $p_1 = 1$, and equating the constant terms gives $p_0 = \frac{5}{2}$. Therefore a particular integral is

$$y_p = x + \tfrac{5}{2}.$$

(b) Substituting $y = p_1 x + p_0$ and its derivatives into the differential equation gives

$$0 + 2p_1 + (p_1 x + p_0) = p_1 x + (2p_1 + p_0) = 2x.$$

Equating the coefficients of x gives $p_1 = 2$, and equating the constant terms gives $p_0 = -4$, so a particular integral is

$$y_p = 2x - 4.$$

Solution to Exercise 14

We try $y = p_2 t^2 + p_1 t + p_0$, which has derivatives $y' = 2p_2 t + p_1$ and $y'' = 2p_2$. Substituting these into the differential equation gives

$$2p_2 - (p_2 t^2 + p_1 t + p_0) = -p_2 t^2 - p_1 t + (2p_2 - p_0)$$
$$= t^2.$$

Hence, separately equating coefficients of t^2, t and 1, we get $p_2 = -1$, $p_1 = 0$, $p_0 = -2$, so a particular integral is

$$y_p = -t^2 - 2.$$

Solution to Exercise 15

We try a solution of the form $y = pe^{-x}$, which has derivatives $dy/dx = -pe^{-x}$ and $d^2y/dx^2 = pe^{-x}$. Substituting these into the differential equation gives

$$2pe^{-x} + 2pe^{-x} + pe^{-x} = 5pe^{-x} = 2e^{-x}.$$

Hence $p = \frac{2}{5}$, and a particular integral is

$$y_p = \frac{2}{5}e^{-x}.$$

Solution to Exercise 16

We try $y = p\cos 3t + q\sin 3t$, which has derivatives

$$\frac{dy}{dt} = -3p\sin 3t + 3q\cos 3t, \qquad \frac{d^2y}{dt^2} = -9p\cos 3t - 9q\sin 3t.$$

Substituting into the differential equation gives

$$(-9p\cos 3t - 9q\sin 3t) - (-3p\sin 3t + 3q\cos 3t)$$
$$= -(9p + 3q)\cos 3t + (3p - 9q)\sin 3t$$
$$= \cos 3t + \sin 3t.$$

Hence we have a pair of simultaneous equations

$$-9p - 3q = 1,$$
$$3p - 9q = 1.$$

Adding three times the second equation to the first shows that $q = -\frac{4}{30} = -\frac{2}{15}$, hence $p = -\frac{1}{15}$. A particular integral is thus

$$y_p = -\frac{1}{15}\cos 3t - \frac{2}{15}\sin 3t.$$

Solution to Exercise 17

(a) Try $y = pe^{3x}$.

(b) Try $y = p\cos 3x + q\sin 3x$.

Solution to Exercise 18

(a) The complementary function is
$$\theta_c = C\cos 2t + D\sin 2t.$$

To find a particular integral, try $\theta = p_1 t + p_0$. Substituting this and its derivatives into the differential equation gives
$$4(p_1 t + p_0) = 2t.$$

Hence $p_1 = \frac{1}{2}$, $p_0 = 0$, and a particular integral is
$$\theta_p = \tfrac{1}{2}t.$$

Therefore the general solution is
$$\theta = C\cos 2t + D\sin 2t + \tfrac{1}{2}t,$$

where C and D are arbitrary constants.

(b) The complementary function is
$$y_c = C\cos 2x + D\sin 2x.$$

The right-hand-side function is $10\sin 3x$, so we try $y = p\cos 3x + q\sin 3x$. The derivatives are
$$\frac{dy}{dx} = -3p\sin 3x + 3q\cos 3x,$$
$$\frac{d^2y}{dx^2} = -9p\cos 3x - 9q\sin 3x.$$

Substituting into the differential equation gives
$$(-9p\cos 3x - 9q\sin 3x) + 4(p\cos 3x + q\sin 3x)$$
$$= -5p\cos 3x - 5q\sin 3x = 10\sin 3x,$$

so $p = 0$ and $q = -2$, and a particular integral is
$$y_p = -2\sin 3x.$$

Therefore the general solution is
$$y = C\cos 2x + D\sin 2x - 2\sin 3x,$$

where C and D are arbitrary constants.

(c) The complementary function is
$$y_c = Ce^{-2x} + De^{2x}.$$

The right-hand-side function is $15e^{-x}$, so we try $y = pe^{-x}$. The derivatives are
$$\frac{dy}{dx} = -pe^{-x}, \quad \frac{d^2y}{dx^2} = pe^{-x}.$$

Substituting for d^2y/dx^2 and y into the differential equation gives
$$pe^{-x} - 4pe^{-x} = -3pe^{-x} = 15e^{-x},$$

so $p = -5$, and a particular integral is
$$y_p = -5e^{-x}.$$

Therefore the general solution is

$$y = Ce^{-2x} + De^{2x} - 5e^{-x},$$

where C and D are arbitrary constants.

Solution to Exercise 19

We split the task of finding a particular integral into two parts, by first finding particular integrals for

$$2\frac{d^2x}{dt^2} + 3\frac{dx}{dt} + 2x = 12\cos 2t \tag{63}$$

and

$$2\frac{d^2x}{dt^2} + 3\frac{dx}{dt} + 2x = 10. \tag{64}$$

In equation (63), the term $12\cos 2t$ on the right-hand side suggests the trial solution $x = p\cos 2t + q\sin 2t$. This has derivatives

$$\frac{dx}{dt} = -2p\sin 2t + 2q\cos 2t, \qquad \frac{d^2x}{dt^2} = -4p\cos 2t - 4q\sin 2t.$$

Substituting into the left-hand side of the differential equation gives

$$2(-4p\cos 2t - 4q\sin 2t) + 3(-2p\sin 2t + 2q\cos 2t) + 2(p\cos 2t + q\sin 2t)$$
$$= 6(q - p)\cos 2t - 6(p + q)\sin 2t.$$

Equating this to $12\cos 2t$ from the right-hand side of equation (63) gives $p + q = 0$, $q - p = 2$. Hence $p = -1$, $q = 1$, and a particular integral is

$$x_{\mathrm{p}} = -\cos 2t + \sin 2t.$$

Now consider equation (64). In this case we try a constant function $x = p_0$. Substituting into the differential equation gives $2p_0 = 10$, so $p_0 = 5$, and a particular integral is

$$x_{\mathrm{p}} = 5.$$

Therefore, using the principle of superposition, a particular integral for the original differential equation is

$$x_{\mathrm{p}} = -\cos 2t + \sin 2t + 5.$$

Solution to Exercise 20

(a) The associated homogeneous equation has auxiliary equation

$$\lambda^2 + 4\lambda + 5 = 0,$$

which has solutions

$$\lambda = \frac{-4 \pm \sqrt{16 - 20}}{2} = -2 \pm i.$$

So the complementary function is

$$u_{\mathrm{c}} = e^{-2t}(C\cos t + D\sin t).$$

To find a particular integral, try $u = p_0$. Substituting gives $5p_0 = 5$. Hence $p_0 = 1$, and a particular integral is

$$u_\mathrm{p} = 1.$$

Therefore the general solution is

$$u = e^{-2t}(C \cos t + D \sin t) + 1,$$

where C and D are arbitrary constants.

(b) The associated homogeneous equation has auxiliary equation

$$3\lambda^2 - 2\lambda - 1 = (3\lambda + 1)(\lambda - 1) = 0,$$

which has solutions $\lambda_1 = 1$ and $\lambda_2 = -\tfrac{1}{3}$. So the complementary function is

$$y_\mathrm{c} = Ce^x + De^{-x/3}.$$

The right-hand side function is e^{2x}, so to find a particular integral, we try $y = pe^{2x}$. The derivatives are

$$\frac{dy}{dx} = 2pe^{2x}, \quad \frac{d^2y}{dx^2} = 4pe^{2x}.$$

Substituting gives

$$3(4pe^{2x}) - 2(2pe^{2x}) - pe^{2x} = 7pe^{2x} = e^{2x}.$$

Hence $p = \tfrac{1}{7}$, and a particular integral is

$$y_\mathrm{p} = \tfrac{1}{7}e^{2x}.$$

Therefore the general solution is

$$y = Ce^x + De^{-x/3} + \tfrac{1}{7}e^{2x},$$

where C and D are arbitrary constants.

Solution to Exercise 21

(a) The derivative of the general solution $u = C \cos 3t + D \sin 3t$ is

$$u' = -3C \sin 3t + 3D \cos 3t.$$

Remember that $\cos\left(\tfrac{3\pi}{2}\right) = 0$ and $\sin\left(\tfrac{3\pi}{2}\right) = -1$.

Substituting the initial condition $t = \tfrac{\pi}{2}$, $u = 0$ into the general solution gives $D = 0$. Substituting the initial condition $t = \tfrac{\pi}{2}$, $u' = 1$ into the derivative gives $C = \tfrac{1}{3}$. Hence the required particular solution is

$$u = \tfrac{1}{3} \cos 3t.$$

(b) The derivative of the general solution $u = e^{-2t}(C \cos t + D \sin t) + 1$ is

$$u' = -2e^{-2t}(C \cos t + D \sin t) + e^{-2t}(-C \sin t + D \cos t)$$
$$= e^{-2t}[(D - 2C) \cos t - (2D + C) \sin t].$$

Substituting the initial condition $u = 3$, $t = 0$ into the general solution gives $C = 2$. Substituting the initial condition $u' = 1$, $t = 0$ into the derivative gives $D - 2C = 1$, so $D = 5$. So the required particular solution is

$$u = e^{-2t}(2 \cos t + 5 \sin t) + 1.$$

Solution to Exercise 22

(a) The derivative of the general solution $u = C \cos 2x + D \sin 2x$ is

$$u' = -2C \sin 2x + 2D \cos 2x.$$

This part specifies an initial-value problem.

The initial condition $u(0) = 1$ gives $C = 1$. The initial condition $u'(0) = 0$ gives $D = 0$. The required solution is therefore

$$u = \cos 2x.$$

(b) This is a boundary-value problem.

The boundary condition $u(0) = 0$ gives $C = 0$. The boundary condition $u\left(\frac{\pi}{2}\right) = 0$ gives $C = 0$ also. D therefore remains arbitrary, so there is an infinite number of solutions, of the form

$$u = D \sin 2x.$$

(c) This is an initial-value problem.

The initial condition $u\left(\frac{\pi}{2}\right) = 0$ gives $C = 0$. The initial condition $u'\left(\frac{\pi}{2}\right) = 0$ gives $D = 0$. The required solution is therefore the zero function

$$u = 0.$$

(d) This is a boundary-value problem.

The boundary condition $u(-\pi) = 1$ gives $C = 1$. The boundary condition $u\left(\frac{\pi}{4}\right) = 2$ gives $D = 2$. The required solution is therefore

$$u = \cos 2x + 2 \sin 2x.$$

Solution to Exercise 23

The differential equation given in this question is the real part of equation (58), so its solution is the real part of equation (59). Hence a suitable particular integral in this case is

$$x(t) = a_0 \frac{(\omega_0^2 - \omega^2) \cos(\omega t) + 2\Gamma\omega \sin(\omega t)}{(\omega_0^2 - \omega^2)^2 + 4\Gamma^2\omega^2}.$$

Using equation (31), the amplitude is the square root of the sum of the squares of the coefficients of $\sin(\omega t)$ and $\cos(\omega t)$, and so is given by

$$A = \left[a_0^2 \frac{(\omega_0^2 - \omega^2)^2 + 4\Gamma^2\omega^2}{\left((\omega_0^2 - \omega^2)^2 + 4\Gamma^2\omega^2\right)^2} \right]^{1/2} = \frac{a_0}{\sqrt{(\omega_0^2 - \omega^2)^2 + 4\Gamma^2\omega^2}}.$$

This is the same as equation (61), which is not surprising. Changing the right-hand side of the equation from $a_0 \sin(\omega t)$ to $a_0 \cos(\omega t)$ corresponds to changing the phase constant of the external force (which depends on the origin chosen for time). It is to be expected that this does not affect the amplitude of the steady-state forced damped oscillations.

Solution to Exercise 24

(a) Considering the expression

$$A = \frac{a_0}{\sqrt{(\omega_0^2 - \omega^2)^2 + 4\Gamma^2\omega^2}}$$

when $\omega \ll \omega_0$, we can neglect ω^2 in comparison with ω_0^2. We can also neglect $4\Gamma^2\omega^2$ in comparison with ω_0^4 (because $\Gamma < \omega_0$ for an underdamped oscillator). We therefore have the approximation

$$A \simeq \frac{a_0}{\omega_0^2} \quad \text{for } \omega \ll \omega_0.$$

In this case, the amplitude is a constant that is independent of the angular frequency of the external force or the damping parameter of the oscillator.

(b) When $\omega \gg \omega_0$, we can neglect ω_0^2 in comparison with ω^2. In the underdamped case, $\Gamma < \omega_0$ and we can also neglect $4\Gamma^2\omega^2$ in comparison with ω^4. We therefore have the approximation

$$A \simeq \frac{a_0}{\omega^2} \quad \text{for } \omega \gg \omega_0.$$

In this case, the amplitude decreases steadily as the angular frequency of the external force increases. The sluggish system is unable to keep up with the fast oscillations of the external force.

(c) Substituting $\omega = \omega_0$ into the general formula for the amplitude gives

$$A = \frac{a_0}{2\Gamma\omega_0}.$$

This is the amplitude at the peak of resonance. It increases without limit as the damping parameter Γ is decreased.

Acknowledgements

Grateful acknowledgement is made to the following sources:

Figure 13: Taken from http://en.wikipedia.org/wiki/File:Sony-walkman-srfs84s_0001.JPG. This file is licensed under the Creative Commons Attribution-Share Alike 3.0 Unported licence.

Figure 14: Ericl Liu. This file is licensed under the Creative Commons Attribution-Share Alike 3.0 Unported licence.

Figure 15: Andrew P. Harmsworth, Science, Space, Education & IT Skills. www.harmsy.freeuk.com/fraunhofer.html.

Every effort has been made to contact copyright holders. If any have been inadvertently overlooked, the publishers will be pleased to make the necessary arrangements at the first opportunity.

Index